THE
INNOVATION
FACTORY

HOW PARTNERING WITH ACADEMIA AND START-UPS SUPPORTS NEW PRODUCT INNOVATION IN THE TWENTY-FIRST CENTURY

Prith Banerjee, Ph.D.

Fulton Books
Meadville, PA

Published by Fulton Books 2022

ISBN 979-8-88505-315-0 (paperback)
ISBN 979-8-88505-316-7 (digital)

Printed in the United States of America

To my mother, Anima, for teaching me to be a well-rounded person and to respect others and for encouraging me to pursue my dreams; to my father, Sunil, who valued education and sent me to the best schools, colleges, and universities; and to my wife, Swati, for being my lifetime love and partner and for always being by my side during my multiple career choices

CONTENTS

FOREWORD

Innovation is one of the many words in our modern lexicon that gets overused. Madison Avenue will have you believe that every new product is packed full of innovation. Résumés are brimming with key search terms like "out of the box" and "innovative." Even simple goods and services promise innovation, just in case we need a new approach to taking portraits of our pets or for securing insurance for a boat. We know that innovation is crucial to our future successes, whether they be in business or in life. For many of us, though, we are just no longer sure what innovation even means because of its overuse. In fact, it is fair to say that the word *innovation* is no longer, well, innovative.

That is what makes Prith Banerjee's study of innovation so refreshing and exciting. This book is more than simply a case study of a single company's innovation journey. Rather, it is a broad-based examination of this intriguing topic, which executives across industries will value. Prith couples his own research and keen insights with a series of interviews with leaders in business and academia to explain the heart of innovation and how it drives our world forward. He details how the innovation process—from ideation, to funding, and to execution—occurs in universities, in start-ups, and in large enterprises. He also advises how large companies can pursue long-term disruptive innovation by better partnering with academia and start-ups.

Prith calls this idea the Innovation Factory, an evocative title that forces us to rethink our approach to the products we create, the processes we follow, and the strategies we develop. He describes how innovation itself can be turned into an ongoing process—literally an innovation factory—during which new ways of approaching familiar challenges can be industrialized at scale.

Over the course of his thirty-five-year technology career, which includes academia and start-ups as well as managing innovation in large companies, Prith has become a legend and a trusted adviser on the topic.

Over the course of my career, I have had the opportunity to observe many chief technologists and have served in the role myself. Prith is one of the most effective leaders I have ever encountered in that role. His intelligence, passion, commitment, and unbridled energy inspire those around him to constantly push the boundaries of what is possible through the promise of technology. Those traits have enabled him to develop deep, lasting connection with other visionaries in the technology community.

As the CTO of Ansys, the global leader in engineering simulation, Prith is responsible for setting the company's long-term technology strategy. He has taken an intricate strategy and has simplified that vision into a series of key pillars, including numerical methods, artificial intelligence / machine learning, and the cloud. As a result, our strategy is more easily understood and embraced by customer, partners, and even our own employees.

His participation in the global technology community has inspired Ansys engineers to play more active roles in the greater business ecosystem. The technology strategy that Prith drives has paid tremendous dividends for Ansys and for our customers. Prior to Prith's joining, Ansys was already the market leader in engineering simulation. But with his guidance, we have extended our product leadership and our overall strength in the industry.

Prior to his time at Ansys, Prith led a remarkable career spanning academia, start-ups, and the corporate world. He spent more than twenty years as a professor, chairman, and dean at the University of Illinois and Northwestern University. He founded two start-up companies: AccelChip and Binachip. Finally, as the director of the iconic HP Labs and Accenture Labs and as the CTO of ABB and Schneider Electric, Prith managed large research organizations.

We are fortunate that Prith has found the time to share some of his unique perspectives, valuable learning, and keen business insights with us in *The Innovation Factory*. I believe this book will serve as a blueprint for companies large and small across any industry or geography to follow. It is time for all of us to start building our own innovation factories.

Ajei Gopal
President and CEO, Ansys

PREFACE

Even though a quarter of a century has passed since Clayton Christensen's *The Innovator's Dilemma* was first published, business thought leaders still find themselves confronted with the same problem: a profound disconnect too often exists between innovation development and business outcomes. Companies say they want the stimulus of innovation and even handsomely fund their in-house R&D. Yet when it comes time for a call to action, such as launching a new product or service, they often back away from the risk. Sadly, American corporations' decision makers all too often decide to play it safe, and the innovation doesn't go into play at all.

In my thirty-five-year technology career—from academia, to my own start-ups, and to managing innovation in enterprise environments—I have encountered many large companies that have R&D collaborations with academia and with start-ups. Open innovation with academia and start-ups, the focal point of this book, is not new. Henry Chesbrough, director of the Garwood Center for Corporate Innovation at the University of California, Berkeley, Haas School of Business, has written extensively about it. Unfortunately, many of these collaborations do not result in true innovation. My book explores the ingredients of the secret sauce required to generate successful open innovation.

The Innovation Factory provides essential, practical guidance for all parties wishing to work toward successful collaborations that achieve innovation in its many aspects. Perhaps you have already launched some partnerships; if so, this book will help both of you make them more successful. Whether you have or have not, this is the only book you need to launch and partner in open innovation initiatives.

The Innovation Factory is organized as follows: Chapter 1—"An Introduction to the Innovation Factory"—introduces the definition of innovation and distinguishes it from basic discovery. It describes innovation in products and processes and goes on to discuss the three horizons of innovation model developed at McKinsey & Company. Horizon 1 is short-term, horizon 2 is medium-term, and horizon 3 is long-term (and is often Christensen's) disruptive innovation.

Larger companies typically excel in horizon 1 and also do a good job in horizon 2 innovation. Universities typically focus on long-term horizon 3 innovation; however, they often end their work at the discovery phase. Start-up companies excel in taking horizon 3 disruptive innovation to market. Large companies typically struggle with long-term horizon 3 disruptive innovation. In this chapter, we interview Monty Alger, professor at Penn State University and formerly with GE Global Research, and discuss how innovation happens in academia and large companies.

Chapter 2—"Innovation in Academia"—discusses how discovery and innovation take place in academia. It explains that most fundamental scientific and engineering discovery happens in academia; however, the metrics of innovation in academia are commonly tied to publications in conferences and journals and to obtaining research funding. Professors are usually promoted based on funding, publications, graduate student supervision, and awards and recognition, such as being appointed as fellows of professional societies.

Most professors are not interested in transferring their technologies to businesses, although a small number of faculty do start companies and transfer the technologies they have been developing. Increasingly, large companies are funding research programs in universities with the intent of transferring the technologies they have funded to a viable product or process for their business. In this chapter, we interview Alberto Sangiovanni-Vincentelli, a professor at UC Berkeley and cofounder and board member of Cadence, and we discuss how universities pursue basic research and discovery and how technologies get transferred to companies.

Chapter 3—"Innovation in Start-Ups"—discusses how innovation develops in start-up companies. While large companies mostly focus on research and development for a diverse portfolio of projects, a start-up is usually interested only in one niche, product, or process on which to focus their R&D and sales and marketing effort. It is, therefore, easier for start-ups to practice disruptive innovation. Also discussed is how start-up companies create business plans to launch a business to pursue disruptive innovation. The various funding stages that start-up companies employ, such as seed, Series A, Series B, Series C, and initial public offering (IPO), are explained. The chapter concludes by describing how start-ups go about forming partnerships with large companies to scale their business. In this chapter, we interview Amit Narayan, CEO of AutoGrid, a start-up in the renewable energy industry, on how start-ups pursue disruptive innovation with funding from venture capitalists.

Chapter 4—"Innovation in Large Companies"—discusses how innovation is practiced in large companies. Start-ups tend to focus on a single project for their R&D effort while a large company typically has multiple products across multiple organizations or divisions. How large companies manage a portfolio of R&D projects and how they try to grow their top-line revenue and bottom-line savings through innovation are detailed. In this chapter, we interview Brad Feldmann, CEO of Cubic Corporation, and we discuss how large companies invest strategically in research and development.

Chapter 5—"The Role of the Central Research Lab"—focuses on the role of a central research lab (CRL) and how it is essential to supporting long-term disruptive innovation. Central research labs at Bell Labs, IBM Research, Microsoft Research, HP Labs, and GE Global Research have been very successful over the past thirty years in pursuing truly long-term R&D topics—for example, the invention of the transistor, the hard disk computer drive, and the laser. Several have won Nobel Prizes.

More recently, as the business environment has changed, some CRLs have found that they need to reprioritize their research to balance short-term and medium-term projects with their previous emphasis on long-term innovation. In this chapter, we interview Peter Lee, corporate vice president of Microsoft Research and Incubations, and we discuss how central research labs, such as Microsoft Research, are pursuing long-term disruptive innovation.

Chapter 6—"How Large Companies Can Support Long-Term Innovation"—proposes how large companies can develop short-term innovation using the portfolio approach described in chapter 4 yet can simultaneously pursue long-term disruptive innovation by leveraging a central research lab, as described in the previous chapter. However, the organic work on innovation needs to be complemented by partnering with academia and start-ups to achieve open innovation. Examples of how new businesses can be incubated in large companies using this approach are described. In this chapter, we interview Mallik Tatipamula, chief technology officer, Ericsson Silicon Valley, and we discuss how large companies engage with start-ups and academia to bring disruptive innovative ideas from outside the company.

Chapter 7—"Funding Models for Innovation"—discusses funding models for innovation. Government funding agencies, such as the National Science Foundation (NSF), the Department of Defense (DOD), the Department of Energy (DOE), the National Aeronautics and Space Administration (NASA), and the National Institutes of Health (NIH), typically fund long-term research programs at universities. The DOE and DOD also fund applied research programs at their own central labs, such as Oak Ridge National Laboratory or the Air Force Research Laboratory. Venture capitalists (VCs) actively fund start-up companies at seed, Series A, Series B, and Series C. Large companies fund their own R&D programs, often by fiat from the CEO and the board.

Increasingly, there is a cross-pollination of funding among academia, start-ups, and large companies. For example, large companies routinely fund work in academia and participate in strategic investment rounds for start-ups. Agencies of the US government often fund start-ups using either the Small Business Innovation Research (SBIR) or the Small Business Technology Transfer (STTR) funding programs. In this chapter, we interview Erwin Gianchandani, assistant director of the directorate for Technology, Innovation, and Partnerships (TIP), National Science Foundation, and discuss how NSF funds basic research among US universities.

Chapter 8—"Digital Technologies Driving Product Innovation"—addresses the role of various digital technologies essential to driving product and process innovation in the twenty-first century. We discuss technologies such as

- CAD/CAE simulation-driven product innovation
- semiconductors and nanotechnology
- photonics and optical interconnects
- quantum computing
- wireless communications
- additive manufacturing
- virtual reality / augmented reality
- blockchains
- cybersecurity
- high-performance computing
- cloud computing
- AI / machine learning
- Internet of Things (IoT)
- platforms

In this chapter, we interview Gamiel Gran, senior vice president at Mayfield, and discuss how venture capitalists fund various start-up companies in each of these digital technologies.

Chapter 9—"Building the Twenty-First-Century Innovation Factory"—offers concluding remarks on how large companies can set up long-term disruption as an innovation factory by complementing the organic innovation with central research labs, academic partnerships, and start-ups. Attracting, retaining, and promoting business innovation talent is essential. In the global business world, such talent is often found in the top ten cities as measured in terms of innovation and what it takes to sustain innovation. How is an innovative culture created and practiced in larger companies?

Finally, a long-term perspective on funding models that will foster more innovation in the US—for example, government funding of the United States Innovation and Competition Act of 2021 (USICA) to create a new directorate within the National Science Foundation that focuses on technology and innovation. In this final chapter, we interview Henry Chesbrough, professor of Haas School of Business at UC Berkeley, and discuss the concepts of open innovation that many companies have successfully applied to drive disruptive innovation.

(Disclaimer: the opinions expressed in this book are the personal views of the author and do not represent the views of Ansys.)

ACKNOWLEDGMENTS

The idea to write this book came out of various interactions with CTOs of different Ansys customers during my role as CTO of Ansys. I had numerous discussions with the CTOs of other companies in multiple industries and the challenges they faced in driving disruptive innovation as part of their digital transformation journey. In 2019, I was first invited to speak on this topic to all the engineering talent at Cubic Corporation, a company where I served on the board of directors. I subsequently participated in several podcasts on innovation that Gamiel Gran hosted at Mayfield, Albert Chou at Mission North, and Ken Forster at Momenta Partners. The idea for this book came out of these podcasts.

I am fortunate to have worked in different organizations on innovation. I have spent more than twenty years in academia at the University of Illinois and Northwestern leading research, supervising PhD students, and writing more than 350 papers. I have founded two start-ups, AccelChip and Binachip, and have learned how start-ups innovate. Finally, I have been managing large R&D organizations at Hewlett-Packard, ABB, Accenture, Schneider Electric, and Ansys for the past fifteen years. I have learned so much from my colleagues in these organizations and want to acknowledge their contributions to the ideas described in my book.

I want to acknowledge the excellent education I received during my BTech degree in electronics engineering at Indian Institute of Technology Kharagpur, one of the premier engineering institutes in India. I want to recognize my professors: J. Das, G. S. Sanyal, N. B. Chakrabarti, S. K. Lahiri, P. Dasgupta, S. DeSarkar, and others. From them I learned the fundamentals of engineering. I also want to recognize my BTech thesis adviser, S. K. Lahiri, who taught me how to pursue fundamental research. Next, I want to acknowledge the excellent graduate education I received at the University of Illinois

Urbana-Champaign. My professors—Jacob Abraham, Ed Davidson, Janak Patel, David Kuck, Mac Van Valkenberg, and others—taught me how to think creatively. I want to thank Professor Jacob Abraham, my MS and PhD thesis adviser, who taught me how to invent new technologies and communicate them in journal papers and conference presentations. The main thing about a PhD education is not the particulars of the PhD thesis topic but the art of learning something and discovering new knowledge. Professor Abraham taught me to be a lifelong learner.

I want to recognize my academic colleagues at the University of Illinois—Professors Jacob Abraham, Ed Davidson, Ravi Iyer, Janak Patel, Wen-Mei Hwu, and Bill Sanders. I participated in multiple collaborative research programs funded by NSF, SRC, and NASA. I want to acknowledge my colleagues at Northwestern University—Professors Abe Haddad, Alok Choudhary, Scott Hauck, Prem Kumar, and Dean Jerry Cohen. I worked on several collaborative research projects with NSF, DARPA, DOD, and NASA. I want to recognize my colleagues at the University of Illinois in Chicago, including Professors Peter Nelson and Mitra Dutta. We worked on various big bet proposals to the NSF's Engineering Research Centers.

After spending twenty wonderful years in academia working on long-term innovation, I had the opportunity to start two software companies. I learned so much about innovating in start-ups from my cofounders at AccelChip—Alok Choudhary, Malay Haldar, and Anshuman Nayak—and my cofounders at Binachip: David Zaretsky and Gaurav Mittal. I also learned a lot about the venture capital business from AccelChip, Arch Venture Partners, Interwest Capital, and Greylock Partners investors. I have also learned a lot about how start-ups innovate from my son, Swaraj Banerjee, and his wife, Anurati Mathur, who cofounded Sempre Health, a health care start-up. We have discussed the challenges and opportunities of working with their customers and investors.

Finally, I learned so much about innovating in large companies at companies like HP, ABB, Accenture, and Ansys. I learned a lot about disruptive innovation while leading HP Labs, from six hundred of the brightest researchers at HP Labs across seven locations worldwide, from the CTO of HP, Shane Robison, and from the CEO Mark Hurd. I carried out the learning at HP Labs to Accenture Labs under CTO Paul Daugherty and CEO Pierre Nanterme.

I want to recognize my colleagues at ABB, where I learned how large industrial companies drive innovation, led by our CEO Joe Hogan. I also want to acknowledge my colleagues at Schneider Electric, led by our CEO Jean-Pascal Tricoire.

I want to recognize my superb colleagues at Ansys, including Shane Emswiler, SVP of products, from whom I learned how to drive innovation across multiple products; Rick Mahoney, SVP of sales, from whom I learned how to support innovation for customers; Nicole Anasenes, CFO and SVP of finance, from whom I learned how to drive innovation using the right financial levers; Maria Shields, SVP of administration, who taught me how to scale a company; Matt Zack, VP of corporate development, from whom I learned who to develop partnerships with in large companies, startups, and academia, as well as mergers and acquisitions; Julie Murphy, VP of HR, from whom I learned how to drive the culture of innovation in a company; Lynn Ledwith, VP of marketing, who taught me how to communicate the vision around innovation; Janet Lee, VP of legal, from whom I learned how to protect innovation using patents and who reviewed my book; Tom Smithyman, whom I worked with to perfect my communication skills; Renee Demay, chief of staff, with whom I have regular conversations about how to engage with sales and R&D; Dipankar Choudhury, Ansys fellow, my partner in the CTO office, who helped me drive innovation across Ansys; and finally, our leader and CEO, Ajei Gopal, who has been mentoring me all these years. We have been driving innovation at Ansys for the past four years, and I have tried to write about my learning in this book. I am grateful to my CEO, Ajei Gopal, for writing a foreword for this book.

I want to thank all the leaders of innovation whom I interviewed for the various chapters in my book: Professor Monty Algers, professor of chemical engineering at Penn State University, for his insights in chapter 1 related to the topics of innovation in general; Professor Alberto Sangiovanni-Vincentelli, professor of electrical engineering and computer science at the University of California, Berkeley, for his discussion in chapter 2 related to innovation in academia; Dr. Amit Narayan, CEO of AutoGrid, for his insights about innovation start-ups in chapter 3; Brad Feldmann, CEO of Cubic, for sharing his ideas about innovation in large companies in chapter 4; Dr. Peter Lee, corporate vice president of Microsoft Research and Incubations, for sharing his insights in chapter 5 on the role of a central research lab in a large company in driving innovation; Dr. Mallik Tatipamula, chief technology officer, Ericsson Silicon Valley, for discussing his ideas on how large companies can practice disruptive innovation by partnering with academia and start-ups; Dr. Erwin Gianchandani, assistant director of the directorate for Technology, Innovation, and Partnerships (TIP), National Science Foundation, for discussing funding models of innovation in chapter 7; Gamiel Gran, senior vice president at Mayfield, for his insight on digital technologies to drive product innovation in chapter 8; Professor Henry Chesbrough, professor of Haas School of Business at UC Berkeley, for discussing open innovation in chapter 9.

I want to thank Jack Rochester, who worked with me to plan, review, and edit this book. We spent countless hours discussing the various topics of this book. Finally, I learned a lot about innovation from my elder brother, Professor Sanjay Banerjee. He is a professor of electrical engineering and director of the Microelectronics Research Center at the University of Texas at Austin. My brother and I have similar academic and career records. We both got our BTech degrees in electronics engineering from IIT Kharagpur in India. We both earned our MS and PhD degrees in electrical engineering from the University of Illinois Urbana-Champaign, and we both worked in academia and industry. We spend hours every week discussing how innovation happens in academia, in start-ups, and in large companies. Sanjay has been a mentor throughout my career of thirty-five years. He has guided me every step of the way.

CHAPTER 1

An Introduction to the Innovation Factory

Interview: Monty Alger, professor, Penn State University

Monty Alger is a professor of chemical engineering at the Pennsylvania State University, where he is director of Institute for Natural Gas Research. His over thirty years of experience in the chemicals and energy industries includes positions as vice president and chief technology officer at Air Products and Chemicals Inc. and as senior vice president of research at Myriant. He spent twenty-three years at General Electric (GE), where he led technology development at the

Global Research Center of GE Plastics and was the general manager of technology for the advanced materials business. Before GE, he was the director of MIT Chemical Engineering Practice School at GE Plastics.

He is a member of the National Academy of Engineering and serves on advisory boards for certain organizations, including the Shenhua National Institute of Clean and Low-Carbon Energy and PTTGC (Thailand). He is also a former member of the Council on Competitiveness's Technology Leadership and Strategy Initiative. He earned SB and SM degrees from MIT and a PhD from the University of Illinois Urbana-Champaign, all in chemical engineering. He served on AIChE's board of directors (2010–2012) and finance committee and worked on investment priorities to align them with member value.

INTERVIEWER. Monty, thank you very much for agreeing to be interviewed for my book *The Innovation Factory*. Tell me about your background in the corporate world and academia.

INTERVIEWEE. After my PhD, I joined the MIT Department of Chemical Engineering as an assistant professor and practice school director at GE Plastics for two years, which involved two sites in the GE Plastics business. I got to know various people at GE and subsequently joined the GE Global Research Center in Schenectady, New York. I worked on projects for several GE businesses—plastics, medical systems, appliances, motors, and lighting. Through this experience, I got to see how GE research operated in the early years.

After several years, I moved to GE Plastics and had many in technology working with sites around the world. Also, as GE globalized, GE opened facilities in Bangalore and Shanghai and worked on globalization technology. Also, during this time, I was part of the GE Six Sigma initiative. That turned out to be transformational for me. I learned how to use output measurements to diagnose products and processes. I was part of a major effort to improve the capacity in the Lexan business in GE Plastics, and we developed techniques for sharing and benchmarking across plant sites. Using data changed the approach to make it much more c with open sharing and translation of practices across sites.

I was then the technology leader for the Noryl business and, subsequently, of the Silicones business in GE Plastics. Coincidently, those two businesses were where we had the MIT practice school station years before. During my time at the Noryl business, we developed new innovation practices and learned much more about how innovation happened in the past and today.

GE Silicones was sold to a private equity firm in 2007, and GE Plastics was later sold also. I left GE and joined Air Products and Chemicals as CTO in 2007. That was a move to a very different business model, one that was much more focused on engineering than on end use products. At the time, Air Products was two separate businesses with chemicals and industrial gases. All that shifted through several divestitures and acquisitions.

Later, in 2013, I joined a small start-up company, Myriant, that had a bio route to succinic acid. I was interested in joining a start-up, and they were building a 30 mm lb demonstration plant in LA. After two years at Myriant, we learned many challenges of the route proposed; and eventually, the business was shut down. PTT in Thailand is the parent investor in this and continues to seek new innovation projects.

Following Myriant, I joined Penn State University as the director of the Institute for Natural Gas Research. Penn State had broad research capabilities in oil and gas, and with the fracking boom, they desired to build a new partnership to pull through technology. This led to several efforts over the last several years. I will add details below. I also learned about the current challenges universities faced with a rapidly changing marketplace. Ultimately, Penn State decided to not pursue a recommended direction, and so INGaR was disbanded, and I moved to the chemical engineering department as a professor. I also finished three years at the AIChE as president and worked to implement many of the concepts I initially learned at Penn State.

INTERVIEWER. Can you define *innovation*? What about *discovery*? How does something move from the process of basic science and discovery to innovation?

INTERVIEWEE. *Discovery* is turning money into science. *Innovation* is turning science into money. I forgot who first said that phrase, but many have heard it and used it. Moving science to market is not a linear practice. It usually involves multiple people coming together, often by chance. Looking at history, one can see how big things happened. People have been seduced into thinking investing in discovery will lead to new market innovation. Without the proper steps and practices, it will only produce science. One of the most critical outcomes of scientific research is the technical talent that is produced. Most technology transfers happen by those who did the work.

INTERVIEWER. What is the mission of a research university like Penn State? How do you, as a faculty member, integrate your roles of teaching, research, and service? How has that mission changed?

INTERVIEWEE. I am the wrong person to answer this question. I have views not held by many at the university. There are two parallel worlds at a university—the academic faculty and the administration. The administration is challenged with the business model of the university. The academic faculty is engaged with education and research. In recent years, there seems to have been an acceleration of research effort. This appears to be across most universities. I think the economic model as the driver of change is worth exploring following that money can lead to important insights. University financial statements are available online. Tuition is usually the most significant source of revenue. The faculty is a primarily independent operator. Various collaborations, centers, institutes, etc. are formed to bring people together. Often, it is around technology and not a market solution.

INTERVIEWER. How does Penn State or other universities facilitate technology transfer to the industry?

INTERVIEWEE. Penn State has an innovation practice outlined in https://www.research.psu.edu. There is a desire to engage companies as part of the overall research plan. It is primarily designed around Penn State offerings and less on what companies need.

INTERVIEWER. You have worked at an industrial research lab like GE Research. How has the role of corporate research labs transformed over the years? How do they work with the larger companies?

INTERVIEWEE. I did a study of GE innovation from 1950 back to the beginning. I found a report written by William White, who was Irving Langmuir's lab assistant. In it, he wrote, "History shows that every big thing was discovered while working on something that was considered more important at the time." This observation, too, has been my experience. One doesn't have a big idea, study it, and then commercialize. There is an iteration between market need and solution. Technology typically enables unique features in an offering, but there is more required to demonstrate. New to world applications are usually the biggest but are not known until introduced to the market. Lots of examples in the tech world of these types of applications. Or Henry Ford: "If I had asked customers, they would have said a faster horse."

Let me add some of my personal insights into GE's history. The early years of business evolved from the core lighting business—power generation, distribution, transformers, turbines, aircraft engineers, etc. There is a history of GE innovation written by George Wise. He is a historian and has really good views of GE. I have not talked to him in many years, but there was a long company culture of innovation. The other thing I observed about the early GE was, there was a percolation path from university to business. The faculty would give talks at the research center. The research center would hire students. Work done at R&D was connected to businesses and back to universities. Many from the research center would go out to work at the company, which created a connection from market back to university. This all changed in the nineties with globalization and downsizing—cycle times shortened, etc. I also had experience in GE Plastics where we created new innovation practices. We built a team to create new projects, not the project. It was iterative with customers and research.

INTERVIEWER. Professors in academia work on fundamental research problems, and the output is peer-reviewed papers in conferences and journals. However, it takes a lot more work to take the results of their basic research and translate them to industry. Can you speak about how that can be improved in the future?

INTERVIEWEE. This is a huge need. It is the culture and business model that need to change. Let me discuss a collaboration model we developed at Penn State for Energy University. We had money from GE to run innovation sessions, which worked very well. Sadly, the university leadership lost interest, so it all collapsed. That was when I joined AIChE for three years, and we started the institute for learning and innovation. It is designed around the same concepts using students connecting ideas to market and integrating education and research. So much is changing with connectivity, accessibility of information, and money. The three recent company breakups—GE, Toshiba, and J&J—highlight the need for a different value proposition in the marketplace.

INTERVIEWER. How can large companies better partner with academia in the future?

INTERVIEWEE. I believe the connected model makes the most sense, but we need new behaviors on all sides as well as new practices. This is what has come out from the National Academy of Engineering (NAE) study so far.

INTRODUCTION

What is innovation? Innovation begins life as a need and becomes an idea for a way to satisfy that need. It is the conduit between the idea and its solution as a product or service. In short, innovation connects a problem and a solution and is most likely to happen at the grassroots level, which I believe is the collegiate postgraduate teaching and learning environment. However, such an environment can be as straightforward as two colleagues discussing a frustrating situation over coffee—the legendary tale of scribbling an idea on a paper napkin that goes on to change the world. University graduate students often become involved in innovation problem-solving project(s) assigned by their professors. Often, the professor becomes an innovation consultant for business partners.

These relationships grow and take new directions as graduate students discover innovation opportunities and create start-ups of their own. They are rarely linear but rather are multipronged—work on one innovation may spawn work on others, seemingly unrelated. In most instances, when your company begins partnering with a university, a start-up, or a complementary business, a collaborative bond begins to form and is hopefully sustained throughout the life of the partnership and into greater business maturity for all. For example, when the city of Portland, Oregon, decided to create a bike-sharing program, it partnered with Nike and Motivate for sponsorship and help with implementation. Biketown PDX launched in 2016 and is still today operated by the rideshare company Lyft. It took time, but here is a caveat: Don't expect technology transfer to happen overnight or to benefit your company exclusively. All parties should derive valuable outcomes from the partnering.

Clayton Christensen demonstrated how successful companies could do everything right and still lose their market leadership or even fail as unexpected new competitors rise and take over the market. For example, HP invested in cloud computing. Yet they could not keep their market share as the largest computer company with more than $100 billion in revenue and ultimately had to split off into two companies—HPE, focused on servers and software, and

HP Inc., focused on personal computers and printers—and still lost its leadership to new entrants, such as Amazon Web Services and Microsoft Azure. There are two key aspects to this dilemma.

1. *Value to innovation is an S curve.* Improving a product takes time and many iterations. The first of these iterations provides minimal value to the customer, but the base is created in time, and the value increases exponentially. Once the base is made, then each iteration is dramatically better than the last. At some point, the most valuable improvements are complete, and the value per iteration is minimal again, so in the middle is the most value. At the beginning and end, the value is minimal.

2. *Incumbent-sized deals.* The incumbent has the luxury of a considerable customer set but high expectations of yearly sales. New-entry, next-generation products find niches away from the incumbent customer set to build the new product. Latest-entry companies do not require the annual sales of the incumbent and, thus, have more time to focus and innovate on this smaller venture.

For this reason, the next-generation product is not being built for the incumbent's customer set, but this large customer set may not be interested in the innovation and continues to demand more innovation with the incumbent product. Unfortunately, this incumbent innovation is limited to the product's overall value, as it is at the tail end of the S curve. Meanwhile, the new entrant is deep into the S curve and is providing significant value to the new product. When the new product becomes attractive to the incumbent's customers, it is likely too late for them to react to the new product. Further, it is now too late for the incumbent to keep up with the new entrant's rate of improvement, which by now is on the near-vertical ascent of its S curve trajectory. Figure 1.1 shows the challenges between sustaining innovations and disruptive innovations.

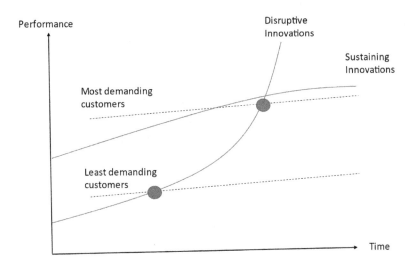

Fig. 1.1. Innovations from sustaining technologies and disruptive technologies (courtesy of Clayton Christenson, *The Innovator's Dilemma*)

Decision makers may think introducing a new product or service won't return a satisfactory ROI. They may perceive the market as unreceptive to change. These reactions may be due to the inherent conservatism of business leadership, resisting market challenges and change in favor of sticking with the product or service they know, how it has always been made and sold—the safety of the bottom line. Yet large companies most often excel at innovation by releasing new and improved versions of an established product. For example, when I was CTO at ABB during 2012–2013, ABB introduced numerous new versions of their transformers, switchgear, and robots.

That said, once a product or service is established in the marketplace, the business may honestly think there is no reason to improve or reinvent it unless they deploy a disruptive innovation. Business leaders think that is risky. Perhaps they don't believe Christensen's dictum, that if they continue doing only what the business leaders have already been doing, they are dooming their business to stagnation. But running a risk-free business is the most significant risk of all.

Apple was primarily in the business of making personal computers, such as the Macintosh and MacBook. In 2007, they created a disruptive product called the iPhone, which was revolutionary in how smartphones worked by combining a mobile phone with a camera and creating the iOS platform for iPhone apps. Finally, Apple was able to create a platform for music and videos using the iPhone. Subsequently, Apple created the iPad in 2010 as a device that straddled a personal computer and an iPhone. This is the kind of disruptive innovation we will explore in this book.

Idea versus Innovation

Innovation is one of the most used and, at the same time, most frequently misunderstood terms in the business vocabulary. Innovation is not the old-fashioned light bulb going off above one's head. That is just an idea. Rather, innovation is translating an idea into goods or a service that either creates value customers will pay for or provides some societal benefit.

To be called an innovation, an idea must be replicable at an economical cost and must satisfy a specific need. Innovation involves the deliberate application of information, imagination, and initiative in deriving greater or different values from resources. Innovation encompasses all processes by which new ideas are generated, developed, and transformed into useful products. In business, innovation is often the result when a company applies fresh ideas to existing products or services to further satisfy its customers' needs and expectations, in some cases before the customer even recognizes the need.

Product and Process Innovation

A product innovation introduces goods or a service that is either new or is significantly improved concerning its characteristics or intended uses. These include significant improvements in technical specifications, components and materials, incorporated software, user-friendliness, or other functional features. Product innovations include both new products and new uses for existing products.

- *New products.* These goods and services differ significantly in their characteristics or intended uses from products previously produced by the firm. For example:
  1. Thomas Edison's light bulb changed the world's relationship with nighttime.
  2. The transistor replaced the vacuum tube and, in the process, redefined the history of the world.
  3. The smartphone, pioneered by Apple, combined discrete technologies into a handheld device that could make a phone call and take pictures. Overtime, it became the personal computer of many.

- *New uses for products.* The development of a further use for a product with only minor changes to its technical specifications is product innovation. Perhaps one of the most brilliant adaptations was Napster, which combined the Internet, peer-to-peer computing, and MP3 recordings to distribute music.

Process innovation is the implementation of a new or significantly improved production or delivery method. This includes significant changes in techniques, equipment, and software. For example, sufficient computer data storage was an issue from the beginning. Large companies were constantly purchasing more and more costly disk drives until the rise of the Internet, which facilitated cloud computing, once referred to as software as a service, or SaaS.

Process innovations can decrease production or delivery unit costs, increase quality, or produce or deliver new or significantly improved products. They can be distinguished by production methods, delivery methods, or both.

- *Production methods.* The means of production involves a specific set of techniques, equipment, and software used to produce goods or services. The purpose is usually to speed up or enhance manufacturing methods to make the product better, less expensive, or more available. Robotics and other mechanical automation is one example. Another is computer-aided design, or CAD, which has made older methods of product development obsolete.

- *Delivery methods.* These concern the logistics of transporting the product or service from the firm to the customer. Logistics encompass equipment, software, and techniques to source inputs, allocate supplies, or deliver final products. RFID (radio-frequency identification) is a commonly used goods tracking system, as is NFC (near field communication), which is also based on RFID protocols but utilizes Bluetooth technology.

- *Both.* Federal Express was an early logistics innovator. Of course, the FedEx truck would come to your facility to pick up or deliver your products. But in the 1980s, FedEx went a step further and set up its logistics office in the company's warehouse, so there was no time or expense involved in moving a product between the business and its shipping service. This innovation was followed by the first tracking number, the use of handheld computers to scan barcodes, and the first personal, computer-based shipping system for its customers.

The Distinction between Discovery and Invention

It took Frederick W. Smith ten years—from the college paper he wrote about the need for speedy package delivery to the first FedEx planes and trucks. The key to understanding innovation is to not confuse it with discovery, which is finding certain attributes or characteristics of an innovation asset that may have potential value. Smith's discovery required a decade's work to become the logistics network it is today. Real innovation is not an invent-first-find-a-market-later process. The value must first accrue to the business—financial, technological, and social. But the value must also accrue to the customer—emotional, financial, technological, or social.

Recall our example of the iPhone, which Steve Jobs considered primarily a phone. Yet its innovation value accrued rapidly once people began using it to take pictures, listen to music, and surf the web. Since its introduction in 2007, hardly anything about making a phone call has changed. If the iPhone had been a phone only, there would have been nothing to innovate. It was the apps—additional tools and services—that transformed the iPhone into one of the most innovative technologies on the market, its camera's performance rivaling that of expensive DSLR cameras, and the App Store gave it myriad opportunities to do more and more things with the device.

Apple understands their product and their market. They talk to customers. They continually innovate their products into better versions. They know how to sell a good product, whether it is the iPhone, iPad, or MacBook. But Apple also recognizes the limitations of just being a hardware company and has pursued the next level of innovation by creating Music (formerly iTunes) and the App Store, thereby leveraging the innovation ecosystem of developers around the world, and they are also adding two very successful revenue streams.

THE THREE INNOVATION HORIZONS

Innovation inherently means a change in a process, a structure, or a business's product or service direction. In 2000, Mehrdad Baghai, Stephen Coley, and David White, consultants at global consulting management firm McKinsey & Company, published the landmark study of business innovation entitled *The Alchemy of Growth: Practical Insights for Building the Enduring Enterprise*. Their book described the three innovation horizons, a concept that is still widely held as the most understandable to this day. In brief, the three horizons are the following:

- Horizon 1 (H1)—short-term innovation, mainly in the core product or service offered, e.g., sustaining, renewing, or in some cases, reinventing the core offer. Strategic companies invest 70 percent of their R&D portfolio in this category.

- Horizon 2 (H2)—medium-term innovation introduced in the core or adjacent offer but driven at the business level. Strategic companies invest 20 percent of their R&D portfolio in this category.
- Horizon 3 (H3)—long tail disruptive innovation, often introduced or driven by an outside influence—for example, acquiring a start-up. Strategic companies invest 10 percent of their R&D portfolio in this category.

Rideshare, founded by Uber in 2009, quickly became a booming business. Lyft, its primary competitor, started three years later. Ridesharing is itself a potent innovation, offering more personalized experiences than a conventional taxi. Lyft further distinguished itself from Uber by innovating into vehicles for hire—motorized scooters, a bicycle-sharing system, and rental cars. Here was how Lyft innovated in each of the three horizons.

- H1—innovated over its competitors that offered ridesharing by understanding the basic principles of human relationships and socialization, making it possible for riders and drivers to learn something about each other prior to accepting a ride.
- H2—branched its core concept to scooters and electric bicycles; like Uber, Lyft also began offering food delivery.
- H3—disrupted its rideshare/taxi business model of high overhead and hiring costly human drivers by developing self-driving auto technologies. Then in 2021, Lyft saw that the endeavor was not an essential part of its core business and so seized the opportunity to sell its self-driving business to an automaker.

Consider another example, how Amazon innovated with each of the three horizons.

- H1—innovated beyond its competitors by pushing the concept of an online bookstore, beating brick-and-mortar bookstores, like Barnes & Noble.
- H2—branched into its innovative brick-and-mortar bookstores and further into online retail in all categories of products, competing with the likes of Walmart, which had remained a bricks-and-mortar business at the time.
- H3—throughout its twenty-plus-year history, Amazon has continued to create disruptive innovation through acquisitions (Whole Foods, the *Washington Post*, pop-ups); its Amazon Web Services (AWS) cloud business has become the leading player in the field over Microsoft Azure and Google Cloud Platform.

In our book *The Innovation Factory*, we will discuss how large companies can emulate Apple, Lyft, and Amazon to drive H3 disruptive innovation.

THE DISCONNECT

Once something is developed through R&D innovation processes, it's up to the marketing and sales staff to sell it. Yet if it is something new or different, they may not know how to do so, or they may think it is not a marketable product or service. Consider James Bond movies. There is an innovation-to-business disconnect between Q's innovation-building lab and 007's practical needs, as Bond rarely uses all the gadgets Q has had designed for him. R&D—or wherever your innovation occurs in the twenty-first-century business organization—is frequently not considered an essential link in the value chain. Unfortunately, once that is the perception, an absence of trust arises, leading to a disconnect difficult to repair.

Take the mouse and the graphical user interface invented at Xerox's Palo Alto Research Center (PARC). Xerox's core business was manufacturing and selling copiers and printers while PARC was a pure research lab tasked with developing future technologies. There was a clearly defined disconnect between innovation and the company's product lines. Xerox sales reps sold business products, not research ideas, thus promulgating one of the most significant technology appropriations of all time. That occurred when Steve Jobs, head of Apple, visited Xerox PARC, saw the immense potential of its personal computer technology ideas, and realized they were his for the taking. In 1984, Apple was able to develop and market both the GUI and the mouse successfully on the Macintosh.

Horizon 3 Innovation—the Most Significant Risk and Return

Most large companies excel in developing incremental improvements to their existing products, solutions, and services, typically referred to as horizon 1 innovation. Many companies manage to do well in developing adjacent products and solutions, which is the horizon 2 innovations. But the sad fact remains: most companies struggle with bringing genuinely innovative new products and solutions—the genuinely disruptive, game-changing ones of horizon 3 innovation—to market.

Yes, gambling on disruptive innovation can be risky and expensive. The new product could fail in the marketplace. Yet what is the price of not innovating? Probably incalculable. In 1964, IBM introduced a new computer system, the System/360. A *Fortune* magazine article called it the company's $5,000,000,000 gamble. IBM's own Bob Evans revealed, "We called this project You Bet Your Company."

IBM knew the risks. Its leadership also understood the consequences of not taking the risk and the potential rewards if the innovative new computer was the success they thought it could be. This is why many products, especially high-tech devices and services, become one-trick ponies and eventually reach a dead end.

There seems to be nothing left to improve upon and no path back to re-innovation. This was certainly how IBM perceived its eponymous Personal Computer, which with its very different marketplace did not fit with its policy of upgrades once every five years. Led by Compaq, a dozen competitors introduced innovations so fast and far-reaching that IBM couldn't sustain its market dominance, so it sold its PC business to Lenovo.

Four Zones of Innovation

Geoffrey Moore, in his book *Zone to Win*, describes four zones of innovation for large companies. The book employs several disruptive ideas as the innovation drivers. Moore's first disruptive idea is that companies need to innovate to keep growing, yet disruption by its nature creates a ripple effect. The best way for a company to grow rapidly is to introduce a new product or service that turns an industry on its head. Consider the innovations of online marketing; cloud computing; or electric scooters, bicycles, and autos. Being an innovative market leader can be extremely profitable, often yielding 20 percent revenue growth over the first five to seven years after a new product or service is introduced.

On the other hand, if you miss the wave, there is usually no way to catch up. You are best off searching for another swell to carry you into innovation waves, as Lyft did. Companies experiencing continuous growth are experts at catching innovation waves. For instance, Apple caught not one but four waves in the last ten years: digital music, smartphones, tablets, and its App Store. In each disruption, the company completely transformed the market for mobile technologies.

Disruptive innovations, however, can also throw entire industries off-balance; a disruption in one field can have far-reaching effects in others. With the release of the iPhone, the market for mobile phones was disrupted, as was the commercial airline business. Phone calls onboard an aircraft were (expensively) handled by a third party; now any passenger may use their phone to make calls at a much lower cost yet potentially causing signal interference with the aircraft's electronics. The airlines had to adjust to this new reality; and yet another: customers wanted to use their smartphones to book trips, download boarding passes, and track their flights. This disruption didn't require just a simple infrastructure upgrade. The smartphone forced airlines to reconfigure almost all customer-facing processes—from check-in, to lounge services, and to boarding—requiring substantial investments that didn't immediately result in additional profits. So disruptive change can certainly be difficult for companies to handle. This is why it is essential to recognize and prepare to manage horizon 3 disruption when it comes knocking at your company's door.

Moore's second idea is that established companies can compete with disruptive start-ups by creating four zones of management, as shown in figure 1.2. Young companies are typically focused on a single goal—building a new product—while established companies have to balance maintaining the current business model and handling market disruptions simultaneously, aware that everything is going to change. Established companies need to consider restructuring operations into Moore's four zones to compete effectively in a disruptive world.

The first is the performance zone. This is where employees who sell an existing product are located. For example, in the automotive industry, this zone would be populated by people who sell cars or generate direct income for the company. The second is the productivity zone. This zone encompasses all activity that doesn't directly generate revenue but instead provides the necessary support for revenue generation. Producing cars, marketing the company brand, providing customer service, and managing human resources are all found here.

The third is the incubation zone. This group is responsible for seeking out innovative solutions to boost the growth of the company. This zone may focus on developing more reliable new types of self-driving systems in the automotive industry, for example. Moore's incubation zone is where the innovation factory's H3 innovation takes place. The final zone is the transformation zone. It focuses on finding ways for the company to adapt to their competitors' disruptive innovations. For instance, if a competitor is developing a more efficient, faster-charging battery for electric vehicles, this zone would form a competitive response.

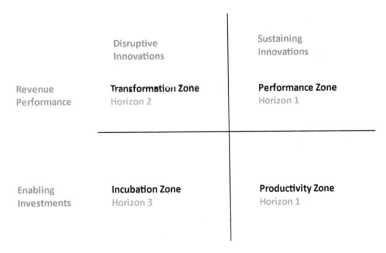

Fig. 1.2. Four zones of innovation (courtesy of Geoffrey Moore, *Zone to Win*)

THE TWENTY-FIRST-CENTURY BUSINESS MODEL

At the root, most business planning and strategy are rote, lazy, and even fear based, often the result of relying on a familiar old horizon or business model that has become impractical and outdated. In many instances, the innovation defines itself as respecting its particular horizon; thus, there is no need to assign one. Similarly, there is no one-size-fits-all business model for developing, integrating, and producing innovation any longer; in fact, perhaps there never was.

Every line of business (LOB) has its prescribed parameters with predetermined insertion points for innovation, but what if no one has a brilliant new idea at that particular link in the value chain? Or what if the company is attempting to expand into new economic environments? Most of this kind of activity demand distinctive new business models, and they require their own unique innovation as one of the many conditions for business process execution, and so innovation becomes an integral aspect of that business process.

OPEN INNOVATION: WHAT THE INNOVATION FACTORY IS ABOUT

Disruptive innovation is not the only form of innovation, but it is the most transformational aspect in the modern corporation. The business graveyard is littered with corporations attempting growth and success while playing it safe when implementing any form of innovation, disruptive or not. No pain, no gain. No risk, no reward.

Of equal importance: thinking you can build your disruptive innovation strategy all by yourself is rarely the best approach. In my experience, companies engaged in the most powerful, transformative innovation strategies without the participation of outside partners are rarely able to achieve the successful outcomes they seek. Put simply, you need fresh perspectives to succeed with innovation, because it is different in every different business circumstance. You need to partner.

This type of partnering is called open innovation. The business enterprise brings in partners from academia and start-ups to lend their thought leadership, insights, and often, experience. This collaboration may well persist beyond the conclusion of a single successful innovation. You might move into a deeper and even more collaborative relationship with your academic partner. You might find that you are so impressed with your start-up partner that you offer to buy or invest in the company. Once your vision for innovation is shared and successful, your partners will want to continue working with you. Each of you will want to scale up the partnership.

In a nutshell, *The Innovation Factory* posits that innovation must be profoundly integrated into the business value chain, and this is most successful when the company partners with academia and start-ups. It describes how large companies can successfully partner to acquire external perspectives and ideas from both start-up companies and universities and merge them into its internal start-up incubators to foster truly disruptive innovation. This does not mean that every idea will see the light of day or that every innovative product or service, once implemented, will succeed. Both success and failure are necessary for business growth, because each teaches new perspectives. Yet we should not shrink from innovating. Without fully integrating innovation into the business value chain, the business will wither and even die. And if we do not partner, success with our innovation initiatives is measurably more difficult, if not impossible.

I hope to make it clear to the business book reader that we need fresh thinking, new perspectives, and an environment that supports and encourages change, risk-taking, and innovation. But this initiative demands new strategic thinking and new business models more suitable to the ever-changing twenty-first-century economic environment. We seem to be locked into doing what we did yesterday or earlier today, but not what we are going to do tomorrow. How do we escape the rigors of business as usual? By working with other innovators. Here are the examples of the major approaches to innovation.

By partnering. Adidas was the premier shoe and footwear maker in the world for over fifty years. Suddenly, it found itself in dire competition with Nike and Reebok, both of whom were innovating the sports shoe. Adidas could not compete efficiently because its shoes were being manufactured in factories using old technologies. Company executives knew they had to find innovative new technologies to make new shoes people would want to buy.

They discovered additive manufacturing / 3D printing. They thought if they could 3D-print the footwear, they would develop some exciting products quickly and less expensively. The company could have launched an internal group to pursue 3D printing with metals, binder jets, or plastics; but that would have taken too long. Instead, they looked around at a dozen 3D printing start-up companies with whom they might partner. They found one, Carbon, which had developed a specific differentiated technology called digital light synthesis (DLS) that was just right for designing and manufacturing their footwear products.

Carbon worked with Adidas for several years to build the first 3D printed shoes, then scaled them into production to manufacture in the millions. Their story is one of true open innovation. Each company brought what they were good at to the partnership, and by innovating together, they created a new and extraordinarily innovative shoe-manufacturing process. Adidas is once again a top-selling sports shoe.

By acquisition. Let us look at Google, which many consider one of the top five innovative companies. Google's search technology, developed by two Stanford grad students, is the company's core asset. Yet Google soon recognized that its search engine was a natural for serving not just content but also advertising. That evolved into targeting the most relevant ads to specific consumers. At the outset, the Google search tool was only available on desktop computers. When Google decided to move search to mobile devices, like phones and tablets, in 2005, it acquired Andy Rubin's company, Android. Google partnered in developing the open Android operating system. The Android OS is an open system and runs on more devices than any other, including the Apple iPhone. It is the leading OS for mobile devices.

Google partnered with many other companies and researchers to grow the company. In 2005, it formalized these partnerships under the umbrella name Alphabet. The following year, Google acquired YouTube, now the largest video content platform in the world. Many of its holdings were open-source, such as Chromium. Chrome (considered proprietary freeware) is an OS and a browser with its own array of specialized apps—Gmail, Drive, Docs, Workspace, and hundreds of others—which further enhance Chrome's usefulness and deepen its bond with customers. To date, Google has acquired or formed partnerships with around 250 companies.

The point is, disruptive innovation in the most innovative companies, such as Google, were rarely done by creating the technology solely in-house. A far wiser and likely less costly approach was smartly scouting for technologies and opportunities outside of the mother ship, integrating them into the larger company and selling the expanded set of products to existing customers as well as attracting a new and expanded customer base. This role, played by innovators (often in the person of the chief technology officer) in larger companies, is similar to that of talent scouts in the NBA and NFL businesses, identifying outstanding talent at the high school or college level to recruit as teammates during drafts.

Avoiding the not-invented-here (NIH) syndrome. I have worked with innovation all my career—first in academia, twice as a start-up founder, and then in charge of innovation for several large companies. While a professor at Northwestern University, my grad student research team created a technology called the MATCH compiler, which could compile MATLAB programs onto field-programmable gate arrays. This was an important research innovation for digital signal processing (DSP) synthesis. The prototype, built in the year 2000, was nowhere near becoming a commercial product. I took leave from the university, founded AccelChip with my graduate students, and worked closely with Xilinx to build the Accel FPGA tool. We integrated it with their system generator tool, and together, we conquered not-invented-here and created magic. Recognizing our abilities, Xilinx bought AccelChip in 2006.

By innovating to do it better. Again, this is another key observation. Many amazing disruptive technologies are created at universities. For example, Merck and Novartis are partnering with MIT to drive innovations at their companies; the USC Marshall Greif Incubator program is incubating several start-up companies; the Mosaic browser development at the University of Illinois, which was funded by the National Center for Supercomputing Applications (NCSA) and the National Science Foundation (NSF), was the enabling technology behind the browser Netscape Navigator.

What is essential is for the disruption to not remain a laboratory experiment. It must be brought to the very point of commercialization. That was where Mosaic stood in the early 1990s until Marc Andreessen, a grad student and Mosaic team leader, partnered with James Clark of Silicon Graphics to produce Netscape Navigator. They took browser technology to the next level and made it into a commercial product. Although one of the first web browsers, its tenure was short-lived, but it left its mark. In 1995, Microsoft licensed the technology and created its own web browser, Internet Explorer, giving Mosaic a second commercial life.

Interestingly, innovation begets more innovation, as the story of Mosaic proves. It seems to be human nature to see something potentially useful and try making it even more useful. Netscape Navigator inspired Internet Explorer, which in turn inspired Google's Chrome, and so on. Every tech company wanted its own browser—Axis, Edge, Firefox, Opera, and Safari—to establish its hegemony and, of course, to make money. Each was dominant at the outset until a competitor out-innovated it. Chrome today is more of a computing environment than just a simple browser. Who knows where innovation will lead us with the next iteration? A browserless web environment?

GAFAM platform innovation. Many regard GAFAM (a term coined by CNBC television host Jim Cramer) companies—Google, Apple, Facebook, Amazon, and Microsoft—as leading the list of the most innovative companies of the twenty-first century. They are—in particular, when it comes to platform innovation. GAFAMs have a combined market capitalization of more than $9 trillion because their revenues are growing significantly each year, and they are consistently very profitable. Many observers and analysts do not realize that each of these companies is leveraging the platform innovation concept to drive their growth. We discuss this in more detail in chapter 8.

At their core, each of these companies, not just Google with its Chrome browser, has created a software platform with open APIs for third-party developers and partners to innovate and develop their applications. Those innovative apps often remain exclusively on each sponsoring GAFAM platform, thereby enriching both sponsor and developer. For example, a third-party developer, such as TikTok, Zoom, or Zynga, creates an app for the host company that sits on top of either the iOS platform from Apple or perhaps the Google Play platform using Android from Google. As the app attracts users and, thus, grows in revenue, Apple and Google each earn 30 percent of the proceeds. This is the ultimate achievement of open innovation—leveraging the innovation of third-party developers. Industrial companies, such as GE, ABB, and Schneider Electric, are trying to emulate this type of platform innovation by creating the GE Predix Platform, ABB Ability, and Schneider Electric EcoStruxure Platform.

We discuss platform technologies in chapter 8 and how it is leveraging the open innovation concept.

THE TRANSFER OF TECHNOLOGIES

Technology transfer involves moving from ideation through various value chain linkages toward the creation of a mature product or service in the marketplace. It rarely occurs the same way in every instance and does not occur often when the entire process takes place within the cloistered walls of a single company. It can happen when that company buys another company or technology product and they synergistically innovate together. It happens more organically and successfully when a professor with an idea decides to take a sabbatical leave of absence, starts a company, builds a focused product, and then either obtains funding or sells it to a large company. This is well-documented successful technology transfer. There are many examples. Below are to name a few.

- Professor Tom Leighton left MIT in the late 1990s to cofound Akamai Technologies, known today as an internationally respected cybersecurity, web services, and cloud computing platform, headquartered in Cambridge, Massachusetts, and valued at more than $3.6 billion.
- Professor Nick McKeown left Stanford to launch Nicira Networks in 2007, providing software-defined networking and network virtualization services; in 2012, Nicira was acquired by VMWare, a cloud computing and virtualization technology company, for $1.5 billion.
- Professor Alberto Sangiovanni-Vincentelli from UC Berkeley started Silicon Design Automation; SDA was folded into Cadence Design Systems, a developer of software, hardware and silicon structures for circuit design. Cadence has acquired over thirty partner companies and today is a more than $3 billion company with headquarters in San Jose, California.

Perhaps this recent and possibly the most successful example of the academic-to-business technology transfer is Professor Jennifer Doudna from UC Berkeley, who is credited with codeveloping the gene-editing technology called CRISPR. It took Dr. Doudna about two decades of development. For her work, she was awarded the Nobel Prize in Chemistry in 2020. Even then, it was considered a brilliant innovation in search of a practical application; then the COVID-19 pandemic hit the world. It took a start-up company, BioNTech, to seize the opportunity to leverage Doudna's CRISPR and mRNA technology and develop vaccines for COVID-19. In one of the perfect innovation partnerships from academia to commerce, BioNTech passed the baton to Pfizer, which quickly delivered this serum technology to the world. Dr. Doudna says, "I imagine having little CRISPR-based devices so that people can come to work, spit in a tube, and in thirty minutes, get an answer, telling them whether they need to be quarantined or not."

These two superb innovation resources—academia and start-ups—are readily interested in partnering with the large company. In fact, recognizing the shortcomings of doing it themselves, all three actively seek partners with which to innovate. Each brings fresh new perspectives to the innovation process and creative problem-solving for your business. Neither partner requires vast outlays of time or money. An academic relationship provides guidance, research, and highly motivated students to work with your R&D people. Start-ups are often much more involved in the dynamics of disruptive innovation, as it impacts business and commerce, so let them do what they love. You should consider partnering your innovation projects with either or both simultaneously. Both are eager and attentive partners. Chapter 2 discusses how discovery and innovation are pursued in academia, and chapter 3 presents how innovation is pursued in start-ups.

Open innovation with academia and start-ups is not new. *The Innovation Factory* provides essential, practical guidance, largely based on my experience, for all parties wishing to work toward successful collaborations to launch innovation in its many aspects. Perhaps you have already launched some partnerships; if so, this book will help both of you make them more successful. In either case, it is the only book you need to launch and partner in open innovation initiatives.

CHAPTER 2
Innovation in Academia

Interview: Professor Alberto Sangiovanni-Vincentelli, UC Berkeley, founder and board member of Cadence.

Alberto Sangiovanni-Vincentelli is the Edgar L. and Harold H. Buttner Chair of Electrical Engineering and Computer Sciences at the University of California, Berkeley. From 1980 to 1981, he was a visiting scientist at the mathematical sciences department of IBM's T. J. Watson Research Center. In 1987, he was a visiting professor at MIT. He has over eight hundred papers, seventeen books, and two patents in design tools and methodologies, large-scale systems, embedded systems, hybrid systems, and innovation. He was a cofounder of Cadence and Synopsys, the two leading companies in electronic design automation, and the founder and scientific director of the PARADES Research Center in Rome. He has been a member of the board of directors of Cadence, KPIT Cummins, Sonics, and Expert System.

INTERVIEWER. Alberto, thank you very much for agreeing to be interviewed for my book *The Innovation Factory*. Tell me about your background.

INTERVIEWEE. I am the Edgar L. and Harold H. Buttner Chair of Electrical Engineering and Computer Sciences at the University of California, Berkeley. From 1980 to 1981, I was a visiting scientist at the mathematical sciences department of IBM's T. J. Watson Research Center. In 1987, I was a visiting professor at MIT. Since July 2019, I have served as special adviser to the dean of engineering of the University of California, Berkeley, for entrepreneurship and as chair of the academic advisers of the Berkeley SkyDeck Accelerator. I am an honorary professor at Politecnico di Torino.

I have coauthored over one thousand papers, nineteen books, and two patents in design tools and methodologies, large-scale systems, embedded systems, hybrid systems, and innovation. I am a cofounder of Cadence and Synopsys, the two leading companies in electronic design automation, and the founder and scientific director of the PARADES Research Center in Rome. I have been a member of the board of directors of Cadence, KPIT Cummins, Expert.ai, CY4GATE, and EXIN. And I am the chairman of the board of Quantum Motion, Phoenix, Innatera, and Phononic Vibes.

In 2001, I received the Kaufman Award of the Council on Electronic Design Automation for pioneering contributions to EDA. In 2008, I was awarded the IEEE/RSE James Clerk Maxwell Medal "for groundbreaking contributions that have had an exceptional impact on the development of electronics and electrical engineering or related fields" with the following citation: "For pioneering innovation and leadership in electronic design automation that has enabled the design of modern electronics systems and their industrial implementation."

In 2009, I received the first ACM/IEEE A. Richard Newton Technical Impact Award in Electronic Design Automation to honor persons for an outstanding technical contribution within the scope of electronic design automation. In 2012, I received the lifetime achievement award from EDAA. I have been a member of the National Academy of Engineering, the highest honor bestowed upon a US engineer, since 1998. I have consulted for several companies during my career, including Harris Semiconductor, IBM, Bell Labs, and HP.

INTERVIEWER. What is the mission of a research university like UC Berkeley? How do you integrate your teaching, research, and service roles as a faculty member?

INTERVIEWEE. The mission of UC Berkeley is to serve society as a center of higher learning, providing long-term societal benefits through transmitting advanced knowledge, discovering new knowledge, and functioning as an active working repository of organized knowledge. Faculty members at a research university such as UC Berkeley integrate the roles of teaching, research, and service by balancing three objectives.

1. One objective is the teaching of undergraduate (BS) and graduate students (MS, MBA, and PhD). This includes classroom teaching through lectures and labs and advising the MS and PhD thesis of the graduate students.
2. Fundamental research is measured through publications and funding. This includes writing proposals for research grants from organizations like the NSF and DARPA and industries and directing the research.
3. Service to the community may include technology transfer.

The first two objectives are the most important to faculty in a research university like UC Berkeley. Technology transfer is a natural outcome of research and knowledge created at the university.

INTERVIEWER. How does UC Berkeley facilitate technology transfer to the industry?

INTERVIEWEE. UC Berkeley is uniquely positioned to combine basic with applied research. Our breadth of top-tier programs, including in engineering, biosciences, business, and law, provide a powerful platform for innovation, entrepreneurship, and technology commercialization. The Office of Intellectual Property and Industry Research Alliances (IPIRA) provides a one-stop shop for industry research partners to interact with the campus. IPIRA's mission is to establish and maintain multifaceted relationships with private companies and thereby enhance the research enterprise of the Berkeley campus. These relationships include sponsored research collaborations and intellectual property commercialization, i.e., technology transfer.

IPIRA comprises two divisions: the Office of Technology Licensing (OTL) and the Industry Alliances Office (IAO). OTL handles the patenting and licensing of intellectual property generated by Berkeley research. The Industry Alliances Office is responsible for negotiating contracts and grants with industrial partners. Together, they work to enhance cooperation between the campus and industry and ensure the optimal and appropriate transfer of intellectual property generated by Berkeley researchers into products and procedures that improve private enterprise and public benefit. IPIRA's goal is to maximize the benefits of Berkeley's research to the economy and quality of life in the Bay Area, the state of California, the nation, and the world.

IPIRA works closely with all segments of the campus community in brokering and facilitating industry-sponsored research support and development, working to overcome obstacles to these relationships, and ensuring they remain consistent with the university's mission of education, research, and public service. IPIRA provides a one-stop service for both faculty and industry—industry-affiliate program agreements, industry-sponsored research agreements, material transfer agreements, data use agreements, patent and copyright licenses, intellectual property protection and licensing outreach to industry, start-up company licensing equity agreements, and resources for start-ups. In performing its functions, IPIRA works closely with the campus Sponsored Projects Office on research contracts and grants and with the campus Office of Foundation Relations and Corporate Philanthropy on industry gifts to research.

"UC Berkeley has a long legacy of innovations and leaders that have created groundbreaking products, revolutionary companies, and entirely new industries. The university plays a critical role in California's economy" (https://vcresearch.berkeley.edu/innovation/highlights). Last year, the campus expanded the dynamic ecosystem that fosters research and translation into real-world applications. As of June 2020, UC Berkeley owns 1,577 total active inventions, 360 active license agreements, 818 active licenses US patents, and 1,002 active foreign patents.

INTERVIEWER. What are some examples of successful inventions or innovations or products that have come out of UC Berkeley from your EECS department or your group?

INTERVIEWEE. Since 1988, over 250 start-up companies have been founded to commercialize IP rights under license from UC Berkeley. As of July 2020, companies under the IP licenses from Berkeley have commercialized more than 730 products. Steve Wozniak of Apple, Gordon Moore of Intel, Masayoshi Son of SoftBank, and Eric Schmidt of Goggle are many UC Berkeley alumni who have founded and run successful corporations.

Other prominent companies founded by UC Berkeley affiliates include 4D Molecular Therapeutics, Exelixis, PowerBar, Amyris, Gap, RedOctane, Apple, Google Earth,

Renaissance Technologies, Cadence Design Systems, Intel, Revolution Foods, Caribou Biosciences, Kaiser Permanente, Rodarte, Chernin Entertainment, Marvell, SanDisk, Corelight, Mendel Biotechnology, Sun Microsystems, National Semiconductor, and Tesla. My research group at UC Berkeley has fundamentally transformed the electronic design automation (EDA) industry. I have personally cofounded three companies: Cadence, Synopsys, and Exemplar Logic (acquired by Mentor Graphics).

INTERVIEWER. Professors in academia work on fundamental research problems, and the output is peer-reviewed papers in conferences and journals. However, it takes a lot more work to take the results of their basic research and translate them to industry. Can you speak about how that can be improved in the future?

INTERVIEWEE. The role of a professor is to train undergraduate and graduate students and direct fundamental research in arts and sciences and engineering. The results of the discoveries are published in peer-reviewed conferences and journals. These results are picked up by industry and introduced into new products. This is how technology transfer has been happening over the last one hundred years. It is not the professor's job to develop new products but instead to create new knowledge and understanding.

Large companies innovate in new areas by working with professors at universities, but the primary way that large companies pursue disruptive innovation is by acquiring companies. Unfortunately, public companies are at the mercy of Wall Street investors. Therefore, it is much harder for public companies to invest a lot of R&D funds in truly long-term disruptive innovation without showing the return on investment. It is easier for a large company to invest a lot of cash to acquire new technology and a product and the market and revenue associated with the product than to invest in a long-term R&D project over five years.

INTERVIEWER. Many professors have taken leaves from academia and started companies as a way to transfer technology. Is that an effective way to do tech transfer?

INTERVIEWEE. When professors or graduate students leave the university and start companies, that is the best way to transfer technology. Tech transfer happens best with the people. In contrast, there are many examples of professors leaving the university to start their companies (e.g., Jason Cong left UCLA to start Aplus, and Nick McKeown left Stanford to create Nicira Networks). However, not all professors leave the university to start companies. For example, I started three companies (Cadence, Synopsys, and Exemplar Logic) but never left UC Berkeley. However, it is essential for graduate students working on research projects to join these start-up companies. Many of my students working on SPICE, Espresso, TimberWolf, MIS, and SIS tools joined Cadence, Mentor Graphics, and Synopsys to transfer their technologies. We have also found many cases of innovative products that came out of universities. For example, Mark Zuckerberg created the social networking platform Facebook while a student at Harvard. Larry Page and Sergey Brin invented the page-ranking algorithms while pursuing their PhD at Stanford.

Another way to transfer technology to the industry is by making the technology available in the open domain. This is different from open-source, where there are some restrictions for companies to use open-source software using GPL license agreements. We have made the results of our EDA research on tools such as SPICE, Espresso, MIS, SIS, and TimberWolf available to anybody in the industry without paying any licensing fees. All they need to do is acknowledge that the product was built on top of UC Berkeley tools. We have found this as the best way for research from UC Berkeley to be transferred to the industry. The most famous examples are Berkeley Unix, RISC architecture, SPICE, Workstations, and RAID technology.

INTERVIEWER. Are funding models in universities changing? Are you getting more funding from industry than the government?

INTERVIEWEE. The funding models of public research universities, such as UC Berkeley, are changing. While still an important revenue source, the state's financial support has diminished significantly: Thirty years ago, 50 percent of the university's revenue came from California; but today, the state provides just 14 percent of the university's revenue. To offset declines in state funding, the university has sought to increase revenues from other sources, such as student tuition and fees, indirect cost recovery, and private giving. Examples of restricted funding include federal research and infrastructure grants and private support. Examples of unrestricted funds include student fees (tuition and other fees), private industry, state general funds, and UC general funds (nonresident tuition, some portions of public contract and grant overhead, some Department of Energy lab fees, patent royalties earned by UC inventions, interest earnings, and application and other fees).

I feel that unrestricted funding from companies provided as a gift with no overhead is the best way to engage with academia. While companies may think that the company does not own the intellectual property, the reality is that in the technology world, it is more important to leverage the technology and bring great products to market faster than it is to own the IP. Another excellent way for companies to engage with professors is to recruit them as consultants on their research projects. For example, I have consulted for several companies, including Harris Semiconductor, IBM, Bell Labs, and HP.

INTRODUCTION

Chapter 1 defined *innovation* as translating an idea into goods or a service that creates value either because it is something customers will pay for or because it provides some societal benefit. The key to understanding innovation is not to confuse it with discovery, which is finding specific attributes or characteristics of an innovation asset with potential value. Innovation begins life as a need and becomes an idea to satisfy that need. Innovation is the conduit between an idea and its solution as a product or service. In short, innovation provides the connectivity between a problem and a solution. Innovation inherently means a change in a business process, structure, or product or service direction. You recall there are three horizons of innovation.

1. H1—innovation in the short-term, mainly in the core product or service offering
2. H2—medium-term innovation introduced in the core or adjacent offer but driven at the business level
3. H3—long tail or disruptive innovation, often introduced or driven by an outside influence such as academia and start-ups

This chapter focuses on the role of academia in innovation, specifically its involvement in horizon 3 innovation. Universities work primarily on discovery, basic research, and applied research. Professors work with graduate students on solving basic scientific and engineering problems. Their research is commonly funded by research and development funding from the federal government—agencies like the National Science Foundation, NASA, or DARPA—and from funding from large companies. The professors work on these research problems with graduate students. After about five years, these students earn their PhD degrees; some continue postdoctoral studies. The university professor's objectives remain research, teaching, and service.

A research paper written by Schneider and Sørensen at Copenhagen Business School stated the following:

> Academic research affects productivity, and
> corporate R&D. The main conclusions are that
> (i) spillovers from academic research to the rest

of the economy do exist, (ii) the diffusion of academic research to the rest of the economy occurs with long lags, (iii) academic research complements private R&D, rather than crowing it out, (iv) the overall value of academic research to society is large.

Technology transfer to commerce is usually not a very important objective. University research in the US is designed to solve complex technical problems; the desired outcome is to see the research and conclusions published in a respected journal or presented at a conference, but it rarely results in innovative products. This chapter discusses how research results in universities can ultimately be transferred to companies with the innovation resources to build disruptive products and services.

RESEARCH UNIVERSITIES IN THE US, THE ENVY OF THE WORLD

Many of the most significant research in American universities focus on science, technology, and biosciences. The US's higher education system is more effective in concentrating resources in these hard sciences because they attract the brightest students, the best faculty, and the most funding. Table 2.1 shows the ranking of the top research universities in the world. Eight of the ten are in the US. Kevin Williamson, writing in the *National Review*, said, "If you are among the world's best in any significant intellectual field, the chances are excellent that an American university is a place you want to be."

Ranking	University	City, Country	Global Score	Enrollment
1	Harvard University	Cambridge, USA	100	21,261
2	Massachusetts Institute of Technology	Cambridge, USA	97.9	11,276
3	Stanford University	Stanford, USA	95.3	16,223

4	University of California, Berkeley	Berkeley, USA	89.8	39,918
5	University of Oxford	Oxford, UK	87	15,000
6	Columbia University	New York, USA	86.7	27,384
7	California Institute of Technology	Pasadena, USA	86.3	2,238
8	University of Washington	Seattle, USA	86	46,258
9	University of Cambridge	Cambridge, UK	85.8	19,580
10	Johns Hopkins University	Baltimore, USA	85.1	16,432

Table 2.1. List of top ten research universities in the world, 2021

Table 7.2 shows the ranking methodology. The first two categories show subjective factors, like research reputation. Universities like Harvard and MIT are prestigious and well-regarded by other academic institutions, getting high rankings. Reputation can only accrue to a university over time, often decades or longer. The remaining three criteria—books, journals, and conferences—are university research outputs that vary in quality and frequency from year to year. When professors and graduate (more often PhD) students perform new research, they discover new knowledge. If that knowledge is novel, they share it with the academic community. Typically, papers and conference presentations are accepted through a peer-review process to determine if the idea is truly novel or not. Only the most original papers are accepted.

Innovation is measured by both quantity and quality. The quantity of innovation is measured through publications and conference presentations. The quality of innovation is measured through where the authors have published their work. Each technical field (e.g., IEEE/ASME or ACM) maintains a list of the most prestigious conferences and journals in their area. Only the most innovative manuscripts are accepted in those outlets. The second way to measure the quality of a publication is by looking at the number of citations in the paper (e.g., how many other researchers' works are referenced) and, subsequently, the number of citations for your work once it has been published. If your paper is genuinely novel and innovative, other people cite your work. (In both instances, this is the academic version of stamping a like on a Facebook post.)

Ranking Indicator	Weight
Global research reputation	12.50%
Local research reputation	12.50%
Publications	10%
Books	2.50%
Conferences	2.50%
Normalized citation impact	10%
Total citations	7.50%
Total publications that are in 10 percent top citations	12.50%
Percentage of publications that are in the top 10 percent citations	10%
International collaboration	5%
International collaboration (relative to country)	5%
Number of cited papers that are in the top 1 percent in their field	5%
Percentage of papers that are in the top 1 percent in their field	5%

Table 7.2. Methodology to rank top research universities

THE METRICS OF INNOVATION IN ACADEMIA

As mentioned earlier, universities are designed to support three objectives.

1. Teaching of undergraduate (BS) and graduate students (MS, MBA, and PhD)
2. Research (measured through publications and funding)
3. Service to the community, which may include technology transfer

These are very straightforward objectives. The difficulty lies in assessing the value of a professor's contributions. The metrics may be skewed toward pure academic contributions. Writing a textbook or an article for a nonscholarly magazine is commonly not considered an academic metric. Neither is starting companies and transferring technology. Without that constrained set of metrics, a professor on tenure track may not be as motivated to pursue technology transfer or innovation. Universities have typically worked with companies in terms of research funding. They know how to do it; it has an apparent, well-defined quid pro quo. The same cannot always be said of technology transfer activities.

The bottom line could be expressed thus: What the professor does that enhances the university and academia is a measurable metric; what serves a business or a commercial interest is not. However, some universities have perceived the value of technology transfer and have established offices and policies to develop these opportunities. Without this established interest, there are no metrics for assessing the importance of this work. Put another way, if there is no reward for developing technology transfer, there is no reason to do it. So typically, developing innovative products is not on the academic agenda.

RESEARCH GRANTS IN ACADEMIA

Most professors write a single investigator grant to support two to three graduate students over three years during their work on a PhD degree. The research projects are narrowly focused. The intended result is published in respected academic journals or presentations at academic conferences, ultimately producing PhD and MS graduates. This is how university professors are measured.

A recent trend is large block grants in which four to six professors write such a grant that may be broadly defined as and may last for three to five years. An NSF Engineering Research Center (ERC) example states that it "supports convergent research that will lead to strong societal impact" in technology transfer. Each ERC has interacting foundational components beyond the research project, including engineering workforce development at all participant stages and a culture of diversity and inclusion where all participants may gain mutual benefit and create value within an innovation ecosystem that will outlast the lifetime of the ERC.

More recently, the NSF has created the Industry-University Cooperative Research Centers (IUCRC) to encourage more break-through research by enabling close and sustained engagement between industry innovators, world-class academic teams, and government agencies. Programs such as this encourage universities to engage in technology transfer.

The NSF is also creating innovation centers in critical technology areas, such as the future of wireless 5G and 6G technologies. A 2021 workshop managed by the NSF and the National Academy of Engineering (NAE) discussed these concepts of the importance of technology transfer to industry in addition to academic contributions. Global R&D centers bring together university professors and graduate students with industry leaders and entrepreneurs. Professors could develop new intellectual property on a technology platform like 6G, and entrepreneurs will work to create businesses from such technology platforms. There is great promise in government agencies supporting programs such as this.

The Role of Students in Innovation

In the role of faculty advisers, professors typically oversee research performed in academia by graduate students. The master of science (MS) degree program consists of eight courses and usually takes two years to complete while PhD students complete sixteen courses and typically take five years to graduate. The coursework is intensely focused on research interests; for example, students who take courses in signal processing and wireless communications will do their doctoral research on 5G or 6G wireless systems and may work for companies like Nokia and Ericsson. Students studying computer programming, database, and artificial intelligence / machine learning (AI/ML) are inclined to do their doctoral research on big data analytics and search engine optimization (SEO); they may work for companies like Google and Facebook.

Here is the key to successful research universities: The research of the National Association of Colleges and Employers has determined that computer science is the STEM major with the highest job offer and job acceptance rate in the US. The best research universities have faculty who are leading authorities in their technical fields. It is academia's job to fulfill the expectations of its student clientele, and that is precisely what top universities strive to accomplish.

RESEARCH FUNDING IN ACADEMIC INNOVATION

To perform university-level research, professors need to provide mentorship support for their graduate students. They also need to help them find financial assistance to cover their cost of living over the years of academic studies. These students are typically funded by teaching assistantships (TA), graduate fellowships, or research assistantships. TAs and fellowships are only available to graduate students in their first two years. Therefore, these students need to be supported by research assistantships in their remaining three years but often for all five years.

Assistantship students typically receive a monthly stipend as living expenses and may be granted a tuition waiver. The cost of external research funding to support one graduate student for a year with full university overhead, including tuition support, is about $100,000 in a US research university with full overhead. Therefore, to support a single investigator research project involving one professor and two graduate students over three years from, say, the National Science Foundation, NASA, or DOD, it would cost about $250,000 per year for three years, at a total cost of $750,000. This is explained in more detail in chapter 7.

Each graduate student approaching the end of their PhD program would likely discover some new technologies they could write about in five to ten conferences or journal publications. Translated into return on investment, a research funding of about $1 million would produce about ten conference or journal publications. A small number of these publications will be submitted for patents by the university from the intellectual property (IP) management office. We will discuss this in more detail in a later section.

One of the metrics professors are rated on is their ability to secure external research funding. To run a successful research program, a professor of engineering at a top research university will likely be tasked with securing about $1 million of funding per year to support a group of ten graduate students.

THE ROLE OF FACULTY IN ACADEMIC INNOVATION

Universities always try to recruit the brightest faculty. They anticipate that the best PhD graduates will be recruited to join the faculty at other well-placed colleges and universities. For example, MIT PhD graduates often become professors at Stanford, UC Berkeley, Caltech, and vice versa. They are typically hired as assistant professors in their respective departments. They are put on a tenure track and have six years to prove to their department and the university that they are a leading authority in their field and ought to be awarded a lifetime appointment. The promotion ensures that the university has the confidence in a tenured professor to grant them academic freedom and freedom of speech by protecting them from dismissal for controversial or nontraditional research, publications, or expression of ideas.

A distinguished faculty can enhance a university's opportunities for research funding from well-heeled government organizations, like the NSF, NIH, DOD, DOE, NASA, and others. The funding contract from such government agencies typically allows the intellectual property of any inventions to be retained by the university, which is a powerful incentive for the university to encourage advanced research projects from its faculty and grad students. Typically, an agency puts out a call for proposals with specifications and due dates. Chapter 7 will go into more detail about the different types of research funding in other countries.

The case study "Invention of Discrete Cosine Transform (DCT)" by Professor Nasir Ahmed in 1972 pointed out the typical academic, team-based process and the difficulties researchers encountered when proposing new ideas. It was a lossy compression algorithm he conceived while working at Kansas State University.

He proposed the technique to the National Science Foundation. He originally intended the DCT for image compression. Ahmed developed a working DCT algorithm with his PhD student T. Natarajan and friend K. R. Rao in 1973, and they presented their results in a January 1974 paper. It described what is now called the type-II DCT (DCT-II) and the type-III DCT (IDCT).

The DCT is widely used for digital image compression. It is a core component of the 1992 JPEG image compression technology developed by the JPEG Experts Group and standardized jointly by the ITU, ISO, and IEC. Companies like Dolby Labs use these technologies to create advanced audio coding. These AACs are then licensed to chip companies like Samsung and Sony, audio receiver companies like Denon and JVC, and speaker companies like Polk Audio. A tutorial discussion of how DCT is used to achieve digital video compression in various international standards defined by ITU and MPEG (Moving Picture Experts Group) is available in a paper by K. R. Rao and J. J. Hwang, which was published in 1996. The image and video compression properties of the DCT resulted in it being an integral component of the following widely used international standard technologies. This example shows how basic research done on technology such as the discrete cosine transform at a university is used by so many companies in their products in the future.

RESEARCH FUNDING FROM PRIVATE COMPANIES

In addition to government funding, some faculty also get funded by companies. Companies typically support shorter-term research since they try to get the research results into innovative products. They are in business to make a profit and do not wish to see research projects languish. For example, when I was CTO at Hewlett-Packard, we had about eighty research projects with universities worldwide every year with an average cost of one hundred thousand dollars. The projects were aligned with the big bet projects that HP Labs was working on during 2007–2012. We will discuss these big bet projects at HP Labs in chapter 5.

These research projects with universities and corporate research labs, such as HP Labs, satisfy two broad objectives. The professors and graduate students working on these research projects in the universities bring alternative perspectives to the research agendas being pursued in the company. In addition, the companies recruit these graduate students working on the research projects as summer interns during their PhD and permanent hires when they graduate.

INTELLECTUAL PROPERTY OWNERSHIP FROM ACADEMIA

A key difference in research funding from the government and companies is the treatment of intellectual property (IP). When a research project is funded by a government agency, such as NSF, NASA, or DARPA, results are published as open (as in open-source) literature in journals or conferences, because the funding agency is primarily interested in promulgating new knowledge in the field. Of course, the articles are protected by copyright laws, but professors rarely try to file patents for owning the intellectual property they have worked on. After all, it is rare that all the IP is vested in a single individual in any case. We will discuss intellectual property and patents in chapter 5.

However, when a private enterprise provides a university with funding for research on a particular topic, the company intends to protect the IP. Companies often demand that if they provide the funding, they ought to have exclusive rights to the IP. This is often a quarrelsome point of negotiation. In such instances, it usually means publication of the research results in the open literature is withheld until a patent is filed to protect the IP. The company that offers to fund university research often holds the right to the IP.

The Bayh-Dole Act, spearheaded by Senators Birch Bayh of Indiana and Bob Dole of Kansas, formerly known as the patent and trademark act amendments, is a federal law enacted in 1980 that enables universities, nonprofit research institutions, and small businesses to own, patent, and commercialize inventions developed under federally funded research programs within their organizations.

In essence, it shifted ownership from the US Patent and Trademark Office, which was essentially clogging the works by withholding commercial patents, to the university that originated the idea and, by extension, the private companies that would transform that idea into a viable product or service. It was a monumental advancement in technology transfer.

Technology transfer is achieved by filing a patent to protect a particular intellectual property. Say a professor and graduate students invent new technology for improving Bluetooth signal strength. The professors must work with a patent attorney to file an invention disclosure. That work begins with a patent application that clearly enumerates how this new method and apparatus advances knowledge state of the art and is an original claim of invention. The process is long and complicated. It often takes years to register the copyright.

For example, while I was in academia at Northwestern University, I led research on the MATCH compiler. Before publishing our work at the IEEE FPGA Custom Computing Conference, we published our patent registration: P. Banerjee, A. Choudhary, M. Haldar, A. Nayak, "Methods and Apparatus for Automatically Generating Hardware from Algorithms Described in MATLAB" (US Patent Number 7,000,213, granted Feb. 14, 2006). Northwestern University owned this patent. When I founded my start-up company AccelChip, the patent owner was transferred to AccelChip. In exchange, AccelChip agreed to pay Northwestern University about 2 percent in royalties on any revenue based on the patent and generated by AccelChip.

Now here is the challenge. Companies often believe that just because they are funding the research project at a university, they should have exclusive rights to any IP created by the university and the professors and graduate students working on the project. This, of course, means they should also earn revenue from it. Universities are now becoming increasingly aware that the IP ought to belong to them and that companies should have to license the technology (for a fee) from the university. The offices of the vice president of research at most major research-intensive universities now have an intellectual property office, which assists professors in filing invention disclosures and patents and then helps negotiate to license these IPs to private companies.

Unfortunately for most universities, this is not a significant revenue stream, but exceptions exist. For example, the University of Wisconsin (WARF) earns substantial revenues from a patent covering the milk pasteurization technology.

Table 2.3 shows the intellectual property royalty license revenue from the top ten universities in the USA with gross licensing revenues of $15 million to $155 million (https://ssti.org/Digest/Tables/121203t.htm).

Rank	Adjusted Gross Licensing Revenues	Institution
1	$155 million	Columbia University
2	$82 million	University of California
3	$62 million	New York University
4	$54 million	Sloan Kettering Institute
5	$52 million	Florida State University
6	$50 million	Stanford University
7	$42 million	University of Rochester
8	$39 million	City of Hope National Medical Center and the Beckman Research Institute
9	$32 million	WARF / University of Wisconsin-Madison
10	$31 million	University of Florida

Table 2.3. Top ten universities in terms of royalty licenses of their intellectual property

In recent years, several universities and companies in the USA have come to a common understanding of research funding and IP ownership and royalty revenue. When I was director of HP Labs, we created a standard template for a research agreement between HP Labs and about one hundred universities. The basic idea is as follows: A company provides funding to a university for research into a topic. The professors and students are set to work, and discoveries and knowledge are created. The university is encouraged to submit an invention disclosure on the researched topic before submitting the paper to any conferences or journals.

Once the patent is granted, the university owns the intellectual property. The company that funded the research can purchase a non-exclusive, royalty-free license to the technology or, if they prefer, a royalty-based, exclusive license. The idea is, say, the technology that has been discovered and patented by the university pertains to this technology would be of interest to some the investing company and some of its competitors.

Here was how a similar situation unfolded for me. The University of Illinois received funding from Hewlett-Packard for a novel cache coherence protocol software for shared-memory multiprocessors. Other computer server companies, such as Dell or IBM, would have undoubtedly been interested. But if HPE funded the work, it would want a nonexclusive, royalty-free license to the technology. Now the University of Illinois owned the IP and could undoubtedly offer to license the technology to HPE's competition in return for royalty payments of 1 percent of revenue from any server that used the software technology. However, HPE would not want to see the technology they helped create and fund get into the hands of the competition. So in this hypothetical instance, HPE would likely agree to a royalty-based, exclusive license.

TECHNOLOGY TRANSFER FROM UNIVERSITIES TO PRODUCTS IN COMPANIES

In the context of research institutions, technology transfer (or tech transfer) is how new inventions and other innovations created in those institutions' labs are turned into products and commercialized. This is typically done in two ways: by licensing patented intellectual property to corporations and creating start-up companies, which also often license the IP created by faculty. What many people don't realize is just how many products and technology advances that we take for granted originated in university and federal laboratories, then ultimately reached the marketplace in large part through technology transfer efforts.

There are many examples of successful technology transfer from universities to industry. The first example is that of Larry Page and Sergey Brin, who were PhD students at Stanford, and they developed the BackRub search algorithm for searching webpages on the internet in 1996. This technology was transferred to Google, founded by Page and Brin, in 1998, and Stanford was given equity ownership of Google. Google became the most successful search company globally with a business model enabled by advertising. Google/Alphabet today has $182 billion in annual revenue and a market cap of $1.9 trillion.

A second example is that of the invention of Gatorade from the University of Florida. The beverage was first developed in 1965 by a team of researchers led by Dr. Robert Cade. It was initially made for the Gators at the University of Florida to replenish the carbohydrates that the school's student-athletes burned and the combination of water and electrolytes that they lost in sweat during rigorous sports activities. Originally produced and marketed by Stokely-Van Camp, the Gatorade brand was purchased by the Quaker Oats Company in 1983, which, in turn, was bought by PepsiCo in 2000. As of 2010, Gatorade is PepsiCo's fourth-largest brand based on worldwide annual retail sales.

Gatorade and Google are two often-cited examples, but thousands of others have made an impact on virtually every scientific field and every walk of life—lifesaving drugs and medical devices, alternative energy solutions, computer hardware and software, new modes of transportation, blockchain technologies, artificial intelligence, vaccines, robotics, cybersecurity, environmental solutions, agricultural innovations, aerospace, and countless others. Technology transfer professionals have a crucial role in protecting the intellectual property associated with these valuable innovations to be licensed and commercialized and brought to the marketplace for society's benefit.

Table 2.4 shows some statistics of the technology transfer activity from universities to companies. The first metric is the number of invention disclosures, a subset of which result in patent applications, and a subset of them result in patents being issued to universities. The second set of metrics is the number of licenses from these patents to various companies. The third metric is the number of start-up companies formed based on these patents and licenses and the number of operational start-up companies. As can be seen from the table, there has been an increase in technology transfer activities from universities to industry in the past ten years—from 2007 to 2017.

Technology Transfer Activity	Year 2007	Year 2017
Invention Disclosures and Patents		
Inventions disclosed	14,398	24,998
Patent applications	11,797	15,335
Patents issued	3,622	7,459
Licensing		
All licenses, total active in a year	30,351	45,657
Licenses issued	4,354	6,283
Start-Up Companies		
Start-up companies formed	555	1,080
Operational start-ups	3,388	6,050

Table 2.4. Technology transfer activity from universities to the industry from 2007 to 2017

But over the years, technology transfer has become about much more than protecting IP. Tech transfer professionals are involved in a wide array of activities to support the commercialization process, including

- working with attorneys to secure patent and other intellectual property rights,
- assessing the commercial potential of new inventions,
- marketing available technologies to potential licensees and partners,

- educating researchers on commercialization principles and strategies,
- assisting with faculty start-up creation and development,
- securing funding for early-stage research and start-ups
- negotiating partnerships and license agreements,
- organizing a business plan and start-up competitions,
- helping to build innovation ecosystems and support structures that promote innovation and economic development, and
- creating programs that encourage students and faculty to innovate in labs and makerspaces and engage in entrepreneurship to bring those innovations to the marketplace.

Technology transfer is a big, multifaceted, and complex job. It may just be the most important job that nobody knows about. Successful technology transfer has benefits for universities, companies, regional and national economies, and society. For universities, it can bring revenues that can be plowed back into research and recognition of its scientists and their innovations, which can help with faculty recruitment and grant funding. For companies, benefits include the ability to tap into research advances without spending on internal R&D and introducing new products that can drive the success of their businesses forward.

Technology transfer is critical in growth through innovation, creating new ventures and more robust industries that create more jobs for regional and national economies. And for society at large, the benefits are valuable in terms of lives saved, improved health, a cleaner environment, and countless technological advances that bring new capabilities and drive local, regional, national, and global economies forward through innovation.

Technology transfer from universities to the industry is complicated. It often happens when students who have worked with technology graduate and work at commercial companies. Companies often recruit students as interns while they are still in school, then hire them as permanent employees; 90 percent of tech transfers happen like this.

FROM ACADEMIA TO START-UP TO LARGE COMPANY ACQUISITION

Recently, many professors have started to transfer the fruits of their research into start-up companies either by licensing their technology or simply by founding a new company. This is how most tech transfer occur. For example, I started AccelChip in 2000 based on the MATCH compiler project founded at Northwestern University during 1997–2000. Larger companies, such as Xilinx, invested in AccelChip, then later acquired it.

There are many other examples of professors (or graduate students) taking university leave to start companies. A sample list is given below.

- Professor Nick McKeown of Stanford University worked on software-defined networking with NSF funding and started a company called Nicira Networks, which VMWare purchased.
- Professor John Hennessy of Stanford University worked on Reduced Instruction Set Computer architectures, then started MIPS, which became a public company.
- Professor Andreas Goldsmith of Caltech and Stanford worked on wireless communications and started Quantenna Communications, which ON Semiconductors acquired.
- Professor Janak Patel of the University of Illinois worked on test generation of digital circuits and started Sunrise Test Systems; Mentor Graphics acquired it.
- Professor Anant Agarwal of MIT converted his courses for online learning at MIT online and started edX, which 2U recently acquired.
- Larry Page and Sergey Brin wrote a research paper on page-ranking algorithms at Stanford, then applied it by starting Google, which became a public company.
- Professor Mendel Rosenblum of Stanford researched virtualization, then found VMWare, which became a public company.

- Sanjit Biswas and John Bickett were PhD students at MIT and worked on the Roofnet project and experimental 802.11b/g mesh network. They left MIT to found Meraki Networks in 2006, which was sold to Cisco in 2011.
- Professor Jason Cong of UCLA worked on FPGA design automation algorithms and founded Aplus Design Technologies, which developed an FPGA synthesis tool acquired by Magma Design Automation in 2003.
- Professor Jonathan Rose of the University of Toronto worked on FPGA architectures and founded a start-up company, Right Track, in 1998, acquired by Altera Corporation in 2000.

RELATIONSHIP BETWEEN LONG-TERM RESEARCH AND INNOVATIVE PRODUCTS

University professors engage in long-term (often ten to twenty years) R&D projects. Almost all discovery and basic R&D happen long-term in academia.

- The theory of relativity in physics by Albert Einstein at the Max Planck Institute in Germany
- Particle physics by Richard Feynman at Caltech
- Relational databases by Professor Héctor Garcia-Molina at Stanford University
- Deep learning by Professor Geoffrey Hinton at the University of Toronto
- The Internet browser by Professor Larry Smarr at the University of Illinois
- Internet communications by Professor Leonard Kleinrock at UCLA
- Wireless communications by Professor Irving Jacobs at UC San Diego
- Gene editing by Professor Jennifer Douda at UC Berkeley

However, Professor Leonard Kleinrock did not just happen to invent the Internet himself one day. He leveraged twenty years of research done by other academic researchers and put it all together into a demonstration of the power of the Internet in DARPA-based work at UCLA. Professor Jennifer Douda, professor of chemistry at UC Berkeley, worked on gene editing for twenty years and reinvented the CRISPR technology by leveraging the work of others and won the Nobel Prize in Chemistry. But she did not start a company. Instead, Moderna and Pfizer-BioNTech received regulatory approval for the mRNA, producing the first two COVID-19 vaccines to become commercially successful, based on the early work done by Professor Douda.

THE BEST WAYS TO PARTNER WITH UNIVERSITIES

It is clear by now that truly fundamental and long-term research is done best in academia. Companies interested in pursuing horizon 3 disruptive innovation need to look to academia for guidance and partnering. Here are some lessons from my experience.

1. About 1 percent of the company's total R&D budget should be spent on funding and developing projects from academia. This way, the researchers in the companies will stay on top of the latest research challenges and opportunities in the field. Otherwise, the researchers in the companies risk only incrementally developing the research ideas they have within the company. Companies like IBM, GE, HP, Google, and Microsoft know this. They have long-established academic research programs, which they fund from their central research labs. This is explained in chapter 5.

2. When funding the research with an academic institution, the company needs to sign agreements regarding the rights of IP ownership of the technology. Standard practices negotiate these rights either as nonexclusive, royalty-free licensing or an exclusive, royalty-based license.

3. The company must realize that the projects funded with academia rarely result in completed products. Instead, they are proofs of the innovation's concept intended to illustrate what the technology can ultimately produce. Much work needs to occur in the company's labs to move the academic research ideas and prototypes into viable, completed products.

4. If a company finds a particular professor and decides to build a product, hiring the professor as a consultant makes sense. Professors are typically permitted to consult 20 percent of their time (one day a week). In this circumstance, any intellectual property created by the professor remains company property. It must be advised that a written agreement is essential. Be aware that the professor should be used as a consultant, proffering advice to the company engineers working on the innovative product, rather than the professor building the product.

5. One of the most effective ways to have successful technology transfer from academia to private companies is to hire graduate students who have previously worked on the research project. Often, they are recruited for summer internships, which allows the company to become more familiar with them and their abilities. This, of course, paves the way for offering a full-time position upon graduation. IBM, GE, and Microsoft have had a very successful academic internship and recruitment programs based on this model.

6. Suppose you are a professor who wishes to step up your career as an innovator. In that case, you need to understand the above points and be willing to participate with private enterprises in creating innovative products. If you are interested in partnering to build an innovative product, consider taking a sabbatical leave from the university, starting your own company, making a product, and selling your company to a large company.

CONCLUSION

Innovation works best when academics and businesses partner. This is particularly true of long tail horizon 3 projects, which academia is particularly good at. Just as horizon 3 projects usually have a long development time, building interpersonal relationships are essential to any innovation project's success. Your company need not do a horizon 3 disruptive innovation project on its own; it should not, for it might have a beginning and no end. Bringing a savvy professor and a team of energetic graduate students on board gives your innovation project much better chances to get it to a successful product. Chapter 3 will detail how professors and graduate students can incorporate innovations and discoveries from academia into start-up companies. Chapter 6 will describe how larger companies can better partner with academia to drive this long-term disruptive innovation.

AUTHOR'S PERSONAL EXPERIENCE IN ACADEMIA

After getting my BTech degree in electronics and communications engineering from Indian Institute of Technology Kharagpur, I came to the USA in August 1981 to pursue my MS and PhD in electrical and computer engineering from the University of Illinois Urbana-Champaign. A research assistantship supported me, which gave me a full tuition waiver and monthly living expenses. At the same time, I took three courses per semester while pursuing research toward my MS thesis—"Fault Characterization of CMOS Circuits"—under my adviser, Professor Jacob Abraham. The Department of Defense's VHSIC Program funded my research assistantship.

I completed my MS thesis in December 1982 and then started work on my PhD. I received an IBM fellowship during this time, which allowed me to work on any research topic. Again, as part of the fellowship, I received a full-tuition waiver and monthly living expenses. In consultation with my academic adviser, Professor Jacob Abraham, I decided to work on my PhD thesis on "Algorithm-Based

Fault Tolerance in Multiprocessor Systems," which I completed in December 1984.

During the period of my MS and PhD, I published five papers in journals and ten papers in conferences. While my MS and PhD theses added to knowledge in the field and resulted in numerous publications, there was no innovative product that resulted from my thesis. The results translated to the industry through diffusion, and you could point to many products that used concepts from my publications but not a direct transfer of technology. Again, I want to point out that the current university system and its metrics encourage basic research and discovery but not directly product innovation.

I was fortunate to receive a research assistantship and a graduate fellowship during my MS and PhD, which allowed me to graduate quickly, while other students were not as fortunate. The fact that US universities have such a robust funding mechanism for supporting graduate students (MS and PhD) and the fact that US universities can recruit the very best graduate students from all over the world are some of the reasons that US universities are so far ahead in rankings and reputation. When they graduate from these US universities, they join companies and contribute to innovation.

When I graduated with my PhD, I had offers to join universities such as Carnegie Mellon, University of Michigan, University of Wisconsin, Purdue University, University of Southern California, UCLA, and the University of Illinois and industrial research labs such as Bell Labs and IBM Research. I joined the Department of Electrical and Computer Engineering at the University of Illinois Urbana-Champaign as an assistant professor in 1985. I got promoted to associate professor in 1989 and received full professorship in 1993. In 1996, I joined Northwestern University as a Walter Murphy professor and the chairman of the Department of Electrical and Computer Engineering. In 2004, I joined the University of Illinois Chicago as a UIC distinguished professor and dean of the College of Engineering and worked there until 2007.

During this period of twenty-two years in academia, I pursued basic research on parallel computing architectures, parallel algorithms for electronic design automation, and parallel compilers. My research was supported by government funding from the National Science Foundation, NASA, DARPA, the Office of Naval Research, and an industrial grant from the Semiconductor Research Corporation, IBM, and Intel. My academic research has resulted in more than 360 publications, including one book, ten book chapters, 100 journal papers, and 250 conference papers. As part of my large body of research work in academia, I was fortunate to have received numerous awards and recognition, including election to the IEEE Fellow, ACM Fellows, and AAAS Fellows and IEEE Taylor Booth and ASEE Terman Award. This is how professors in universities are recruited, retained, promoted, and recognized.

I have contributed to discovering new knowledge in the field, and I have contributed to training undergraduate and graduate students in electrical and computer engineering. These students have gone to work in various companies and have contributed to creating innovative products, but these are all indirect ways of contributing to innovation. As CTO of Ansys, I have seen much of my work in parallel algorithms for electronic design automation implemented as high-performance computing versions of the Ansys products, such as Fluent for fluid dynamics and HFSS for electromagnetics using shared memory message-passing parallelism. This is an example of an indirect technology transfer of the work done in academia to industry.

As chairman of the Department of Electrical and Computer Engineering at Northwestern University or as dean of the College of Engineering at the University of Illinois Chicago, I recruited dozens of new faculty members. I promoted them to associate and full professors. We recognized their contributions in basic research and discovering new knowledge, publications in top-tier journals and conferences, and their awards and recognitions in their professional societies, such as IEEE and ACM.

During my twenty-two years in academia at the University of Illinois Urbana-Champaign and Chicago and at Northwestern University, I have worked with dozens of graduate students and supervised thirty-seven PhD students and forty MS students. I have supported these students with research assistantships from funding from the National Science Foundation, NASA, ONR, and DARPA. These students have graduated from the university, worked for various companies, and contributed to their innovation. My personal experience in academia as a graduate student, professor, department chairman, and dean of engineering has allowed me to appreciate how innovation and discovery are carried out in top research universities in the USA.

CHAPTER 3
Innovation in Start-Ups

Interview: Amit Narayan, CEO of AutoGrid

Amit Narayan is the founder and CEO of AutoGrid Inc. From 2010 to 2012, he was the director of Smart Grid Research in Modeling and Simulation at Stanford University. He led an interdisciplinary project related to modeling, optimizing, and controlling the electricity grid and associated electricity markets. Before founding AutoGrid, Amit was the vice president of products at the publicly traded company Magma Design Automation Inc. (Nasdaq: LAVA). He led the product development and product management teams responsible for Magma's flagship product in the design implementation.

Over one-third of all semiconductor chips used in consumer electronic devices, such as smartphones, Blu-ray players, and video games, were designed using products developed by Amit's team at Magma. Before joining Magma, Amit founded Berkeley Design Automation Inc. (BDA), a venture-backed company in analog and radio-frequency semiconductor design software, and served as its founding CEO and, later, vice president of engineering, responsible for all research and product development activities and customer engagements.

Under Amit's leadership, BDA saw its products adopted by over one hundred semiconductor companies globally, including twenty out of the top twenty-five. For his work at BDA, Amit received the EDN innovation of the year award in 2006. Amit received his BTech in electrical engineering from Indian Institute of Technology Kanpur and PhD from the University of California, Berkeley. He has published over twenty-five papers about design automation, holds seven US patents, and is an active adviser to several start-up companies in the Bay Area.

INTERVIEWER. Amit, thank you very much for agreeing to be interviewed for my book *The Innovation Factory*. Tell me about your personal background.

INTERVIEWEE. Hi, Prith. Thanks for the opportunity to share my background and work for your book! I was born in England and grew up in India. My father was a professor at IIT Kanpur, so I was fortunate to grow up on the campus as part of a very academically vibrant community. I did my undergraduate in electrical engineering from IIT Kanpur also and then came to the US for my PhD in EECS at UC Berkeley. My research was in electronic design automation to design semiconductor chips. I founded a company called Berkeley Design Automation based on my research on wireless chips, which was acquired by Mentor Graphics (now Siemens). Then I worked at a company called Magma Design (Nasdaq: LAVA), which was a public company and subsequently acquired by Synopsys (Nasdaq: SNPS). After that, I spent some time at Stanford University as a visiting researcher, where I started looking at renewable energy and got the idea for my current company, AutoGrid.

INTERVIEWER. What is the mission and value proposition of your start-up AutoGrid? What are some of your products?

INTERVIEWEE. AutoGrid was founded in 2011 with the mission of accelerating access to sustainable energy to combat climate change. I started AutoGrid when my elder son was just starting kindergarten and my younger daughter was about to be born. I started thinking about the world they will have to grow up in and the dangers of climate change. I realized that the electricity sector was one of the major sources of carbon emissions but also the biggest opportunity to transition into a sustainable world. If we could deploy solar and wind and use these renewable energies to power our cars and homes, we would make a big dent in the problem. However, I soon realized that the architecture of our power grid would need to be reimagined. This was when I started AutoGrid, to become a catalyst for transition into clean energy.

Over a hundred years, our centralized, one-way power system has been built with the core assumption that electricity consumers are random actors, and the only way to keep the system stable is by utilities dispatching their generators. This paradigm has led to utilities spending hundreds of billions of dollars in building peaker plants, which are only fired up when the electricity demand is excessively high—say, during a hot and sticky summer afternoon. There are more than one thousand peaker plants across the US (map), costing over a trillion dollars. Many of these plants sit idle 80 to 99 percent of the time.

In New York City, the eighteen peaker plants run at an average capacity factor of 6 percent (five hundred hours per year), making them very expensive to operate. In New York City, the average cost of peaker plant electricity is 1,300 percent higher than the overall average cost of electricity, costing consumers approximately $4.5 billion over a ten-year period. These peaker plants are four times dirtier on average, even by fossil fuel standard, but even worse, they are socially unjust with almost half of them located in disadvantaged communities. Not only this, these plants are often unreliable, because the transmission and distribution lines that carry the power from a centralized location are subject to disruption from hurricanes and storms. For example, a 128-megawatt generation unit failed to provide power during Hurricane Ida, which hit sixteen years to the day after Hurricane Katrina.

At AutoGrid, we have been pioneering the concept of a virtual power plant for a decade, which is a disruption to the traditional fossil fuel industry. Just like how Zoom virtualizes meetings and cloud virtualizes computing, AutoGrid is virtualizing power generation and distribution infrastructure. By doing so, AutoGrid's software can aggregate and direct power from millions of electric vehicles, batteries, rooftop solar, utility-scale wind, thermostats, building systems, and other distributed energy resources to balance supply and demand across the grid to keep it working reliably so that utilities don't have to build fossil fuel-based peaker plants and can provide cheaper, cleaner, and more reliable power from renewable sources, such as solar and wind.

INTERVIEWER. Who are some of your customers, and what value are they getting by using AutoGrid products?

INTERVIEWEE. AutoGrid serves all players within the rich energy ecosystem. This includes tradition utilities and new energy companies who don't own traditional poles/wires. These include electricity retailers, renewable project developers, energy-as-a-service companies, independent power producers, and consumers of energy. AutoGrid Flex software platform offers these customers the ability to build, own, operate, and participate in intelligent and scalable virtual power plants (VPPs) to maximize their return on investment in renewable energy technologies, improve the reliability of the grid, and reduce carbon footprint.

AutoGrid Flex platform is managing over 5,000 MW of VPPs in fifteen countries—everything from an electric car and battery or solar panel in a home, to microgrids in a campus or industrial site, and utility-scale storage and renewable farms—

and is ranked as the number one virtual power plant platform in the world (according to the global ranking published in 2020 by industry-leading research and analysis firm Guidehouse Insights). We are proud to count over fifty utilities and energy companies as our customers. These include Schneider Electric, CLP Group (Hong Kong), Sunrun, Sunnova, GreenStruxure, Shell, Total (Europe), National Grid, Florida Power & Light, Tata Power (India), Eneres (Japan), and others.

INTERVIEWER. Who is your competition? Is it mainly other start-ups or larger companies?

INTERVIEWEE. Our primary competition is education and awareness. We are replacing a product (fossil fuel-based peaker plant) that has been around since electricity was invented. Even though a virtual power plant is a superior product in all respects, we have to educate and drive for reform with stakeholders to reinvent the architecture one step at a time.

Having said that, we are not the only ones trying to do this. There are many companies, such as Tesla, who are trying to do this in-house. However, in most cases, their software works within a closed ecosystem of their own products. Our approach is open and scalable and works with the products of all manufacturers. This approach is needed as energy is inherently a heterogeneous environment. You might have a car from Tesla, solar panels from Sunrun, thermostat from Nest, and appliances from LG; and all this needs to coordinate with one another and with the utility grid, and our platform orchestrates all the different pieces so that they play nice with one another.

In the latest report by independent industry research published by Guidehouse, AutoGrid was ranked the number one virtual power plant platform. Interestingly, all the other companies that were in the top five have been acquired by larger companies who make and sell their own proprietary hardware, making us the only pure-play, vendor-neutral player in the market today.

INTERVIEWER. Where did the technology for AutoGrid originate? Can you share some background of the different funding levels you have gone through—Series A, Series B, and Series C and their timelines?

INTERVIEWEE. The company started with some of my early research at Stanford University, but over the last decade, we have invested heavily in R&D to build out the platform and perfect the algorithms. We have raised close to $150 million in venture funding across several rounds. Most recently, we announced a Series D2 round of $85 million to scale our products and go-to-market. We thought we were a little early in the market when we started, but it gave us time to refine and perfect our technology with real-world deployments around the globe. Energy is mission-critical infrastructure, and customers are rightly a little risk averse before they try solutions from a new start-up. Having over a decade of experience in this area gives confidence and comfort to our customers that they are buying a stable and production-proven product.

INTERVIEWER. Are your investors all pure venture investors, or do you have strategic investors? Can you share your insights about the pros and cons of taking funding from strategic investors?

INTERVIEWEE. After many disappointments in cleantech space, I think the last decade was hard for companies targeting this space. Cleantech space is hard for VCs in general because companies require more time and capital to disrupt a slow-moving, heavily regulated market. However, it also is perhaps one of the largest opportunities of our lifetime. There are three thousand utilities just in the US, many of which have realized that they need to innovate, or else they might go down the path of Kodak or Blockbuster. Some of them have been very active in funding external innovation at start-ups, and we have been fortunate to be able to tap into these strategic investors. Over the years, we have raised funding from some of the largest energy companies in the world, including SE Ventures, National Grid,

Shell Ventures, Total Carbon Neutrality Ventures, CLP Group, Ørsted, Envision Energy, Tenaska, GS Group, and Microsoft Sustainability Fund.

The benefit of taking funding from strategic investors is the knowledge and connections it provides into their business units. Even within these large organizations, sometimes, it is hard for start-ups to identify the visionaries and early adopters of technology. Having someone who can help navigate through this complexity and help identify and qualify the right people can often save a lot of time and effort, which is invaluable for a start-up trying to move fast on a limited budget.

INTERVIEWER. Have you engaged with any technology or business partnership with larger companies? Can you share your insights about the difficulties and advantages of working with large companies?

INTERVIEWEE. We have partners with several larger companies, including energy companies, such as Schneider Electric and Amazon Web Services. The benefits are primarily from the scale and reach these companies can provide through their network and resources. Both Schneider and Amazon have been great channel partners for us, helping us reach new regions in the world. Through their help, we have now been active in fifteen countries and have active customer opportunities in several more. In terms of challenge, perhaps scale is also the biggest. To be able to support the increased activities we have to staff up our team and streamline our processes in parallel.

INTERVIEWER. You have worked in academia, start-ups, and larger companies. In your opinion, where does a start-up really shine. Namely, what are the advantages of innovating within a start-up? What are the challenges?

INTERVIEWEE. This is an excellent question. I think successful start-ups excel at figuring out the product-market fit when the market is undergoing disruption because of a new technology or a new business model. The ability to engage with customers, make agile tweaks to product and business model, and the intensity and focus that comes with limited time and resources in a typical start-up environment are great ingredients for success. Last but not least, start-ups are able to incentivize and empower people in unique ways that is sometimes not possible in a pure academic or in a large company environment. The challenges are numerous also. A typical start-up has fewer resources in terms of people, time, and money and needs to find this product-market fit as quickly as possible.

INTERVIEWER. What has been your relationship with the board and the investors of AutoGrid? Have they helped you with product strategy? Have they helped you with customers? Have they helped you with growing your business and business models?

INTERVIEWEE. We operate in a market that is quite complex for traditional Silicon Valley VCs. As such, the bulk of our investors and board members have been strategic—large companies who are either customers or can be channel partners. We have had several such strategic investors, including SE Ventures, CLP Holdings, Total Carbon Neutrality Ventures, Shell Ventures, National Grid Partners, and SolarEdge, who are all important customers for AutoGrid.

Having strategics on the board can be immensely powerful and creates a win-win on both sides. As a small company, it is valuable to have a channel open that can facilitate conversations with business units at a more strategic level. The customers who have a seat around the table feel more secure in doing business with smaller start-ups. They are also able to identify visionaries/early adopters within their own organizations, which is critical when a start-up is trying to determine product-market fit and is crossing the chasm. These investors also have deep industry knowledge and networks outside of their own companies, which can be very valuable for a young start-up with limited sales resources. The investors also know that the start-up's products are differentiated and share in the upside with company's success.

INTERVIEWER. Are funding models in the VC world changing? In the past, you could get $2 million Series A funding with a simple business plan with no prototypes. Now you need to have a prototype and some customers before you apply for Series A. Can you comment on how hard or easy it is to raise funding if you are new entrepreneur?

INTERVIEWEE. The investors' willingness to take risk changes with market timing. I think these days, entrepreneurs are doing pre-seed, seed, and convertible debt before they come for Series A. Funding is always a complex function of market size, team, technology or business model differentiation, and moat. I believe funding opportunities for first-time young entrepreneurs who have the audacity to dream big and can convince investors about their ability to attract talent and execute are as good as I have ever seen in my twenty-plus years of entrepreneurial career.

INTERVIEWER. What is your exit strategy for AutoGrid—to go IPO or to be acquired by a larger company?

INTERVIEWEE. The market opportunity is massive, as our platform is at the center of hundreds of billions of dollars of investment moving into new energy. I feel we have all the options available to us from an IPO to merging with a larger company to gain scale. Right now, we are fully focused on executing and growing.

INTRODUCTION

Chapter 1 presented the definition of innovation as translating an idea into goods or a service that creates value for which customers will pay or alternately provides some societal benefit. It presented the three horizons or planning models of innovation. This chapter focuses on innovation as it occurs in start-ups, where the focus is steadfastly on horizon 3 innovation. While large companies excel at incremental improvements to their current set of products (horizon 1 or 2), they are not often successful in creating genuinely disruptive products. Horizon 3 is where start-up companies excel. They identify a niche market and develop a focused product for that market, then develop a sales and marketing strategy tailored for that product. Therefore, start-up companies are more successful than large companies in developing long-term disruptive innovation.

This is an excellent time to point out the distinction between what may be termed conventional long-term innovation and disruptive innovation. Typically, they are not the same, although the term *disruptive* is conversationally tossed about in business discussions. Traditional long-term innovation is usually planned, staged innovation of an existing product or service. The business knows what innovations it intends to promulgate over time. For example, a toy manufacturer may introduce a movie character as a plastic statue. Future innovations add moving arms and legs, then a motor for motion, followed by a voice feature. Minor changes in the marketplace, customer feedback, or ideas from the innovators may change plans somewhat. This may be termed incremental innovation, but the trajectory remains relatively the same.

On the other hand, disruptive innovation is not quite so simple to define. Christensen, in his book, essentially said it was a product or service designed for a new set of customers. However, his legacy Christensen Institute has redefined disruptive innovation over the years since he first employed it: "Disruptive innovations are not breakthrough technologies that make good products better. Rather, they are innovations that make products and services more accessible and affordable, thereby making them available to a large population." This definition scorns the notion that innovation is born of a new idea, in one sense, by stating it makes an existing product better when it may be an entirely new product and reinterpreting it as an aspect of marketability.

Neither needs be the case, although they could be. But our purpose is to understand it best in the context of the contemporary business environment as a significant new product or service that redefines the customer experience. The idea and the innovation led to a product or service that had not existed before, but once it did, the innovation fulfilled a recognizable consumer need. Here are a few technological examples.

- The Hewlett-Packard HP-35 Scientific Calculator
- The World Wide Web
- The smartphone
- VisiCalc
- Cloud computing

Each began its life as an idea that led to a start-up venture or company.

How Are Start-Ups Created?

Start-up companies are the lifeblood of innovation in the world. Start-up founders are usually from academia, from large companies, or are serial entrepreneurs. When a founder comes from academia, they have usually solved a complicated technical problem with the help of funding from a government agency, such as NSF, NASA, DARPA, or NIH. They may have already built a software or hardware prototype of their innovation and are trying to commercialize their technology. An example of such a start-up founder is Professor Nick McKeown. He developed his ideas for software-defined networking at Stanford University and then left Stanford to start his company, Nicira Networks, which VMWare subsequently acquired. Another example is Jason Cong, who left UCLA in 2003 to start Aplus Design Technologies, acquired by Magma Design Automation in 2006.

When a founder comes from a large company, they have identified a pain point or a problem that needs to be solved. They may have already built a hardware or software prototype at their company. Still, there is no interest in developing a business from it at the company. The idea is considered too far removed from its core business, so the inventor/founder leaves to start their venture. An example is John Swanson, who used to work at Westinghouse Electric and identified a need to build a finite element analysis software. Still, since Westinghouse was not interested, he left the company and started his own software company, Swanson Analysis Systems, which later became Ansys.

The third kind of start-up founder is the serial entrepreneur, who has previously created some other start-up company. This individual has accrued some experience and, from working with an initial start-up and engaging with customers, has identified a new need or pain point to focus on. Venture capitalists who fund start-ups look most positively at this type of entrepreneur, who has already established a successful track record of founding start-ups. An example is Sanjit Biswas and John Bicket, who cofounded Meraki Networks in 2006 based on work done at MIT and sold the company to Cisco in 2011. They later cofounded Samsara in 2012, which became a public company in 2021.

CRITICAL CRITERIA OF A SUCCESSFUL START-UP

When a start-up founder creates a business plan, they need to demonstrate their understanding of four critical criteria to convince an investor to fund the start-up.

- What is the value proposition?
- Is this a clearly differentiated new technology that creates a sustainable competitive advantage?
- Describe the attainable market share and why this is a significant opportunity for the start-up.
- What superlative talent will you bring to execute your great business plan?

What Is the Value Proposition?

The key to understanding the value proposition is identifying a pain point or the solution's value proposition. This is a need, not simply a want. The pain or discomfort must be alleviated with your solution. There may currently be one or more ways the problem is being addressed; but you, the start-up entrepreneur, have found a better, faster, cheaper way to solve it. Next, you need to quantify the value to the customer. This analysis requires some hard numbers. How much will the customer pay for this innovation to relieve their pain?

When I founded my first start-up, AccelChip, the value proposition was that innovation was based on a prevailing hypothesis in the computing industry: how to do our work better, faster, and less expensive. Engineers in the networking and communications fields typically prototype their algorithms in a language called MATLAB. Once they decide on the specific algorithm and intend to implement it in hardware—in this instance as an integrated circuit chip called a field-programmable gate array (FPGA)—they have to translate their MATLAB algorithm into a language called register-transfer-level VHDL, or Verilog. It typically requires a couple of engineers about six to nine months to perform this translation. AccelChip developed a technology that automatically compiled behavioral MATLAB code into RTL VHDL / Verilog, which could be synthesized into FPGAs in minutes. This accelerated the FPGA design process. This value proposition saved eighteen to twenty-four person months of effort at a hundred thousand dollars and allowed a customer to expedite designing a specialized FPGA and get it to market much faster. For AccelChip, a customer was quite willing to pay forty thousand dollars per copy of the AccelFPGA product.

How Is Your Solution Unique and Differentiated?

Can anyone else copy your solution and bring out a competitive product? Is the intellectual property protected through an invention disclosure or a patent? How hard will it be for a competitor with deep pockets to come into your market with a better product or a lower price?

For the example of AccelChip, there was no similar product in academia or industry that solved this problem. The problem was so hard that DARPA funded it as part of their adaptive computing program in 1998. I was a principal investigator of the MATCH compiler project that created the technology with some graduate students at Northwestern University. We had several publications in conferences and journals that described the technology of the MATCH compiler. However, these technologies were also protected by several patents filed by Northwestern University.

When AccelChip was founded in 2000, it obtained an exclusive license of the MATCH compiler technology from Northwestern University, which included some equity ownership of AccelChip and a percentage of sales of any products sold by AccelChip based on this technology. This is typically how universities try to monetize their innovation and inventions.

IDENTIFYING THE SIZE OF THE MARKET

Knowing market share is a critical success factor. It must be demonstrable. You must carefully and accurately identify your market. Is the product or service business-to-business or business-to-consumer? Ask yourself the what, who, and why questions: What is the known market? Who are the potential customers? Why would they buy the product or service? Is it a growth market or stable? Are there already competing products or services? What is their market share, and how much can you expect? How would you get your product to market? Will you need a sales force? How many customers are there in the country, the world (USA or China or India), and in the particular industry (automotive, aerospace, health care, or manufacturing) who would buy such an innovative product? What is the total available market for the product? Will you have only one product or service, or do you have growth and expansion plans?

TAM, SAM, AND SOM

The model for ascertaining this information is often referred to by the acronyms TAM, SAM, and SOM and are accomplished in the following order:

1. *Total addressable market (TAM)*. Assuming there is no competition, TAM is the potential for sales opportunity in the identified market.
2. *Serviceable available market (SAM)*. What percentage of the TAM can your company's product or service realistically serve in manufacturing output, geographic span, competition, product/service life cycle, etc.?
3. *Serviceable obtainable market or share of market (SOM)*. As framed and quantified by SAM, what portion of the SOM can your company's product or service realistically capture and serve. (Note: it is not one hundred percent!)

You must know your TAM before you can determine SAM and SOM. In many instances, money is well spent to speak with a technology analysis firm, such as International Data Corporation (IDC), Forrester Research, or Gartner. They may have already researched and published reports on what you wish to learn. Of course, you can do your market research, and you should. Those who fund your start-up will be impressed when they know you have done your homework.

With AccelChip, the TAM for electronic design automation (EDA) was estimated at $2 billion in 2000. However, the SAM for the system-level synthesis portion of the EDA market was quite a bit less: about $300 million. We estimated that AccelChip would be able to get 10 percent of the market and reach revenues of $30 million within five years.

It is often challenging for a start-up company to establish the market for its products since they disrupt the current market and status quo. When an investment bank makes a market projection, they might say the TAM for the database software market is $300 billion, of which large software companies like Oracle or SAP may have 20 percent of the market share. Similarly, say the TAM for the computer server market is $500 billion, of which HPE and Dell might have 30 percent of the market share. These large companies and their market dominance pose a severe barrier to entry from a start-up regardless of its product's innovation.

But what kind of market share would a start-up company get for a product or service market where there are no products or services? But what is the market for a start-up company that has created a "device such that blind men can see"? If you do a Google search of a market for such a product, it will be zero since no such product exists. However, one can determine the market of such a product by intersecting some other product markets.

For example, you can look at the total number of blind men globally—about fifty million out of the total nine-billion population. People who are not blind but require correction to their eyesight using glasses pay $100 for a pair of eyeglasses. Therefore, a better product than eyeglasses for a blind man can be priced at $200. Hence, the market for such a product would be $50 million times two hundred dollars or $1 billion.

How Will You Sell the Product, and How Complex Is the Supply Chain?

What is the go-to-market approach for your product? How much will it cost to manufacture? How much to warehouse it? Will you have your own direct sales force, contract with a distributor, perhaps sell only online, or try to leverage an indirect sales channel? What is the exact cost of goods sold (COGS)? Typically, this is the formula: initial inventory plus purchases minus ending list returns the cost of goods sold. What is the cost of selling your product or solution? Once all this data is analyzed, is your product or service profitable?

Hardware companies have a high COGS cost and lower gross margins. Software companies have tiny COGS and, hence, have higher gross margins. Hardware companies have to source their components from their suppliers and then build or assemble the product.

How complex is your supply chain, and what risks—theft, damage, loss, replacement, and so forth—do you need to account for?

In the case of AcceChip, the value proposition for AccelFPGA—saving the customer $200,000 per design—the product pricing set at its introduction was $50,000 per license. The market estimate in 2000 was about six thousand FPGA design starts per year. If 10 percent of those designs used AccelFPGA, the revenue would be about $30 million in five years.

AccelChip planned to sell the product through a direct sales force and an indirect channel. The direct sales force would have a salesperson and an application engineer working as a team to generate $1 million of revenue per year. This meant the pair would be responsible for selling twenty copies of AccelChip to about ten customers per year. In addition, the indirect channel was through distributors who would take 50 percent of the revenue per copy. Still, given that the channel had access to a large customer base, this was acceptable to AccelChip.

How Good Is Your Team?

Does the team have previous experience with start-ups? Have the team members worked together before? Can teammates pivot into a new solution if the team faces a technical or business obstacle? Some VCs say they will instead fund a company with an A-plus team and a B-minus business plan than a B-minus team with an A-plus business plan. This is because an A-plus team will usually be able to determine that the business plan is not working and will immediately pivot to a better business plan.

In the case of AccelChip, the team was comprised of myself as founder and CEO; my cofounder, a professor from Northwestern as VP of business development; a person with industry experience as VP of engineering; an experienced salesperson as VP of sales; and six software engineers, all graduate students at Northwestern University who had worked together on the MATCH compiler project. The team was technically good but lacked experience working for a start-up, so we did face some challenges in the early years.

Most Start-Ups' Business Plans Fall Short

It is essential to know the risks involved with launching a start-up. CB Insights, a private equity market intelligence firm, states that the top three reasons start-ups fail are lack of capital, the wrong team for the job, and no market need. Before you get too excited and decide to become a start-up founder, you should know that creating a successful start-up is arduous. Everyone hears about successful start-ups, like Google, Facebook, Amazon, and Tesla, and their trillion-dollar market caps. We all hear about start-ups that have become unicorns (meaning at least $1 billion in valuation) and have just raised $100 million in a Series D round.

Many entrepreneurs don't understand that the business plan is not a sales pitch. It is a solid blueprint for constructing a business. As I have been pointing out, it must be built on a rock-solid foundation of the highest-quality market research, the formation of a very talented and ambitious team, and a budget that would pass any audit the IRS could throw at it. A business plan that does not meet and exceed these parameters paves the way for start-up missteps and best and failures at worst.

Business Plan for a Start-Up

In most cases, your plan will be a twenty-to-thirty-page document written in straightforward business language. Its main points would be highlighted; there would be lots of bulleted points, some tables, and charts to highlight trends and goals; and most importantly, it would be detailed, absolutely factual, financial projections. To ensure the quality of your business plan, consider hiring a professional editor and a business accountant to review it. Your attorney must approve of it as well. A standard business plan includes seven sections.

The executive summary. This introduction to your start-up presents the highlights of your plan. Note that the most critical reviewers, your lead venture capitalist, may read only this section but will indeed peruse your financials. In the case of AccelChip, the executive summary described the value proposition of reducing the time to design an FPGA chip. As mentioned earlier before, it reduced two design engineers' work to about six to nine months from twenty-four months and then cut the time to convert a design to just a few minutes. This was, as you can see, a powerful value proposition.

The company. A plan for a start-up describes your strategy for creating the legal entity and how the initial ownership will be divided among the founders. It should also include a table that lists start-up costs and initial funding. A plan for a company already existing should describe the legal form of the business, the company history, and the business's past performance. In the case of AccelChip, we explained that the technology was based on the DARPA-funded MATCH compiler project at Northwestern and that we had several patents. The company credentials included the two cofounder professors, the two graduate students, and Northwestern University.

What you sell. Describe in detail the products or services you intend to offer. Emphasize why buyers would purchase them, what benefits accrue, and what pain points they will address and resolve. Chart your costs accurately. They are based upon estimates from proven providers.

Your market. Describe your target market, including demographics, growth, and trends. Display a table or other suitable graphic to show the market forecast. Describe the nature of your industry and the competition you have. In the example of AccelChip, the total available market for electronic design automation was about $2 billion in 2000. However, the serviceable market for the system-level synthesis of the EDA market was about $300 million. We estimated that AccelChip would be able to get 10 percent of the market and have a revenue of $30 million in five years.

Strategy and implementation. Strategy is all about focus; so train your focus on specific target market segments, representative products or services, and cost- and time-saving distribution avenues. Realistically forecast your sales goals and weigh them against the cost of sales. Define your milestones with dates, budget forecasts, and individual and team responsibilities. In the case of AccelChip, we decided to sell the software product AccelChip for $50,000 per copy.

The plan was to generate revenue of about $1 million in year one, $3 million in year two, $7 million in year three, $12 million in year four, and $30 million in year five using a combination of direct sales, indirect channel sales, and maintenance contracts.

Management team. List the names of the key members on your team with their work highlights and responsibilities. Include a table that shows personnel costs. List the gaps in the management team, if any, and how they're being addressed. In the case of AccelChip, I was the founder and CEO, my cofounder was a professor from Northwestern, who was the VP of business development, an experienced person from industry was the VP of engineering, and a professional salesperson was the VP of sales.

Financial projections. Describe your financial strategy and how it supports your projected growth. Include a breakeven analysis that shows risk as a matter of fixed versus variable costs. Include projected profit or loss, cash flow, and balance sheets. In the case of AccelChip, the plan was to generate revenue of about $1 million in year one, $3 million in year two, $7 million in year three, $12 million in year four, and $30 million in year five using a combination of direct sales, indirect channel sales, and maintenance contracts.

To launch AccelChip, we needed to raise $2 million in Series A, $5 million in Series B, and $15 million in Series C to be profitable and grow to a $200 million valuation company. We would do so with direct sales, indirect channel sales, and maintenance contracts. The plan was to develop AccelChip so we could sell it to a large company for a profit. In actual practice, AccelChip could only raise $2 million Series A and $5 million Series B. Before needing to raise Series C, it was sold to Xilinx for $25 million.

OPPORTUNITIES AND BARRIERS TO ENTRY

To create a truly successful start-up, you need to have a sustainable, competitive differentiation or advantage. You may have an excellent idea for creating a new product or a new way to solve a problem. However, you need to protect the concept of your product or solution so that a competitor cannot copy or duplicate your solution. You must convince your investors that someone else cannot simply copy/paste your solution into a competitive product. This is where differentiated technology comes in.

When Google was started in 2007, Stanford grads Larry Page and Sergey Brin wanted to manage all of the world's information. They created their proprietary PageRank algorithm to search every web page globally. To this day, Google Search's power is due to this crucial technology differentiation, although its patent expired in 2019. The Google page ranking system is Google's entry to competitive differentiation while at the same time its barrier to another search engine's attempts to beat it.

Before starting their company, most professors today file for intellectual property protection in the form of a patent or invention disclosure. Investors reviewing a start-up's business plan often look for patent filings before funding the company. With AccelChip, no similar product solved this problem either in academia or industry. I was a principal investigator in the MATCH compiler project mentioned earlier. We had several publications in conferences and journals describing the MATCH technology, and these technologies were all protected by patents filed by Northwestern University. When AccelChip was founded in 2000, it obtained an exclusive license to the MATCH compiler technology, which included some equity ownership of AccelChip and a percentage of sales of any products sold by AccelChip based on MATCH technology. This is typically how universities hope to monetize their innovations and inventions.

WHO FUNDS THE START-UP

Three types of investors fund start-ups in different stages of investment.

- Angel investors
- Venture capitalists (VCs)
- Large companies (trade-offs in investments by strategic investors, conflict with exit target price)

At each stage, an investor typically values the company at a specific price, then invests some funds in exchange for a percentage of company ownership. At the end of the investment, the company receives a post-investment valuation. Suppose a company is trying to raise seed level funding. At that stage, the investor usually employs the critical criteria to decide whether to invest: the nature of its value proposition, the total market, and the quality of the founding team.

Say the investor values the company at a $4 million pre-money valuation. Say there are two founders, each with 50 percent ownership. If the company has ten million shares to begin with, each of the founders will receive five million shares. Suppose the investor puts $2 million into the company. The pre-money valuation is $4 million, meaning each founder's share would be worth forty cents, the post-money would be $6 million, and the investor's percentage ownership would be 33 percent. Therefore, the investor would end up with five million shares.

After the investment, each founder's share would go down from 50 percent to 33 percent. Based on this $2 million investment, the founders would get to work on the innovation product. They would create a hardware or software prototype and start selling the product, if only in concept or beta, to accrue some revenue. If they do well, the company's valuation for the next round of investment would be rise, perhaps to $12 million, implying that each share is now worth eighty cents.

Now let us say the company raises an additional $12 million worth of investment. At a post-money $24 million valuation, a Series B investor would get 50 percent ownership of the company. The founders' shares would each go down to 16 percent. But 16 percent of a $24 million company is worth $4 million, so on paper, the founder's equity doubles—from $2 million to $4 million. And the same progression repeats in future investment cycles.

The critical point is to make enough progress in the company at each step of an investment cycle so that the share valuation keeps going up. Ultimately, the company may sell for $200 million, at which point the share price is two dollars, and each founder would make $10 million from the sale of that company. This is how entrepreneurs make money from creating and selling start-ups. Of course, if you are a founder of a billion-dollar unicorn company, you would be worth $100 million!

STAGES IN START-UP INVESTMENT

A start-up business is, by its nature, a higher-risk investment than a mature business. The mature business has assets for collateral and a known cash flow that allows investors and lenders to assess and compensate for various business risks. A start-up business has far greater exposure. Therefore, it is critically important to focus on early-stage and expansion-stage financing (and the multiple phases within each stage) to remain flexible and adaptable to the start-up's unique and often quickly changing business and financing conditions.

SEED FINANCING PHASE

The seed phase. This is also known as the precommercialization stage, the proof-of-concept stage, during which a business idea is tested for its viability. The primary research may have been completed, but the commercial capabilities are not yet proven. A formal business entity has not been formed, because whether to move forward with creating the business has not been decided. During the seed stage, the enterprise generally requires relatively small amounts of financing, which would be used to conduct business feasibility studies, develop prototypes, evaluate market potential, protect intellectual property, and investigate other aspects of the business idea. At the end of the seed financing phase, the entrepreneur must decide whether to create the business (often called the go/no-go decision).

The prelaunch phase. This occurs once the go decision has been made. This phase usually requires more funding than the seed stage, as plans are formed. Angel investors may become interested. Developing a detailed business plan is critical now. So is creating a legal entity for the business, which defines the operational boundaries. The founders may start looking at property, equipment, and other operating assets the business will require. The founder will often hire a management team; they must explore all regulations and acquire needed licenses to operate. The founders and the newly hired management team will create the supply chain and develop distribution and marketing relationships as part of the business plan evolution.

Launch phase (Series A). Also referred to as the start-up phase, this is when production is initiated and sales begin. Employees are hired, and the product lineup and marketplace are firmly established. Now begins bridge financing, spanning from the time the prelaunch phase is funded until operations commence, providing sufficient working capital for smooth operations, funding of any losses incurred during the start-up phase, and ensuring there are contingency funds in case of an unexpected business interruption. Financing for the prelaunch stage and the start-up phase may coincide.

Ramp-up phase (Series B). This is the final phase in early-stage financing. It is characterized by ramping up production and sales. If successful, it validates the company's business model. Business volume may be approaching breakeven, and profitability is within sight. If so, venture capitalists may be interested in financing this phase from a strategic perspective. The ability to accelerate the ramp-up momentum and transform it into growth catapults the company into its growth stage. It establishes profitability and can finance operations from its internal resources.

Expansion phase (Series C). This phase follows first-stage financing and provides working capital for the initial expansion—for example, managing inventories, producing and shipping products, and tending to accounts receivable (AR). Although the company has made progress, there are instances in which it may not yet be profitable—for example, if buyers are slow in paying.

Further expansion phase (Series D). What if your business is growing faster than expected? These funds are used for additional resources expansion, marketing, working capital, or developing products. Here, the company has reached profitability and is ready for its exit.

Exit strategies. Every business has a beginning, middle, and end like life itself. The best way to end your business is on your terms: having an exit strategy. There are many reasons for an exit, and each has different consequences, so you and your investors must give thought to this important event. Common reasons for an exit are your decision, for whatever reason, to sell, to step aside and let someone else run the business, a merger or acquisition, going public (termed an initial public offering (or IPO), or even closing down if business conditions demand it. Making plans for such eventualities is thoughtful contingency planning.

You can do initial public offers (IPO), where you sell a part of your business to the public in shares. Aside from providing an exit strategy by being able to reimburse investors within your start-up, it can be a secondary form of exit for other investors across other companies by taking part in a buyout.

MERGERS AND ACQUISITION

Another critical and often considered exit is an acquisition by a larger company. Your start-up company must exercise the option to merge with another company should cash flow or liquidity become an issue. All investors want to know whether they can get their money back should the deal go south. Ensuring your start-up stays afloat will provide a certain level of security among your investors. I always want to know whether the start-ups I invest in have the knowledge that they can sell the company in a merger acquisition.

THE START-UP FUNDING CLIMATE IN 2021

Venture capital (VC) valuations rose to unprecedented levels in 2021 in large part because of nontraditional investors entering the market. PitchBook prepares a quarterly US VC Valuations Report that examines how start-up valuations across the venture life cycle and sectors change. Record levels of funding and a fierce influx of nontraditional investors into the venture ecosystem have buoyed VC-backed company valuations in the second quarter of this year (https://pitchbook.com/news/reports/q2-2021-us-vc-valuations-report).

Key takeaways from this report include the following:

- Early-stage pre-money valuations notched records in Q2 2021 with a median and average of $50 million and $105.4 million respectively.
- At the late stage, the median and average valuations hit $160 million and $882.4 million respectively, representing a sharp increase from values recorded in previous years. The value growth is partly driven by investor willingness to write increasingly more extensive checks to pre-IPO companies.
- Exit valuations grew at a decade-record rate with median acquisition and public listings step-ups of 2.2 and 1.7 times their last private market values.

HOW TO CREATE A BUSINESS PLAN FOR A START-UP

We will now discuss how to create a business plan for a start-up. Let us assume that a start-up company has an idea for an innovative software product that will change how some tasks are performed in large companies. In the case of AccelChip, the value proposition of this product is that it saves six months for a couple of engineers to do a design problem. Since this saves a company the cost of two engineers at a salary of $100,000 per year over six months, the savings to the customer is about $100,000. Hence, the software product was priced at $40,000 per copy and was available on Windows and Linux.

The product would be sold through a direct sales channel by salespeople and application engineers and a distributor as an OEM channel for $20,000 net revenue to the start-up. The business plan assumes that the start-up can sell 10 copies of the product in the first year, 20 copies in the second year, 350 copies in the fifth year using the direct channel, and about 650 copies using the OEM indirect channel. Hence, the projected revenues for the start-up in years one to five are \$400,000, \$1 million, \$2.7 million, \$12.8 million, and \$30 million. These revenue projections are shown in table 3.1.

Start-Up					
Annual Revenue Projections					
	Year 1	Year 2	Year 3	Year 4	Year 5
Units					
SW Product Linux/ Windows Direct Sale	10	20	40	150	350
SW Product Linux/ Windows OEM Sale		10	45	300	650
Yearly Support		10	30	100	450
Total Software Units Sold	10	30	85	450	1000
Unit Pricing					
SW Product Linux/ Windows Direct Sale	\$40,000	\$40,000	\$40,000	\$40,000	\$40,000
SW Product Linux/ Windows OEM Sale	\$20,000	\$20,000	\$20,000	\$20,000	\$20,000
Yearly Support 20 Percent of List Price	\$8,000	\$8,000	\$8,000	\$8,000	\$8,000
Revenue					
SW Product Linux/ Windows Direct Sale	\$400,000	\$800,000	\$1,600,000	\$6,000,000	\$14,000,000
SW Product Linux/ Windows OEM Sale	\$0	\$200,000	\$900,000	\$6,000,000	\$13,000,000
Yearly Support	\$0	\$80,000	\$240,000	\$800,000	\$3,600,000
Total Direct Sales Revenue		\$880,000	\$1,840,000	\$6,800,000	\$17,600,000
Total OEM Sales Revenue		\$200,000	\$900,000	\$6,000,000	\$13,000,000
Total Revenue	\$400,000	\$1,080,000	\$2,740,000	\$12,800,000	\$30,600,000

Table 3.1. Example business plan revenue projections for a start-up

Table 3.2 now shows the start-up's cash flow and equity needs in building up the business, $2 million in Series A in year one, $5 million Series B in year two, and $10 million in Series C in year three. At this point, the company would become profitable.

Five-Year Income Statement and Cash Flow					
Income Statement	Year 2001	Year 2002	Year 2003	Year 2004	Year 2005
Revenues	$400,000	$1,080,000	$2,740,000	$12,800,000	$30,600,000
Other Income	$31,107	$75,026	$56,909	$599,300	$714,726
Expenses	$1,253,592	$2,906,017	$5,232,180	$10,101,787	$12,322,307
Income (Loss) before Taxes	-$822,485	-$1,750,991	-$2,435,272	$3,297,514	$18,992,419
Income Taxes 30 Percent on Income	$0	$0	$0	$989,000	$5,698,000
Net Income (Loss)	-$822,485	-$1,750,991	-$2,435,272	$2,308,514	$13,294,419
Cash Flow					
Beginning Cash Balance	$0	$1,167,170	$4,421,281	$11,986,009	$14,294,523
Equity Capital	$2,000,000	$5,000,000	$10,000,000	$0	$0
Other Current Assets	$10,345	-$5,102	$0	$0	$0
Net Income (Loss)	-$822,485	-$1,750,991	-$2,435,272	$2,308,514	$13,294,419
Ending Cash Balance	$1,167,170	$4,421,281	$11,986,009	$14,294,523	$27,588,942

Table 3.2. Example business plan cash flow and equity raise for a start-up

The resultant business plan is shown in figure 3.1.

Projected Income and Cash Flow Statement for Startup

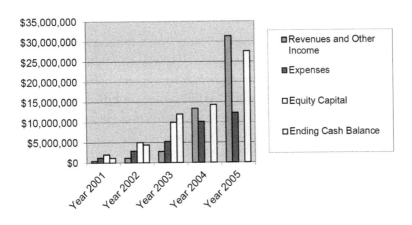

Figure 3.1. Five-year business plan for a start-up company

RAISING FUNDING AND GIVING UP OWNERSHIP

Let us show how equity ownership works for the example start-up business plan illustrated in the earlier section and figure 3.1. When the company is founded, the founders create a total share pool of 7.5 million and allocate 5 million shares to the founders and 2.5 million shares to the future employees and management. At this point, the founders own 75 percent of the company. The company now raises $2 million in Series A funding at a pre-money valuation of $5 million. Thereby, they give up 2/(2+5) = 29% ownership of the company, and the Series A investors are given 3 million preferred A shares.

At this point, the founder's 5 million shares are worth 48 percent instead of 67 percent. The company makes progress on its business and revenue and next tries to raise a $5 million investment at a $10 million pre-money valuation in exchange for 5/(5+10) = 33% ownership of the company and gets 5.25 million preferred B shares. At this point, the founder's 5 million shares are worth 32 percent ownership. The company makes more progress toward its business goals and gets more revenue. The final round of investment is $10 million Series C at a $40 million pre-money valuation, and the Series C investors get 10/(10+40) = 20% ownership of the company.

At this point, the founders' shares of 5 million shares are only worth 25 percent of the company. However, when the company makes its exit as an IPO or an M&A to a larger company for $300 million, the founders make $75 million. This is how start-ups create value for customers, create revenue, and create equity income for the founders and investors. Figure 3.2 shows the company ownership at different levels.

RAISE MORE CAPITAL OR KEEP MORE OWNERSHIP?

The example in figure 3.2 highlights a struggle that every founder/entrepreneur faces as they try to grow their start-up company. The start-up company needs capital (cash investment) to hire employees (developers and salespeople) to build a product and sell the product. The more employees you can hire, the faster you can grow your business and stay ahead of the competition. However, to hire more employees, you need to raise more capital. As you raise more capital, you give up more ownership of your company to your investors. Founders often struggle with this tension. They don't want to give up ownership of their company, which they feel is their baby. However, they do not often realize that there will be no business without significant capital raised; and therefore, there will be no exit. You may own 50 percent of your business, but 50 percent of zero is still zero, whereas 20 percent of $100 million is $20 million, which the founder can make when he sells the company or goes through an IPO.

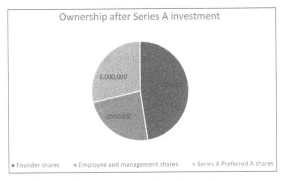

(a) Ownersip after Series A

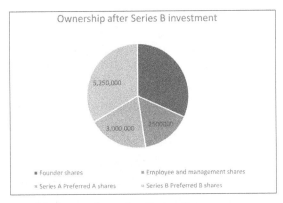

(b) Ownership after Series B investment

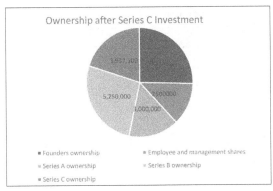

(c) Ownership after Series C investment

Figure 3.2. Company ownership among founders, employees, and investors at various stages of investment

STRATEGIES FOR PARTNERSHIPS FOR START-UPS

Start-up companies have three ways to bring their product to market. While all these directions exist for a start-up, they all have advantages and disadvantages. First, they can sell the product to their customers by having their own sales force. The company can have its own sales team led by a VP of sales. Each salesperson would reach out to potential customers, arrange for a product demo, and bring a field application engineer. The customer may want to see a proof of concept demonstration that the product will work for the customer's problems. Therefore, it is essential to have an excellent field application engineer who can solve customer problems by integrating the product at the customer site.

Typically, a team of salespeople and application engineers will have a quota of $1 million of sales of a product in a given year. For example, the AccelChip product sold for $40,000 per copy, so a sales team at AccelChip had a quota of twenty-five copies of the product to be sold in a given year. The advantage of this approach is that the start-up gets to control its destiny. After all, no one knows the product and its capabilities better than the own team. The sales and application engineering team can directly get feedback on the product from the customer to the product team, and the engineering team can improve the product. Therefore, this is the best way to develop a sales channel in the early phases of a company. The disadvantage is that this approach does not scale. It is not easy for a start-up to build up a truly global sales force across all regions and countries.

The second way to market is through a distributor or a channel. A distributor will typically have multiple products available for sale to a large set of existing customers. A start-up company will have to partner with the distributor, where the distributor will get a 30 percent royalty on each product sold. Because the distributor has a much larger sales force and lots of customers, it is easier for a start-up to establish such indirect channels, especially in countries where the start-up can't build up a lot of sales forces. For example, if a start-up company is based in California, the start-up can't engage with customers in Japan, Korea, or Germany. Hence, the start-up may establish partnerships with distributors in various countries. The advantage of this approach is that the start-up gets to scale to an extensive sales channel using the distributor's sales force. The disadvantage is that a start-up company's products will typically have bugs in them, and it may not be possible for the support organization of the distributor to support the development.

The third way to establish a partnership is with a larger company with products in a related market. A start-up needs to show how their product will fit into an overall solution that a larger company's customer may be interested in selling. For example, Ansys is a simulation company whose customers use simulation to build different products in the automotive or aerospace or manufacturing industries. When the customer is designing a product, it can have various product sizes in different dimensions (width, length, or height). A customer may create the product in different sizes and then determine the optimal size for the product using an optimization loop.

A start-up company called Dynardo developed a tool called OptiSlang to help a customer use a simulator from Ansys to perform this optimization automatically. Dynardo formed a partnership with Ansys such that the Ansys salespeople sold the OptiSlang product to its customers by integrating it with the simulation tools. Ansys put the OptiSlang product on its sales price list, and for every OptiSlang product sold, Dynardo received a percentage royalty similar to a channel or distributor relationship. This kind of partnership is a technology and sales partnership where the start-up's products are integrated with the larger company's products and sold to their customer as a package. Such a relationship is called an OEM relationship.

For example, automotive companies have relationships with many tier 1 suppliers to supply the parts for their automobiles, such as brakes and tires. The advantage of this approach is that the start-up company gets to use the larger company's more significant global sales channel. Still, the disadvantage is that if the product has bugs in it, the sales team of the larger company may not be able to provide that support. Also, there is a danger in establishing a technical partnership with the larger company since the larger company may be able to dedicate some internal R&D resources to build a similar product internally and not extend the collaboration.

The fourth way for a start-up to partner with a larger company is to receive investment from the company as part of a Series A or Series B financing. While venture capitalists typically only provide the financial investment, a larger company will provide strategic investment, money, and strategic direction to the start-up. For example, AccelChip received a strategic investment from Xilinx as part of their $5 million Series B investment. The advantage of getting strategic investment from a larger company in the same industry vertical is that it provides validation of the business to a venture capital.

The final way to work with a larger company is to be acquired. As mentioned in the previous section, the start-up company typically raises multiple investment rounds to become a profitable company. Still, the only way for the initial investors or founders to get rewarded for their investment is to go through an exit process that is either an initial public offering (IPO) or acquired by a larger company. For example, AccelChip was acquired by Xilinx in 2006 for $25 million, and the Series A and Series B investors got a return on their investment. Another example is Dynardo, the company that we discussed earlier, an OEM partnership, acquired by Ansys in 2019.

How Large Companies Can Best Partner with Start-Ups

Large companies have done well with H1 incremental innovations to their existing products but are less adept with H3 / disruptive innovation projects. This is where it makes sense for large companies to partner with start-ups. While we all know experience is a good teacher, start-ups are less risk averse than large companies and can teach the old dogs new tricks. We go into this in more detail in Chapter 6.

Partnerships happen in many ways.

- The large company can invest in the start-up as part of Series A, B, or C financing. This allows the large company to take an equity stake and get a board seat or observer seat in the start-up. It also enables the large company to track the technical and business progress.

- The large company can form an OEM partnership, whereby the start-up products are added to the large company's product portfolio sales pricing list. For example, if the start-up's product lists for one hundred thousand dollars, the giant company will typically offer a royalty payment of 30 percent. Access to the large company's sales channel quickly gets the start-up's product ahead of many more customers. The start-up has more time to build its own sales force with this revenue stream.

- The large company may decide to acquire the start-up after observing its performance and gauging its potential. This is good on the front end and helps determine the best exit strategy.

How Start-Up Companies Can Partner with Academia and Large Companies

How can I improve my innovation success if I am a start-up entrepreneur? How can I better partner with large companies? How can I partner with academia? If I am a start-up entrepreneur, I should ask whether I can go alone to build my dream of the start-up. The start-up will probably have the team to develop the product internally. However, you have a choice of building out a direct sales force to sell the product or having an indirect channel using a distributor or a large company and executing an OEM agreement with that company. It may also be a good idea to take strategic investment from that company. If you executive well, that large company may acquire you in the future.

The Start-Up Ecosystem

Today's start-up ecosystem is extensive and rich, because so much innovation occurs in universities, incubators, governmental organizations, research centers, and large companies seeking new thought. Start-up ecosystems benefit the economy as well as start-ups. Platforms like Crunchbase or StartUs Insights track some 2 million start-ups across 77,000 technologies and 300 locations across the globe. If you are a large company interested in working with start-ups, it is easy to search for potential partners.

CONCLUSION

This chapter intended to describe how start-up companies succeed when working with their specialty horizon 3 disruptive innovation. They are 100 percent focused on building an excellent product, selling it to make a profit, and then scaling that business. This chapter explained

- how a start-up company identifies a unique value proposition to solve a problem that no one else has solved
- how to identify a set of customers and the total available market
- how to create a business plan used to raise capital in multiple phases (seed, Series A, Series B, and Series C)
- ultimately, the decision for an exit strategy, such as an acquisition or an IPO, and
- how start-up companies can partner with intermediaries for sales or large companies form OEM relationships to grow their business.

Chapter 6 explains how large companies can better partner with start-up companies.

AUTHOR'S PERSONAL EXPERIENCE IN START-UPS

From 2000 to 2004, *as AccelChip founder, president, CEO, and, later, chief scientist*, I founded AccelChip based on technology developed at Northwestern University on the MATCH compiler that was funded by DARPA between 1998 and 2001. AccelChip licensed the technology from Northwestern. I was able to raise $2.3 million in venture capital funding in Series A from Arch Ventures and $5 million in Series B from Greylock Capital and Interwest, hired a top management team, and helped to grow the company to about twenty-five employees. During this period, AccelChip developed the first product—AccelFPGA—that automatically converted system-level algorithms written in MATLAB into Register Transfer Level VHDL and Verilog that could be synthesized onto FPGAs. AccelChip generated more than $5 million in revenue and was purchased by Xilinx in 2006 for $25 million.

From 2004 to 2011, *as BINACHIP founder, chairman, and chief scientist*, I founded BINACHIP that was based on technologies developed at Northwestern University and University of Illinois at Chicago on the FREEDOM compiler that was funded by NASA and DARPA. During this period, I helped the company raise funding using SBIR and STTR proposals from NSF, NASA, Army, and DARPA and hired a core group of employees. BINACHIP built the first product—ESLERATE—that automatically converted software binaries for processors, such as the TI DSP and ARM, into Register Transfer Level VHDL and Verilog that could be synthesized onto FPGAs and ASICs. BINACHIP generated revenue of about $1.5 million from government contracts with NASA, NSF, Army, and DARPA and was acquired by QuickStream Media in 2011.

Both these start-ups gave me practical experience about how to take a research prototype from a university lab and develop a product out of it and provide some meaningful value to some customers—in other words, how to convert a discovery into innovation.

CHAPTER 4
Innovation in Large Companies

Interview: Brad Feldmann, CEO of Cubic Corporation

Bradley H. Feldmann has served as president and chief executive officer of Cubic Corporation from July 2014 to December 2021. Overseeing the operations of Cubic's two business divisions, Cubic Transportation Systems and Cubic Mission & Performance Solutions, Feldmann implements management and operation processes and overall strategic vision for the corporation. He was appointed to the board of directors in May 2014 and was elected as chairman of the board in February 2018.

As president and CEO, Feldmann managed Cubic's 2021 sale and transition from a publicly traded company to private ownership. He has led several transformational initiatives throughout his tenure, such as creating the Cubic Innovation Social System. This framework enables Cubic individuals and teams to rapidly transform ideas into differentiated, user-centric products and services that solve Cubic customers' most challenging problems.

Under Feldmann's leadership, Cubic took essential steps to change its global IT infrastructure into a scalable, efficient, and effective system through the rollout of the Global Enterprise Management Systems (GEMS) initiative. Cubic's Diversity & Inclusion initiative seeks to increase Cubic's diverse employee population and supplier base to drive innovation, recruiting, talent development, and corporate responsibility priorities that benefit employees, customers, and the communities Cubic serves.

Feldmann is a graduate of the Stanford Executive Institute and holds a Master of Business Administration with honors from San Diego State University. He is also a distinguished graduate of the US Air Force Academy with a Bachelor of Science in Electrical Engineering and a top graduate of the USAF Squadron Officer School.

Feldmann is NACD (National Association of Corporate Directors) directorship certified He is an active member of the National Defense Industrial Association, serving as a board member, executive committee member, and finance committee chair. He is a fellow of the National Association of Corporate Directors and serves on the board of UrbanLife as finance committee chair. Feldmann also served on the Aerospace Industries Association Board of Governors and was on the executive committee from 2017 to 2019.

Feldmann was recently honored as a *San Diego Business Journal* CEO of the Year (2021) and listed as one of their Most Influential People in 2021. In 2020, he was recognized as one of Wall Street Journal CEO Council's world's most influential business leaders. Feldmann earned the CERT Certificate in Cybersecurity Oversight from the NACD and was honored by the Corporate Directors Forum as Director of the Year for Corporate Governance in 2018.

In 2017, he was recognized as Most Admired CEO by the *San Diego Business Journal* for his exceptional organizational leadership.

He was awarded the Bronze Stevie Award in the Executive of the Year category by the American Business Awards. In 2016, Feldmann received the Duane Roth Distinguished Contribution Awards for Technology by CONNECT for his contributions to elevating San Diego as a global innovation economy.

INTERVIEWER. Brad, thank you very much for agreeing to be interviewed for my book *The Innovation Factory*. I would like to ask you some questions about innovation at Cubic. But before I begin, can you tell me about the company Cubic? What does it do? Who are your customers and your businesses? How many employees? What is your annual revenue?

INTERVIEWEE. Cubic is a technology-driven, market-leading, global provider of innovative, mission-critical solutions that reduce congestion and increase operational effectiveness and readiness through superior situational understanding. Cubic has two businesses: Cubic Transportation Systems and Cubic Mission & Performance Solutions. At Cubic Mission & Performance Solutions (CMPS), we provide networked command, control, communications, computers, intelligence, surveillance, and reconnaissance (C4ISR) capabilities for defense, intelligence, security, and commercial missions. We are a leading provider of live, virtual, constructive, and game-based (LVC-G) training solutions for the US and allied forces.

Cubic Transportation Systems (CTS) is an industry-leading integrator of payment and information solutions and related services for intelligent travel applications. CTS delivers integrated systems for transportation and traffic management, delivering tools for travelers to choose the most innovative and easiest way to travel and pay for their journeys, and enabling transportation authorities and agencies to manage demand across the entire transportation network. We have over six thousand diverse employees (called CUBES) across seventy-five locations in more than twenty countries who serve our global customers. Our annual revenue for the company in 2020 was $1.5 billion.

INTERVIEWER. Let us talk about innovation. What are some of the core technologies that drive Cubic the company? How much does Cubic invest annually in innovation? How does the percentage of R&D to revenue for Cubic compare with the industry (transportation and defense)? Can you speak about your internal R&D and customer-funded R&D?

INTERVIEWEE. Cubic is founded on innovation, so it is no surprise that we have a timeline of technological innovations that have propelled Cubic through the years. Innovation is our lifeblood. Cubic invests in innovation through both top-down investments and bottom-up investments. We invest small to create ideas, increase investment as we gain customer sponsorship, and ensure we have business unit leadership and commitment before significant product launch investments. We regularly review the efficacy of our assets and adjust as necessary.

We invested a record $55.5 million in innovation in 2021, up from $44.6 million the prior year. To put that into context, we invested $18 million in 2015, which was a mere 1.3 percent of sales, compared to now, where we are investing over 3 percent of revenue. We prioritize our internal research and development (IRAD) investment and integrate new acquisition technologies faster for superior returns. We place short, medium, and long-term game changer and total bets to create the best, balanced returns while driving the market share of our sub-businesses. We combine our investment with customer cofunding to ensure that we are also gaining mindshare from our investments. We use discipline to terminate innovation projects that do not contribute to our revenue goals.

While most of our projects are technology focused, our portfolio also involves several projects focused on differentiated business model innovations, particularly digital platforms that enable us to scale applications, create recurring revenue streams, and commercial pricing to drive more value for our customers and shareholders. We develop products and technology solutions shared in a source of funds between customer contracts to Cubic and Cubic research and development or investment. This ranges from prototype and demo, a set of criteria, a customer-funded study or innovation project, or a US government customer CRAD (contract research and development). We had approximately 70 percent of customer codevelopment in 2020 and 2021, highlighting the importance of our customer-centric approach to innovation.

INTERVIEWER. As CEO, you are responsible for growing top-line revenue growth and bottom-line savings to generate more earnings and drive the share price. Can you share your philosophy about how you serve the shareholders of a public company? Is R&D an expense or an investment? You can generate more earnings by reducing R&D. How do you invest in R&D to drive profitable growth in your business? Can you describe the portfolio approach to managing R&D?

INTERVIEWEE. While R&D may be an expense to the financiers, I use it to drive growth and new revenue streams. The portfolio approach that we operate is based on balancing short- and long-term investments, from incremental innovations to game-changing ones, with a level of risk working proportionally.

The portfolio allocation process occurs annually to ensure that innovation projects are linked to customer opportunities that benefit from the R&D expenditures. Additional objectives of the portfolio allocation process are to identify customer-paid development opportunities related to R&D projects and consistently quantify customer codevelopment funding for programs with significant development scope that contribute to progressing technology roadmap pursuits. The result of this process is an overall Cubic portfolio investment plan. The process assures verifiable data through Cubic business systems, and it imposes accountability for affordability and prioritization of established annual R&D portfolios and technology roadmaps. Also, very importantly, it commits critical team members, essential skill sets, and the necessary funding to execute innovation projects efficiently and with prioritized urgency throughout the fiscal year.

INTERVIEWER. Large companies excel in incremental horizon 1 innovation and do well in horizon 2 innovations in the adjacencies in their products. What they struggle with is the horizon 3 disruptive innovation. Since I served on the board of directors of Cubic, I saw how you encouraged horizon 3 innovation using your IdeaSpark program. Can you share some details about this program and how it fostered innovation at Cubic?

INTERVIEWEE. IdeaSpark was developed in 2014 to serve as a comprehensive innovation enablement platform that empowers organic, community-driven ideas and crowdsourced solutions to solve critical business challenges and maximize competitive advantage. IdeaSpark provides a reliable digital forum for employees to engage in creativity and offers Cubic employees direct opportunities to grow new solutions to support overall business strategy. We use community-driven ideas and bounty challenges with crowdsourced solutions as two distinct ways to capture creative input from the Cubic workforce. These methods allow users of various functional disciplines and experience levels to contribute ideas and improvements to reach innovation goals.

Our primary ideation workflow is called Community Driven Ideation. This is a guided ideation workflow and bottom-up approach to ideation. Ideators can propose new products and process improvement ideas to the entire IdeaSpark community. Once an idea is submitted, other users can use social features to vote, comment, and follow arguments. Using collaborative tools based on well-known social media paradigms, the combined innovation team and Business Unit Innovation Council members review and vote on the submitted ideas.

Suppose an idea is advanced to the seedling stage. In that case, the sponsoring Business Unit decides whether to fund the proposal effort for an assigned business development / capture lead and Cubic integrator to explore and validate the potential business case. This validation would include market analysis, user experience surveys, evaluation of current Cubic IP, and rapid development of a minimum viable prototype (MVP). Suppose the idea is validated at this Business Unit adjudication stage. In that case, the Business Unit sponsor will move the concept into one of four potential streams: customer-funded development, rapid prototype, product/technology roadmap, or future R&D project.

The second type of workflow implemented in IdeaSpark is a problem-based workflow called Bounties. Bounties are a top-down innovation approach that enables Business Unit stakeholders to narrow the topics for ideation and enlist the workforce to compete against one another and attempt to solve a customer pain point or offer a new approach for applying technology. Using gamification and discussion forums, the stakeholder can post a problem or challenge in the form of Bounty on IdeaSpark, outline a specific time limit for the challenge, and offer award points and a winner when the time expires. Using this social, crowdsourced format, all ideators can comment on and upvote/downvote on the submitted solutions for the stakeholders. Winning challenges leads to increased social status and points and a Bounty award for the winning submission. This cycle of gamified innovation then repeats as new problems are posted and new solutions are submitted.

The IdeaSpark community hub fosters Cubic's innovation culture with focused communication that speaks directly from and to our innovation community. To keep employees coming back and contributing to the ecosystem outside of idea submissions, IdeaSpark's community pages offer rich media blogs and video support.

INTERVIEWER. What role does strategy play in growing your company? Can you describe some of the work on company strategy led by your internal teams and some work you may have done with strategy consultants about growing your business? How did you engage with the strategy committee of your board?

INTERVIEWEE. Winning customers is critical, and we win customers by solving their most complex problems through innovation. We have technology roadmaps to ensure we invest in the right technologies to solve our customers' future issues. We adopted Willie Pietersen's strategic learning cycle to create winning propositions and continuously learn from strategy creation and execution. Winning proposals are how we make value for our customers and shareholders simultaneously. We create the supporting key priorities with measurable strategic objectives that flow down into the organization, creating buy-in and alignment. We have also realized that strategy execution is critical, and therefore, having more CUBES involved in the strategy creation process ensures even more buy-in from the organization.

Strategy is everything—the essential thing—to grow the company. Whether it is maximizing stock price, optimizing adjusted EBITDA margin, maximizing free cash flow, or reducing debt, it is essential to consider a range of strategic alternatives in our strategic environment and opportunities and consider the best interests of our shareholders. Our situation analysis and critical insights help us frame the strategic options we could feasibly achieve. As part of our strategic alternatives review, we evaluate and actively manage our portfolio of businesses using methods such as the BCG growth-share matrix and real options valuation to determine whether it makes sense to pursue strategic options, including mergers acquisition activities.

We define our strategic choices, which markets we will compete in, which customers we will serve, and what we will offer them. The centerpiece of our strategy is the winning proposition. It is the decisive point. It defines how we will win the competition for value creation by providing the unique benefits we will deliver to our customers, which offer a compelling reason for them to do business with us, and how we will translate this exceptional customer value into superior financial returns enterprise.

Cubic's board of directors (BOD) is highly engaged in strategy. Members of our senior management regularly review the strategy with the board and the operating plan of each of the business segments and the company. Our Strategic Planning Group (SPG) and Executive Management Committee (EMC) work closely with the BOD to continually assess our progress toward achieving our strategic goals. They are committed to a robust, healthy, two-way dialogue with the board based on intellectual honesty and the brutal truths associated with our business.

INTERVIEWER. Many companies use mergers and acquisitions (M&A) as a way to bring in new technology and innovation to the mother ship. Can you speak about some companies Cubic has acquired in the past three to five years and how they have contributed to your growth?

INTERVIEWEE. During the past five years, Cubic has acquired the following companies: GRIDSMART, Trafficware, Gate, Delerrok, Pixia, and Nuvotronics. Our cumulative acquisition returns are above our weighted average cost of capital (WACC). While not every acquisition performs at the same rate, we have had successes that have led to growth, particularly integrating Trafficware and GRIDSMART under one umbrella to create our intelligent traffic systems (ITS) business and realigning pricing strategies for increased competitiveness and global expansion.

The Nuvotronics acquisition in CMPS is an example of when we are initially down from the 8 percent WACC target, as we have worked to expand production capabilities, which will allow us to enter the space and 5G/6G arena. This is important for the future strategic growth of the company over the years to come. It will allow us to enter new markets, but the in-house technology will complement existing products and systems, including developments in our transportation business.

Innovation in Large Companies

This chapter focuses on H3 disruptive innovation in large companies, the nation's backbone. There would be little incentive for start-ups or small businesses to strive if they could not hope to grow large and successful. While many large companies excel at incremental improvements to their current set of products (H1) and may also perform well on medium-term innovation in its expansion into other markets and market segments (H2), all too often, they are not very successful in creating genuine H3 disruptive, innovative products or services.

While a start-up company focuses on a particular product or service in a specific market and tries to take market share and grow revenue in that market profitably, a large company will typically have multiple entries in multiple markets and must manage a portfolio of R&D investments in each of its markets and divisions profitably.

The App Store is an exciting example of how a large company shared its innovation with a developing, if not still a start-up, company. In 1999, Salesforce innovated the concept of a way to work with third parties called the AppExchange and named it the App Store. A few years later, Apple CEO Steve Jobs told CEO Marc Benioff, "You've got to build an application economy." Benioff liked the idea and trademarked the name App Store but in 2006 gave the idea, the name, and the website URL to Jobs. As a result, in 2008, Apple opened its own App Store. Now a mature H3 enterprise, Apple successfully launched its App Store and more recently reinvented and reinnovated its disabled iTunes music player as Apple Music, Apple TV, and Apple Podcasts platforms with great success. Salesforce, a cloud-based customer relationship management (CRM) company, is considered one of the top companies to work for.

Like Salesforce, every large company has its core business. Most of the H1 and H2 innovation occurs here for obvious reasons. What begins as an H3 disruptive innovation may, over time, impact the core business. It is often natural for an adjacent LOB to merge into the primary business. Bain & Company partners Chris Zook and James Allen, writing in their *Harvard Business Review* article "Growth Outside the Core," describe six adjacent ways a large company can grow.

1. Expand along the value chain. This is one of the most challenging adjacency moves.
2. Grow new products and services.
3. Use new distribution channels.
4. Enter new geographies.
5. Address new customer segments, often by modifying a proven product or technology.
6. Move into the white space with a new business built around a strong capability. This is the rarest and most challenging adjacency move to pull off.

BUSINESS BASICS IN A LARGE COMPANY

The CEO of a publicly traded large company is responsible to its stockholders for increasing the share price and the market capitalization/valuation of the company. Just as a start-up company tries to increase its valuation by growing its profits, the CEO and management team of a large company must do the same except that the growth, when scaled over hundreds of products across multiple divisions, is much more complex.

Say a large company has approximately two billion shares outstanding with earnings per share of five dollars and a price to earnings (PE) ratio of about ten. The company price per share is about fifty dollars, and its market cap will be about $100 billion. The objective is to continually increase revenue—in other words, profits—year after year. Companies whose revenue grows at 10 percent per year profitably (or 5 percent about the market growth in that vertical) with about a 15–25 percent net income margin will respond favorably to Wall Street investors and its shareholders.

Many do not understand this simple fact: The only way to grow revenue profitably is to constantly innovate with new products or services that are better than your competition's, thereby continuously increasing your market share. This is the basic principle of business regardless of company size, but it is critical for the large company.

Consider the automobile manufacturing business—for example, Toyota. It is a top-ten automaker with over half a billion dollars in assets. Automakers like Toyota typically manufacture cars in separate divisions—small vehicles, such as the Corolla; a medium-sized division for the Camry; a luxury car division for the Lexus; a truck division for the Tacoma; and a minivan division for the Sienna. Automakers' divisions are often found in different countries where they are closest to the consumer. For example, the Toyota Camry is manufactured in the US while the Toyota Prius is still made in Japan.

Take, for example, the Corolla division. It may sell a model for $15,000 with sales projections of one hundred thousand units in a given year, generating a total estimated revenue of $1.5 billion—fifty thousand units in America, thirty thousand in Europe, and twenty thousand in Asia. Therefore, the revenue is $750 million, $450 million, and $300 million in the three regions.

The division will have to purchase parts from their tier 1 suppliers—also referred to as original equipment manufacturers, or OEMs—such as DENSO or Exide, to build these cars. These parts may be electronics, brakes, steering wheels, tires, or transmissions. Say the brakes are $1,200 and the transmission is $2,000. All these costs are, of course, calculated as line items of cost of goods sold (COGS). Assume the COGS of this Corolla is $12,570. Hence, the gross margin of a typical small car division of a large business is approximately 15 percent. The large company must also account for the spending on sales, marketing, and research and development. The cost of R&D in the automotive business is about 3 percent of revenue, which is about $45 million. After all these expenses, the division's net profit margin may amount to $150 million. The net profit margin (EBITDA, or earnings before interest, taxes, depreciation, and amortization) is 10 percent after paying taxes and amortization.

In the case of Toyota, its sales over the past five years have been relatively flat. Given this problem, what steps must the company consider to grow its revenue? This can only be done through innovation—by creating innovative products that are much better than the competition and even its existing product lines.

Breakdown by items	Division 1	Division 2	Division 3	Division 4	Total
Average sales price of product	$15,000	$25,000	$50,000	$100,000	
Number of products sold	100,000	50,000	20,000	5,000	
Annual revenue	$1,500,000,000	$1,250,000,000	$1,000,000,000	$500,000,000	$4,250,000,000
Cost of goods sold	$1,200,000,000	$950,000,000	$725,000,000	$300,000,000	$3,175,000,000
Gross margin	$300,000,000	$300,000,000	$275,000,000	$200,000,000	$1,075,000,000
Gross margin percentage	20%	24%	28%	40%	25%
R&D expenditure	$45,000,000	$50,000,000	$50,000,000	$40,000,000	$185,000,000
Sales general admin expenses	$49,500,000	$60,000,000	$65,000,000	$56,000,000	$230,500,000
Net income (EBIT)	$205,500,000	$190,000,000	$160,000,000	$104,000,000	$659,500,000
Net income percentage	14%	15%	16%	21%	16%
Depreciation and amortization					$300,000,000
EBITDA					$959,500,000
EBITDA percentage					23%
Total shares					1,000,000,000
Earnings per share					$1
Share price					$10
Market capitalization					$9,595,000,000

Table 4.1. Income statement of a hypothetical large company

Table 4.1 shows an example income statement of a large company with four divisions. Division 1 sells one hundred thousand products at an average price of $15,000 with annual revenue of $1.5 billion. The cost of goods sold is $1.22 billion with a gross margin percentage of 20 percent. The R&D expense of this division is $45 million, and the sales and general administrative costs of this division are $49.5 million. The net income percentage for this division is 14 percent. Division 4, on the other hand, sells a fewer number of products (five thousand) but at a much higher price ($100,000) with a total revenue of $500 million. The total revenue for the company is $4.25 billion, and the total net earnings after amortization and taxes are $960 million. Assuming the company has 1 billion shares, the earnings per share at the end of the year is $9.6. The market capitalization of this company, assuming a PE ratio of ten, is $9.6 billion. The CEO of this company will try to increase the company's market capitalization and share price by 10 percent or 20 percent per year.

For another example of a domestic auto manufacturing business, take a look at the income statement for General Motors in 2020. The total revenue for GM in 2020 was $122.5 billion, which was 10.75 percent less than the 2019 revenue of $137.2 billion. That was a significant decline. The revenue for GM had peaked at $147 billion in 2018. The entire automotive industry faced a 10 percent reduction because of the COVID-19 pandemic. All sales were down. The cost of goods sold was $101.9 billion; hence, the gross profit for GM was $20.5 billion, or 16.8 percent. The R&D expenditure was $6.7 billion, or about 5 percent. Other sales and general administrative expenses were $7 billion. The EBIT margin was $7.1 billion. After paying an income tax of $1.7 billion and depreciation of $12 billion and income from other operations of $7 billion, the EBITDA margin was $20 billion with an EBITDA margin of 16.3 percent. These earnings were distributed to shareholders. With 1.33 billion shares of GM outstanding, each shareholder received earnings per share of $4.30. With a PE ratio of 5.67, the share price of GM was about $48 per share, and a market capitalization of GM was about $70 billion.

This is typical. The auto manufacturing industry is a low-margin business. While the revenue decreased by 6.7 percent in 2019 and 10.75 percent in 2020, GM is investing in innovation (in areas such as electrification and autonomous vehicles) and planning that the revenue will grow in the future and that there will be profitable growth. The challenge faced by large companies such as GM is how you grow your revenue and how you develop it profitably. This is where innovation comes in. For example, in 2020, the entire automotive market went down by 10 percent, and most auto companies struggled to maintain revenue. But then they are all looking at 2025 or 2030 and planning that the automotive industry will bounce back after the pandemic, so they need to invest in R&D in areas such as autonomous driving, electric vehicles, and connected cars to come up with lots of innovation in these areas so that they can sell 120,000 cars in 2025 and take market share away from other auto companies.

In the automated driving area, GM invested in partnership with a start-up company called Cruise, and Ford invested in a start-up company called Argo in the computerized driving area. For any carmaker, the future of innovation lies with moving from internal combustion to battery-powered electric motors.

Organizational Structure of a Large Company Needed to Support Innovation

Figure 4.1 shows the organizational structure of a large automotive company with multiple divisions. Division 1 sells cars, division 2 sells trucks and minivans, and division 3 sells motorcycles and scooters. Division 1 has three lines of business (LOB)—for small cars, medium-sized cars, and luxury cars. Each of these lines of business has a research and development group, a design group, and a product management group. These lines of businesses develop and manufacture the products, and the sales teams for the entire company sell these products in different regions (North America, Europe, and Asia). This is a typical organizational structure of large companies.

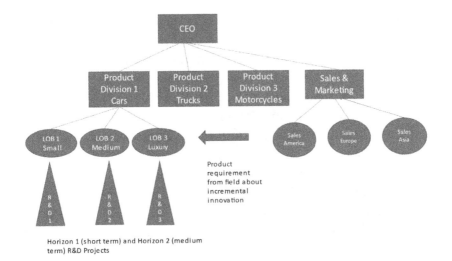

Horizon 1 (short term) and Horizon 2 (medium term) R&D Projects

Figure 4.1. Organizational structure of a large automotive company with three divisions

How to Solve the Problems of H3 Innovation in Large Companies

Large companies do best in near-term/incremental improvements of existing products. Large companies also do pretty well in medium-term/adjacent products. However, large companies struggle with long-term/disruptive products since these are very risky, and they do not know how to sell said products.

Managing a Portfolio of R&D Investments

An idea may become an innovation, at which point it can be appraised and managed as an investment. If progress toward becoming a product or service, it is an R&D investment. Large companies commonly have a portfolio of products, as shown with an automobile manufacturer, and a portfolio of R&D investments. The same is true for its innovation initiatives. A large company may have over a hundred innovation projects underway simultaneously. They must be identified, cataloged, managed, integrated, and connected in the business value chain to demonstrate their purpose and ROI. Each must be addressed and measured in terms of its business performance.

Figure 4.2 shows how large companies manage their R&D investments in a portfolio of businesses. This simplified example shows a company with four divisions, each having its product (yellow, green, red, and blue). The size of the circle represents the amount of revenue. The x-axis shows the net profit percentage by-products, and the y-axis shows the annual revenue growth rate.

You can see from this picture that the blue product is highly profitable, but since it is in a declining business, it is a cash cow. The company should continue investing minimally to maintain the product to generate as much cash as possible. The green product is the best-case division and product. The product is highly profitable and is growing in revenue every year. The company ought to keep investing in R&D in this product and division. The yellow product may be a new product for the company, so investing in its R&D is not profitable yet. But if the company continues to invest, it can probably grow the business and make it profitable. The red product and division are not profitable, and business is declining. This business needs to be closed down. Its people and R&D investments should be retargeted into the other businesses.

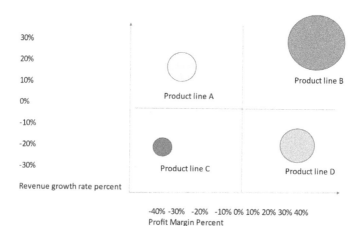

Figure 4.2. Managing a portfolio of R&D investments
in a company with four divisions

How Large Companies Protect R&D Investments Using Patents

Large companies investing in new products and technology R&D must protect their investments, for they are constantly at risk of being compromised or stolen. Examples of new areas of innovation and investments and business intelligence theft are AI / machine learning, 3D printing, Internet of Things (IoT), big data analytics, cloud, mobile devices, autonomous vehicles, robotics electrification, etc. Chapter 8 goes into more detail about various digital technologies employed to drive product and service innovation.

Once a company invents or decides to innovate with new technology, it must immediately take steps to protect its investments by filing invention disclosures and patents. Patents are typically valid for twenty years, give companies a measure of protection from theft and illicit or illegal misappropriation, and help preserve a sustainable competitive advantage. For example, a medical or pharmaceutical company invents a new drug after making an R&D investment of $1 billion. The patent assures the invention has legal protection while the company now has time to recoup its investment. A blockbuster drug can generate revenues of $5–10 billion. However, it requires a substantial R&D investment and the development time, then the clinical trials and FDA approvals for the drug. Consider the COVID-19 vaccine. While it did not take Pfizer-BioNTech, Moderna, or Johnson & Johnson long to create the new vaccine (since its core mRNA was already well-known in that it had been developed as part of the CRISPR genetic engineering work done at universities over the past twenty years), it still took over a year to obtain all the FDA approvals.

Although there are no competitions for the most patents a company has been awarded, it is still considered a sign of an enterprise's success and preeminence. But more importantly, patent development is responsible for developing and sustaining competitive advantage, at least up to a point. Yet perhaps even more critical, producing patent-capable goods and services incentivizes innovators and inventors within the company to work harder and smarter. This then becomes an indirect measure of the amount and the quality of innovation in a company.

Ranking	Company	2020 Patents
1	IBM	9,435
2	Samsung	8,539
3	LG Corporation	5,112
4	Canon	3,689
5	Intel	3,284
6	Raytheon	3,213
7	Huawei	3,178
8	Microsoft	2,972
9	TSMC	2,892
10	Sony	2,886
11	Apple	2,840
12	Dell	2,826
13	Toyota	2,816
14	General Electric	2,417
15	Google	2,379
16	Amazon	2,373
17	Qualcomm	2,297
18	Boeing	2,157
19	Ford	2,090
20	Panasonic	1,929

Table 4.2. Top twenty companies ranked by the
number of patents granted in 2020

It is generally accepted that the companies with the most patents are the most innovative. Another way to look at the most innovative companies is to note how many patents they have acquired over the company history. Table 4.3 shows the top ten companies holding the most patents since their inception. While there are a lot of companies in the top ten in both tables, one exception is IBM, which has consistently been granted the most significant number of patents in the short term (more than Samsung) yet holds only half as many patents total as Samsung. IBM has a very efficient way of managing its most valuable patents. When they determine that some patents do not contribute to protecting IBM's competitive advantage, they sell patents to other companies. IBM, above all, knows when to hold a patent and also wisely knows when to fold it. This is a very well-managed process.

Ranking	Company	Total Patents Held in 2020
1	Samsung	76,638
2	IBM	37,304
3	Canon	35,374
4	General Electric	30,010
5	Microsoft	29,824
6	Bosch	28,285
7	Panasonic	27,298
8	Siemens	25,280
9	Intel	24,268
10	LG Electronics	23,043

Table 4.3. The top ten companies holding the most patents

WHEN INTELLECTUAL PROPERTY IS USED TO DRIVE BUSINESS REVENUE

While most companies use intellectual property tools, such as patents, trademarks, and copyright, to protect their innovations, allowing their products and services to develop a distinct competitive differentiation in the marketplace, some companies use patents as a direct source of revenue.

Ray Dolby founded Dolby Labs in 1965. He invented an audio noise suppression technology and successfully licensed it to audio media and hardware companies. Today, Dolby Labs has approximately 13,200 issued patents and about 4,100 pending patent applications in more than one hundred jurisdictions worldwide, both for audio and video noise suppression. During its fiscal year 2020 ending September 25, 2020, about 93 percent of Dolby's $1.2

billion revenue came from licensing. The remaining 7 percent of revenue came from sales of its products and services, such as Dolby Cinema.

Dolby's licensing revenue comes from a two-tier Dolby patent model. Most of their consumer entertainment licensing business consists of a two-tier licensing model, whereby their decoding technologies, included in reference software and firmware code, are first provided under license to semiconductor manufacturers, referred to as implementation licensees. Implementation licensees are the first to incorporate Dolby technologies in their integrated circuits (ICs), sold to OEMs of consumer entertainment products, referred to as system licensees. These systems license companies or business entities then obtain their licenses, allowing them to make and sell end user products using ICs with Dolby technologies.

Dolby Labs depends on innovations that create new technologies. But more importantly, its business and innovation model depends on these technologies being patentable so they may be licensed to other companies so that the technology can be implemented for their specific business purposes. For example, Atmos, a unique Dolby technology, was custom-designed and implemented in the Lucid Air automobile, delivering a three-dimensional, spatial-audio experience.

PATENT TROLLS

A recent trend in patenting is troll companies that acquire patents from other companies, then use them to sue large companies for patent violation. In international law and business, patent trolling or patent hoarding is an absolute or pejorative term applied to a person or company that attempts to enforce patent rights against accused infringers far beyond the patent's actual value or contribution to the prior art, often through hardball legal tactics. Patent trolls often do not manufacture products or supply services based on the patents. However, some entities that do not implement their asserted patent but merely own it may not be considered patent trolls simply because they license their patented technologies on reasonable terms in advance.

Copyright trolling has existed for several years, commonly concerning music rights. While in most cases, the entities termed trolls are operating within the bounds of the legal system, their aggressive tactics achieve outcomes contrary to the original intent of the patent system as a legislated social contract to foster and protect innovation. The rapid rise of the modern information economy and the Internet has put the global intellectual property system under more strain. Patent trolling has been less of a problem in Europe than in the United States, because Europe has a loser-pays-costs regime. In contrast, the US generally employs the American rule, under which each party is responsible for paying their own attorney's fees.

How Innovation Is Supported in Large Companies

Innovation is a strategy for conducting business. It is essential for a large company so that its products or services do not become obsolete or are surpassed by competitors. Innovation is how a company's offerings are refreshed and invigorated and often begin life as an H1 or H2 outside the core business. At a certain point in development, they can transform into an H3 innovation, which is not to say an H3 innovation cannot occur like a lightning bolt. All innovation must be regarded as valuable and supported through its early ideation stages. When it becomes a possible product or service, the support becomes formalized and quantified as an R&D effort. Some of the means of achieving those outcomes are

- creation of a central research lab and a CTO office,
- creation of centers of excellence that support horizontal technologies,
- organizing company-wide technology conferences and talks,
- programs to solicit innovative ideas from all employees, and
- institutional programs to recognize innovation and create a culture of innovation.

CHIEF TECHNOLOGY OFFICER (CTO) AND A CENTRAL RESEARCH LAB (CRL)

The first way to support long-term innovation in a large company is to create a chief technology officer (CTO), a central research lab, an advanced technology group, or a corporate research center. For example, HPE, IBM, and Microsoft have HP Labs, IBM Research, or Microsoft Research. GE, ABB, and Schneider Electric have corporate research centers. Dolby Labs and Synopsys have advanced technology groups. They all have the same organizational design. Their shared mission is to investigate long-term technology trends relevant to the company's business objectives.

For example, while I was director at HP Labs, we always explored innovations related to printing and imaging technologies, pervasive computing and collaboration, sustainable data centers, exascale computing, and data management and analytics. While I worked at ABB, we had a centralized corporate research center with labs focusing on power electronics, cybersecurity, process automation, robotics, transformers, materials science, and breaker technologies. We will discuss more examples of this approach in chapter 5.

HORIZONTAL CENTERS OF EXCELLENCE IN TECHNOLOGY

The second way to support long-term innovation is to organize horizontal centers of technology. These centers support R&D in distinct product units. For example, Ansys has product units such as Structures, Fluids, Electronics, Semiconductors, and Embedded Software; and two thousand engineers are working on R&D across these product lines. While I was CTO of Ansys, the company created Centers of Excellence around technology areas such as numerical methods, AI / machine learning, high-performance computing, model-based systems engineering, integrated computational materials engineering, and digital twins. Each of the two thousand engineers is part of a product line R&D team and is also a member of one or two centers of excellence. This drives a lot of collaborative discussion and innovation across product silos. Figure 4.3 shows the relationship between product lines and centers of excellence at Ansys.

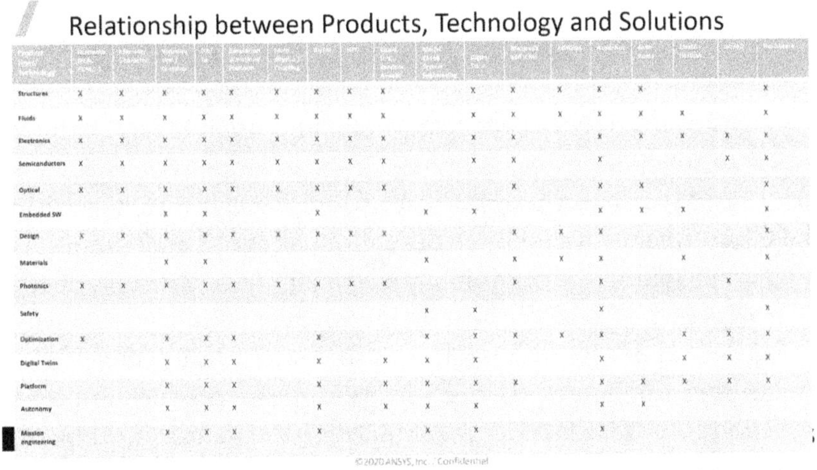

Relationship between Products, Technology and Solutions

©2020 ANSYS, Inc. Confidential

Figure 4.3. Relationship between products and technology centers of excellence at Ansys (courtesy of Ansys)

COMPANY-WIDE TECHNOLOGY CONFERENCES AND TALKS

The third way to foster innovation in large companies is to organize company-wide technology conferences and talks. For example, while I was director of HP Labs, HP organized an annual tech con for about one thousand of its (out of its thirty thousand) engineers to get together for one week to present and share their ideas for the most innovative technologies. These conferences continue to be quite successful. While I was CTO of Ansys, the company created a similar annual tech con for two hundred of its two thousand engineers. While the tech con brought together engineers at one location for one week, Ansys also organized a TechTalk series where engineers presented technical topics once every two weeks (twenty-six talks a year). All engineers attend these TechTalks at Ansys since they are held as videoconferences. These meetings break down silos between product groups and encourage cross-business unit technical collaboration.

SOLICIT IDEAS FOR INNOVATION FROM ALL EMPLOYEES

The fourth way to encourage more innovation in large companies is to solicit ideas for innovation from all employees. For example, Cubic sponsors a program called Idea Exchange supported by the CEO, where any employee can submit an idea for an innovative product or solution at the company. The CEO funds a team of two to four people to take off from their current assignment to pursue this novel, innovative idea for four to six weeks. During this period, the team can build a prototype of an innovative product and solution; and if the idea is good, it is funded at a significant level by the CEO. This is discussed in more detail in the response to the fourth question by Brad Feldmann, CEO of Cubic, at the beginning of this chapter.

CREATING A CULTURE OF INNOVATION WITH INSTITUTIONAL PROGRAMS

The fifth and final way to encourage more innovation in companies is to create a culture of innovation. The best companies recognize employees for their innovation. For example, while I was CTO of Ansys, the company created an annual CEO Innovation Awards program that solicited ideas for new product innovation, new technology innovation, and new solutions innovation. The criteria for the award were the following:

- Is the technology innovative to Ansys and the market?
- Do these nominations have patents, trade secrets, and publications to demonstrate that innovation?

- How significant is the market opportunity for this innovation?
- Is there current proof of customer impact?
- Is this a scalable innovation applicable to many customers and many markets?

CONCLUSIONS

This chapter reviewed how large companies manage a portfolio of R&D projects across multiple products and multiple divisions to support innovation to grow top-line revenue while maintaining profit margins. While large companies excel at short-term or incremental horizon 1 innovations, they also do an excellent job managing horizon 2 or medium-term innovations. But they struggle with pursuing long-term innovations.

There are several ways for large companies to support long-term innovation.

- Creating a CTO office and a central research lab
- Encouraging everyone to innovate 20 percent of their time
- Asking for innovative ideas from all employees and creating an idea exchange
- Creating technology centers of excellence
- Creating a culture of innovation with technology conferences and innovation awards

Chapter 5 will discuss approaches to creating a central research lab in a CTO office to pursue long-term innovation organically. Chapter 6 will discuss approaches for large companies to pursue long-term innovation: combining organic innovation having central research labs combined with partnering with academia and partnering with start-ups.

AUTHOR'S PERSONAL EXPERIENCE IN LARGE COMPANIES

Below are the lessons I learned from my work in large companies—ABB, Schneider Electric, and Ansys.

From 2012 to 2013, ABB, executive vice president and chief technology officer. I was executive vice president, chief technology officer, and member of the executive committee of ABB, reporting to the CEO. In this role, I headed up the technology directions for both corporate and divisional technology, which included more than eight thousand scientists and engineers in seven ABB Corporate Research Centers around the world (China, India, Germany, Poland, Sweden, Switzerland, and the USA) and two Global Labs, Global Labs Power, and Global Labs Automation.

I was responsible for starting some new initiatives at ABB around long-term disruptive innovation involving large, multidisciplinary teams of researchers. Some example areas were big data for services; cloud automation; energy-efficient data centers; single-day robot integration; next-generation power grids; and smarter integration of motors, drives, and applications. We also started some new initiatives around university collaboration and further business incubation. Many of these research projects were transferred into new products for the ABB businesses. ABB practiced open innovation with more than one hundred universities worldwide.

From 2015 to 2017, Schneider Electric, executive vice president and chief technology officer. I was executive vice president, chief technology officer, and member of the executive committee of Schneider Electric, reporting to the chairman and the CEO. In this role, I was responsible for driving innovation and technology differentiation and coordinating the company's R&D activities across its five businesses with eight thousand R&D personnel and a 1.3 billion euro R&D investment. My CTO office had four pillars: (1) the five business CTOs through whom I coordinate the R&D across the divisions and lines of business, (2) central functions, like R&D governance, technology community, and open innovation with start-up companies, universities, and partners, (3) corporate research center, which is the central research arm, (4) and IOT and digitization, where we are building an IOT platform for Schneider Electric. I was also responsible for the development of the EcoStruxure IoT platform.

From 2018-current, Ansys, chief technology officer. In this role, I led the evolution of Ansys's technology and championed the company's next phase of innovation and growth. I was responsible for about $300 million in R&D activities and led two thousand R&D engineers across the seven businesses. I led the long-term technology strategy at Ansys around areas such as AI / machine learning, high-performance computing, multiphysics platforms, model-based systems engineering, and digital twins. We built high-growth solutions at Ansys around autonomy, electrification, 5G, IIoT, and health care. I was also responsible for driving Ansys's new and emerging business (having P/L responsibilities) in three initiatives: (1) AI/ML applied to simulation, (2) digital twins, (3) and simulation opportunities in health care. As part of my role, I worked with Ansys's large enterprise customers on aligning the Ansys long-term technology strategy with the customers' business priorities. We also participated in numerous long-term customer co-innovation projects.

CHAPTER 5

The Role of Central Research Labs in Innovation

Interview: Peter Lee, corporate vice president, Research and Incubations at Microsoft

Dr. Peter Lee is the corporate vice president of Research and Incubations at Microsoft. He leads Microsoft Research across its eight laboratories around the world. He also oversees several incubation teams for research-powered new lines of business, the largest of which is Microsoft's growing health care and life sciences effort. Dr. Lee has extensive experience managing fundamental research to commercial impact in various areas, spanning artificial intelligence, quantum computing, biotechnology, etc. Before joining Microsoft in 2010, he was at DARPA, where he established a new technology office that created operational capabilities in machine learning, data science, and computational social science. From 1987 to 2005, he was a professor at Carnegie Mellon University; and from 2005 to 2008, he was the head of the university's computer science department.

Today, in addition to his management responsibilities, Dr. Lee speaks and writes widely on technology trends and policies. He is a member of the National Academy of Medicine. He serves on the board of directors of the Allen Institute for AI, the Brotman Baty Institute for Precision Medicine, and the Kaiser Permanente Bernard J. Tyson School of Medicine. In public service, Dr. Lee was a commissioner on President Obama's Commission on Enhancing National Cybersecurity and led several studies for PCAST and the National Academies on the impact of federal research investments on economic growth. He has testified before the US House Committee on Science, Space, and Technology and the US Senate Committee on Commerce.

INTERVIEWER. Peter, thank you very much for agreeing to be interviewed for my book *The Innovation Factory*. Tell me about your background in academia, DARPA, and Microsoft.

INTERVIEWEE. I grew up in an academic household with my father being a physics professor and my mother a chemistry professor. The joke is that I was a big disappointment to them when I decided to major in mathematics in college. After finishing my PhD in computer science, I joined the faculty at Carnegie Mellon University, researching programming language theory, mainly aimed at making software more reliable and secure. Of note was the work with my student George Necula on proof-carrying code. During my twenty-four years at CMU, I had a stint as the vice provost for research and, in the end, head of the Computer Science Department.

The change in government brought me to serve at DARPA after the 2008 election. I did under Regina Dugan, who was appointed as the DARPA director. At DARPA, I created a new technology office, essentially a division of this DOD agency, focused on disruptive trends and technologies in computing and related areas, such as the social sciences. An example of the work we did is seen in the DARPA Network Challenge, a worldwide hunt for hidden red weather balloons staged to demonstrate the power of social networks in surveillance applications.

In 2010, I joined Microsoft Research (MSR). My first role was to manage the mother ship MSR lab in Redmond, Washington. About a year later, this role expanded to leadership of the US MSR labs; and then almost another year later, all of MSR worldwide. After Satya Nadella took over as Microsoft CEO, my role shifted away from MSR to create a kind of internal incubator called New Experiences and Technologies (NExT), which, among other things, made Microsoft Cloud for Healthcare, which today is one of the newest businesses for the company and is attempting to expand in part through acquisition. In March 2020, I was brought back to lead Microsoft Research worldwide.

INTERVIEWER. What is the mission of Microsoft Research?

INTERVIEWEE. This year, we are celebrating the thirtieth anniversary of the founding of Microsoft Research. In the founding memo by Nathan Myhrvold and Rick Rashid, the mission of MSR was stated as follows:

1. Advance state of the art in computing and related fields
2. Transfer new technologies rapidly into Microsoft products and services
3. Ensure the future of Microsoft

The management philosophy of MSR was deeply influenced by the founding director, Rick Rashid, and he, in turn, was deeply influenced by his tenure at Carnegie Mellon University. In particular,

1. MSR research works would be peer-reviewed and published openly,
2. MSR researchers would be fully funded and not be required to write grant proposals, and
3. culturally, people in MSR would abide by the reasonable person principle instead of relying on written policies, rules, or review structures and boards.

The first three decades of MSR are marked by the tremendous impact on computing and technology and primarily focused inward on those things. As we enter our fourth decade, as a part of a company that has redefined its mission statement in more outward terms, we define our mission in five goals.

1. Advance foundational technologies, and in turn, advance the state of human knowledge
2. Empower human creativity and achievement
3. Foster a resilient and sustainable society
4. Support a healthy global community
5. Ensure that technology is trustworthy and beneficial to everyone

INTERVIEWER. Can you provide an overview of Microsoft Research today (how many people and locations)?

INTERVIEWEE. MSR today has nine laboratories worldwide (listed in decreasing order of size): Redmond; Beijing; Cambridge, UK; Bangalore; New England; New York; Montreal; Shanghai; and Amsterdam. The entire research staff is about 1,500 people, most PhD researchers, though there are also engineers, designers, program managers, and other support staff. In addition to the lab personnel, there are research teams spread throughout Microsoft, mainly in various product engineering teams but some also in in-field teams, community engagement, and assignments such as chief scientist roles for multiple divisions.

INTERVIEWER. How has the role of Microsoft Research changed over the past thirty years, since its inception?

INTERVIEWEE. Major scientific and technology waves have marked each decade of MSR. The first decade was marked by advances in operating systems design, compiler design, computer graphics, networking, relational databases, and emerging human-computer interaction. Microsoft also had significant technological challenges, such as the shift from 16-bit to 32-bit CPU architectures, for which MSR provided critical solutions. The second decade had a significant focus on large-scale distributed systems, which today forms much of the foundation for cloud computing and software engineering, which includes much of the foundation for Microsoft's developer division.

In the context of Microsoft, the company faced significant challenges in software quality, and MSR's work contributed not only new technologies but also a large number of critical people to engineering leadership positions in our product groups. The third decade has seen a significant rise in machine learning and artificial intelligence, sparked by the work in 2009 on the first industrial-scale experiments and deployments of deep learning. And going along with that are significant efforts to understand how to scale the computing infrastructure to support and deploy AI at scale and, more importantly, to understand the issues of fairness, accountability, transparency, and ethics of AI as it seeps into more and more of daily life.

INTERVIEWER. What are some successful inventions or innovations or products that have come out of Microsoft Research?

INTERVIEWEE. This is a complicated question, because MSR has produced thousands of patents, research papers, and open-source systems. Almost every product Microsoft sells today has MSR ideas, technologies, and code. But here are just four that come to mind, more or less off the cuff.

(1) In 2009, MSR worked with Geoff Hinton and his group to determine whether deep neural networks would be effective for automatic speech recognition. Along with the research effort, MSR also sponsored a workshop at the 2009 NIPS conference on this topic. The results were surprising, and then about a year later, they reinforced them in the computer vision domain by Andrew Ng and Jeff Dean at Google, which created tremendous, community-wide interest in the approach. Deep learning became a dominant form of ML in academic research and commercial applications a decade later.

(2) Continuing on the machine-learning topic, in 2015, MSR invented deep residual networks, commonly referred to as ResNets. ResNets are an industry standard, forming the foundation of deployed computer vision systems at nearly every tech company today and a critical starting point for further refinements and advancements in ML and AI research at universities and industry research labs.

(3) The symbolic Z theorem prover is arguably the most advanced system today for cross-platform satisfiability modulo theories solving. It is used across the spectrum from fundamental research to industrial development. For example, today at Microsoft, the Z prover is used as the core component of systems that do in-depth security testing of all major Microsoft products, including Windows, Office, and Azure.

(4) At the 2012 ISCA conference, we presented a new architecture for accelerating ultra-large-scale data center services, using a technology based on field-programmable gate arrays called Catapult. Besides changing the mindset of designers of large-scale data

centers, this work sparked the arms race at all the major cloud companies (Alibaba, Amazon, Baidu, Google, Microsoft, etc.) in customized silicon and architecture design. Today, Catapult is integrated into every blade, in every rack, and in every datacenter at Microsoft worldwide; and it not only powers low latency distributed computing at a near-zero cost but also provides security and crypto on the fly and ultra-large-scale ML (neural net) inferencing in a service called Brainwave.

There are many others, but these come to mind as examples that have had a foundational impact, involved open publication, academic collaboration, and broad industry contribution.

INTERVIEWER. How does MSR partner with universities with research, internships, and talent hiring?

INTERVIEWEE. Since we operate as an open research lab, encouraging (and rewarding) contributions to the scholarly literature and to open-source (via GitHub), most collaborations with university researchers happen organically and in much the same way that collaborations across universities happen. Our researchers collaborate, write papers, give lectures, and attend conferences. MSR will provide funding to support academic conferences and workshops or provide monetary gifts to support researchers' work in exceptional circumstances. These are equipped to support work, particularly in areas that we feel are underfunded, and to advance the cause of diversity and inclusion in computer science research.

We will engage in a more organized, highly funded, strategic partnership with an academic institution in exceptional circumstances. We have significant strategic collaboration agreements with several top Chinese universities, including Tsinghua University. We recently negotiated a large-scale, strategic collaboration partnership with the Broad Institute in the USA. In some parts of the world, we actively contribute to developing research capability and culture. We have been doing this in Asia for the past twenty years and India for the past ten years.

The fruits of these efforts have been highly beneficial to Microsoft and the world. We have a substantial internship program aimed primarily at PhD students, bringing roughly 1,200 PhD interns to our labs every year. In parts of the world, such as India and Latin America, we also target undergraduate institutions with the idea that we can develop more capability and interest in fundamental research. About three-quarters of the staff in MSR are PhD researchers. We hire from top university research programs around the world.

But a small but growing number of people we hire do not have PhDs. As research has become more specialized in certain areas where universities tend not to do research (e.g., hyperscale neural networks) or where universities are not advancing as quickly as we would like in creating more diversity, we see the need to hire pre-PhD researchers and essentially train them ourselves. We also engage by providing research personnel to community service at CRA/CCC, the National Academies, AAAS, etc. For example, today, Eric Horvitz is a member of PCAST. Finally, more senior research talent is moved from universities and other companies. The amount of movement among significant tech companies that hire research talent (primarily Google and Facebook and, to a much lesser extent, Apple and Amazon) is substantial.

INTERVIEWER. What are some of the key research areas being pursued at MSR today?

INTERVIEWEE. Physical science at the atomic scale has become a significant area. It becomes more apparent that advances in large-scale computation, algorithms, and machine learning may make it possible to make more sophisticated and large-scale simulations and predictions of matter at the molecular level. This is important to Microsoft because it points to a future workload for cloud and AI, which is fundamental to Microsoft's business. But it is also foundational to future understanding of biological processes and applications in areas such as drug discovery.

It is also key to our core businesses in the digital transformation of agriculture (e.g., the discovery of new nitrogen fixation catalysts for better fertilizers) and climate change (e.g., the discovery of carbon catalysts for more effective direct air capture). Fairness, accountability, transparency, and ethics of AI—what we call FATE—is another area emerging as an ample space of research activity at MSR. As we see the inevitability of increasingly capable and general-purpose AI emerging over the coming decade, the impacts on people and communities concerning FATE will become as important as cybersecurity.

Finally, AI continues to be a dominant area of research, continuing to grow in importance and level of activity. There seems to be no end to its increased capability as we achieve a more significant scale. As we approach multitrillion parameter neural systems, the engineering challenges meet fundamental computer science, physics, and electrical engineering challenges, even touching on our considerable quantum computing effort.

INTERVIEWER. How are technologies invented at MSR transferred to businesses?

INTERVIEWEE. There is significant trust between MSR and business groups. For that reason, the bulk of technology transfers happens organically in the sense that collaborations between a product group and MSR researchers form up and lead to new technologies being transferred through that collaborative work. But there are also more structured approaches.

We have a system of RIAs (research innovation areas), which are essentially joint centers formed between MSR and a business group. Typically, a CTO-like role is taken on by a research leader in MSR, and the area has both short-term and very long-term commitments by the business group. For example, in ultra-large-scale storage systems, which today is focused on optical storage, such an arrangement has led to the new plan of record for the Azure business group, leading to a new manufacturing facility for deployment built in the UK. Finally, we graduate an entire research group into a business unit in some cases. This happened recently with our research group working on new health care technologies (internally, the group was called Health Next). Eventually, the research group had enough success, making an impact on actual health care organizations, that it transitioned to being a new line of business in our cloud and AI business unit.

INTERVIEWER. Does MSR incubate brand new businesses?

INTERVIEWEE. Yes. My organization is called Research and Incubations because it is involved in incubating new businesses. As I explained in the previous question, we incubated our latest business in health technology. In recent years, we have incubated several new products and lines of business in areas such as secure IoT (a product called Azure Sphere), AI-powered chatbots (Azure Bot Service), and more. In some cases, such as in health technology or Azure for Operators, MSR gets involved in decisions around acquisitions to build the new business.

INTRODUCTION

Chapter 4 introduced some of the most effective ways for large companies to practice long-term disruptive innovation. One of the most important among these five suggestions is appointing a chief technology officer (CTO) and launching a central research laboratory. This chapter focuses on the role of a central research lab in driving horizon 3 and disruptive innovations in large companies.

A central research lab, or CRL, is a space where a group of engineers gathers with all the tools and resources necessary so they can pursue their ideas and innovate with them in pursuit of a helpful product or service, which will produce revenues and, indeed, respect for the company. In some instances, the CRL is a large common space; it may also be in diverse locations depending upon its human and capital resources yet still regarded as a composite facility.

For our purposes, a CRL is identified as belonging to an enterprise. Still, in the world of the twenty-first century, there are both private CRLs—for example, IBM Research, Microsoft Research, HP Labs, GE Research, Xerox PARC, Google Research, and Google X—and publicly established and funded CRLS, such as the Department of Energy's seventeen National Laboratories, such as Los Alamos National Lab or Oak Ridge National Lab. Depending on the size of the company and the CRL, the CTO oversees the company's technological resources and manages the innovation projects to successful conclusions.

The CRL is an old practice that has come back because it is highly effective. Thomas Edison proved its worth when in 1877 he founded his first research lab in Menlo Park, California, where he invented the first electric light bulb. In 1900, Edison and two partners founded what later became known as the General Electric Research Laboratory in Schenectady, New York. Today, it is a significant innovation hub that coalesces and supports all of GE's innovation and innovation partnerships. It is described in more detail below.

Many other companies have created central research labs during the twentieth century, bringing together technologists and researchers and their ideas to drive long-term technology innovation. The most prestigious of them are Bell Labs, IBM Research, Microsoft Research, HP Labs, Xerox PARC, and General Electric Research.

BELL LABS

In 1880, when the French government awarded Alexander Graham Bell the Volta Prize of fifty thousand francs for the invention of the telephone, he used the award to fund the Volta Laboratory (then known as the Alexander Graham Bell Laboratory) in Washington, DC. It focused on the analysis, recording, and transmission of sound. Bell used his considerable profits from the laboratory for further research and education. On January 1, 1925, Bell Telephone Laboratories Inc. was organized to consolidate the development and research activities in the communication field and allied sciences for the Bell System. In 1967, Bell Laboratories headquarters was officially relocated to Murray Hill, New Jersey. The parent company Bell became Lucent, then merged with Alcatel, a French communications company, and was subsequently acquired by the Finnish company Nokia in 2015. Today, Bell Labs is known as Nokia Bell Labs.

Bell Laboratories was—and is—regarded by many as the premier research facility of its type, developing a wide range of revolutionary technologies, including radio astronomy, the transistor, the laser, information theory, the operating system Unix, the programming languages C and C++, solar cells, the charge-coupled device (CCD), and many other optical, wireless, and wired communications technologies and systems. Nine Nobel Prizes have been awarded for work completed at Bell Laboratories. Bell Labs researchers have won the Turing Award five times. Bell Labs was in its prime in the 1960s and 1970s when it was the central research lab of AT&T. While the parent company had a monopoly on the telephone market, about 2 percent of its revenues went to fund Bell Labs R&D. However, since the government breakup of AT&T into smaller Bell companies and with increased competition from other telecom companies, Bell Labs lost much of its revenue stream and, therefore, its funding for basic research. Although Nokia Bell Labs today has thirteen locations worldwide and still does some basic research, it pales compared to the original Bell Labs.

IBM Research

IBM Research is the largest industrial research organization in the world with twelve labs on six continents. IBM employees have garnered six Nobel Prizes, six Turing Awards, twenty inductees into the US National Inventors Hall of Fame, nineteen National Medal of Technology, and five National Medal of Science. As of 2018, the company has generated more patents than any other business in its twenty-five consecutive years, which is a record.

The roots of today's IBM Research began with the 1945 opening of the Watson Scientific Computing Laboratory at Columbia University. This was the first IBM laboratory devoted to pure science. Starting in the 1950s, it expanded to Westchester County, New York, and elsewhere, including the Yorktown Heights Thomas J. Watson Research Center in 1961. Notable company inventions include the floppy disk, the hard disk drive, the magnetic stripe card, the relational database, the Universal Product Code (UPC), the Fortran programming language, Sabre airline reservation system, DRAM, copper wiring in semiconductors, the smartphone, the portable computer, the automated teller machine (ATM), the silicon-on-insulator (SOI) semiconductor manufacturing process, Watson artificial intelligence, and the quantum experience.

HP Labs

HP Labs is the exploratory and advanced research group for Hewlett-Packard. The development of programmable desktop calculators, inkjet printing, and 3D graphics are credited to HP Labs researchers. On March 3, 1966, founders Bill Hewlett and David Packard sought to create an organization not bound by day-to-day business concerns. HP Labs headquarters are in Palo Alto, California, with eight other labs worldwide.

More than forty key innovations have come out of HP Labs, including HP's first computer, the HP2116A, the first commercially available light-emitting diode (LED), cesium beam atomic clocks, the first pocket scientific calculator, the HP-35, the first programmable scientific desktop calculator, and subsequently, the HP 9100A laser interferometer, capable of measuring to millionths of an inch. They are also credited for the first commercial inkjet and laser printers, 64-bit architecture (Itanium), digital photography, first rewritable DVD system (DVD-RW), the digital publishing, and streaming media, among many others. Later in this chapter, I will detail my personal experience leading HP Labs.

Microsoft Research

Microsoft Research is the research subsidiary of Microsoft. It was created in 1991 by Rick Rashid to advance state-of-the-art computing and solve complex world problems through technological innovation in collaboration with academic, government, and industry researchers. The Microsoft Research team consists of more than one thousand computer scientists, physicists, engineers, and mathematicians, including Turing Award winners, Fields Medal winners, MacArthur Fellows, and Dijkstra Prize winners.

Microsoft's first research lab was founded on the Microsoft headquarters campus in Redmond, Washington, in 1991 and currently employs about 350 researchers. The bulk of its research is, in theory, artificial intelligence, machine learning, systems and networking, security, privacy, HCI, and wearable technologies. Its eight other campuses focus on key technologies, such as machine learning, the user interface, quantum computing technologies, such as the qubit, future applications, and deep learning, to name only a few. During the interview at the beginning of this chapter, Peter Lee provided many valuable details about Microsoft Research.

Xerox PARC

Xerox PARC (Palo Alto Research Center) is a research and development company in Palo Alto, California. Founded in 1969 by Jack Goldman, Xerox Corporation's chief scientist, the company was originally a division of Xerox tasked with creating computer technology-related products and hardware systems. Xerox PARC has been at the heart of numerous revolutionary computer developments—laser printing, Ethernet, the modern personal computer, the graphical user interface (GUI) and desktop paradigm, object-oriented programming, ubiquitous computing, electronic paper, amorphous silicon (a-Si) applications, and the computer mouse and advancing very large-scale integration (VLSI) for semiconductors.

Jack's Advanced Scientific & Systems Laboratory aimed to develop future technologies; it was not intended to reproduce the existing work at Xerox's research laboratory in Rochester, New York, which focused on refining and expanding its copier business. Instead, Xerox PARC was a site for pioneering work in advanced physics, materials science, and computer science applications. Xerox formed Palo Alto Research Center as a wholly owned subsidiary in 2002 and has about two hundred employees today.

GENERAL ELECTRIC RESEARCH LABORATORY

General Electric Research Laboratory was the first industrial research facility in the United States. First established in 1900 by Thomas Edison and his partners, the lab was home to early technological breakthroughs. With funding from General Electric, the lab created a research and development environment that set the standard for industrial innovation for years to come. It developed into GE Global Research and now covers various technological research, ranging from health care to transportation systems, at multiple locations worldwide. Its original campus remains in Schenectady, New York.

It took several years for the lab to follow through with the vision to create original innovations instead of improving on the inventions already in place. GE's earliest project was perfecting Edison's incandescent light bulb. In 1908, engineer and new head researcher William Coolidge invented the ductile tungsten light bulb filament, providing a more durable and long-lasting light filament than the existing technology. In 1932, Irving Langmuir won the Nobel Prize in Chemistry for his work on surface chemical reactions, which helped him develop the gas-filled light bulb in 1916. After patenting many inventions, Langmuir developed his new light bulb, which reinvented lights altogether. By 1928, because of Langmuir's innovation, GE held 96 percent of incandescent light sales in America.

Some notable inventions from GE Research include the electric fan, the electric range, transoceanic radio system, portable x-ray machine, turbosupercharger engine, magnetron vacuum tube, television, autopilot system, solid-state laser, computed tomography (CT) scanner, magnetic resonance imaging (MRI) system, popularization of wind turbines, fuel-efficient Evolution Series locomotive engines, and the first twenty-four-cylinder internal combustion engine.

GE Labs employs three thousand employees at its labs in Schenectady, New York; Oklahoma; Bangalore; India; China; Germany; and Brazil.

THE ROLE OF A MODERN CENTRAL RESEARCH LAB FOR THE TWENTY-FIRST CENTURY

As is evidenced by this brief overview, much of the most significant innovation we know and use today has come from central research labs operated by high-technology large US companies. Although many other innovations have come from university labs and small start-ups, these horizon 3 labs have possessed characteristics that have pushed their projects out into society. This evolution from idea to finished product or service is the hallmark of CRLs. Their significance remains undiminished even though the innovation landscape has changed over the past 120-plus years.

Central research laboratories are facing more significant challenges than ever before throughout the United States and elsewhere. Budgets for research continue to shrink while corporations are demanding faster, more tangible results from their investments. As a result, CTOs and lab research managers are looking for new ways to organize their programs better and motivate their engineers. Although every company is pursuing its strategies nevertheless, across the board, CTOs and lab managers are trying to pull research projects into tighter relationships with other divisions of the company. Some are concerned that management is encouraging H1 and H2 to get more projects out the door to the detriment of the H3 initiatives, which don't produce the quicker ROI. Some argue that genuine innovations will come about as research programs become more attuned to their corporate parent's contemporary problems. They are likely correct, but CRLs have traditionally been somewhat isolated from day-to-day issues and objectives for a good reason. In his interview at the beginning of the chapter, Peter Lee went through the different phases of Microsoft Research, which is very insightful.

The most successful corporate research labs are Bell Labs, IBM Research, Xerox PARC, Microsoft Research, HP Labs, and GE Research.

Managing a Portfolio of R&D Projects

When I was director of HP Labs in 2007, the entire organization became engaged in a deep discussion about the role of a modern CRL and began developing a strategic plan. At the time, HP Labs had about six hundred researchers in five lab locations worldwide. At that time, Hewlett-Packard employed about thirty thousand R&D engineers, distributed among five divisions: printers, personal computers, servers, software, and services. The HP Labs budget of $150 million sat within the larger R&D budget of about $3 billion for Hewlett-Packard.

HP Labs was doing only long-term horizon 3 R&D with projects that would be relevant in ten to twenty years. But we decided that given current business constraints, this kind of work would be viewed as too academic and, therefore, not applicable to HP, possibly terminating HP Labs. On the other hand, HP Labs could work on horizon 1 projects to help the company with projects that would become relevant in six to eighteen months. But we decided that the company's leadership would ask, "Why are six hundred researchers in our CRL pursuing the same research and development as the thirty thousand R&D engineers?" Again, this approach would make HP Labs seem irrelevant and unnecessary.

The decision was to take a portfolio approach to R&D, whereby one-third of our projects would be short-term (horizon 1), relevant to the company in six to eighteen months; one-third would be medium-term (horizon 2), relevant to the company in two to four years; and the remaining third would be long-term (horizon 3), relevant to the company in five to fifteen years.

How Large Are CRL R&D Projects and Teams

In 2007, some six hundred researchers at HP Labs were involved in more than two hundred R&D projects, each with one to three team members. These projects produced publications and patents, similar to the output of academic research. But they did not have the scale to build into useful, impactful products, so we changed our direction toward H3 disruption and went after twenty big bet projects, each with an average team size of twenty-five to thirty people. This approach gave these big bet projects enough scale of investment to have an impact. Each researcher could propose a project characterized by two attributes.

- The technical problem had to be very challenging, and if solved, it would advance state of the art in the field; its proposal would be structured like an NSF or NIH proposal from academia.
- The proposal identified the project's business impact. If the technical problem were solved, it would result in products and solutions that would generate at least $1 billion in annual business for HP.

We received more than one hundred proposals for big bet projects. They were reviewed by an HP Labs advisory board of CRL leadership, selected business unit CTOs, and business unit general managers. The advisory board picked one-third short-term projects, one-third medium-term projects, and one-third long-term projects. The role of the advisory board was modeled after venture capital firms whose partners funded start-up companies with a portfolio distribution—e.g., 25 percent of the funding would be for biotech companies, 30 percent for energy tech companies, and so forth.

It was a good selection process. Everyone at HP Labs had the opportunity to propose ideas, so the idea generation funnel was widened to benefit every researcher. This was great for morale and creating a culture of innovation. As a result, HP Labs was reorganized into eight labs and twenty big bet projects.

- print and content delivery
- mobile and immersive experiences
- cloud and security
- information analytics
- networking
- intelligent infrastructure
- services and solutions
- sustainability

Collectively, the six hundred researchers set to work on twenty big bet research projects focused on addressing these eight lab themes. Examples were exascale computing, Moonshot server, the Central Nervous System for the Earth (CeNSE), memristor nonvolatile memory, software-defined networking, sustainable data centers, and commercial digital print.

TECHNOLOGY TRANSFER FROM LABS TO THE BUSINESSES

CRLs have often struggled with the problem of technology transfer from the labs to the businesses, very similar to attempting technology transfer from academia to industry. Recognizing the problem, HP Labs created the following tech transfer mechanism:

- Short-term horizon 1 projects would follow a type 1 tech transfer to the divisional business units. A defined need guided the research team to create a prototype that would result in a significant product enhancement.
- Medium-term horizon 2 projects were to follow a type 2 tech transfer, so they were transferred to the divisional CTO office for incubation.
- Long-term horizon 3 projects would follow a type 3 tech transfer, so they were incubated at the company CTO level.

As mentioned, the work in R&D is often perceived as disconnected from business goals and operations. By forming the HP Labs advisory board, the business units became instrumental in project selection. As a result, they took a greater interest and funding responsibility for tech transfer and, thus, successful projects.

CRL PARTNERSHIPS WITH UNIVERSITIES

Corporate research labs create strong partnerships with universities, like IBM Research with Harvard, Nokia Bell Labs with Cambridge, or Microsoft Research with UC Berkeley. These relationships endure because labs working on H3 innovation problems are similar to university research. Microsoft Research and IBM Research have traditionally built the most significant relationships with universities. Both research labs have engagements with more than one hundred universities per year.

HP Labs created a strong open innovation program to work with several universities, including Stanford University, UC Berkeley, the University of Southern California, the University of Illinois Urbana-Champaign, MIT, Carnegie Mellon University, Purdue, and Georgia Tech. Each year, HP Labs would send out a request for proposals (RFP) to universities with a budget of about $10 million. This resulted in HP Labs funding eighty to one hundred university projects for $80,000–$150,000 per project, which supported a couple of graduate students at a university.

These funding contracts contained simple provisos for intellectual property ownership, always a delicate matter for the academic institution. Any idea resulting in a written paper generated from the collaboration could be submitted for publication at peer-reviewed conferences or journals. HP Labs held the right to file patents for these ideas, but the universities would own the patents. HP Labs had the right to a royalty-free, non-exclusive license for these patents or a royalty-paying exclusive license to make them into products.

Another way corporate CRLs engage with universities is by recruiting their PhD students as summer interns. Microsoft brings in more than two hundred PhD interns per year from the top computer science departments in the USA to work with the four hundred researchers at Microsoft Research in the US. Thus, Microsoft can make job offers to the very best PhD students.

PARTNERSHIP WITH START-UPS

When I was the managing director of Accenture Labs, we had a robust open innovation program. Various stages of engagement tracked more than one thousand start-ups in the open innovation program. The first stage was the watch list with about 600 start-ups whose technologies were followed by Accenture Labs. The second stage was the prospect list, which had about 250 start-ups with whom Accenture Labs had some preliminary meetings and discussions. The third stage was the qualified list with about 50 start-ups with established relationships and engagements with some businesses. The fourth stage was the committed list, which had 5 start-ups with some committed efforts from the businesses. The fifth stage was the engaged list with about 3 start-ups. The final stage was the scale list with a couple of start-ups with whom Accenture had millions of dollars worth of consulting business.

CHALLENGES OF DRIVING INNOVATION IN A CORPORATE RESEARCH LAB

Corporate research labs can do a great job in basic research on H3 disruptive innovation. Using their technical teams to develop new technology makes it more or less organic or second nature. Yet CRLs for many years have remained vertical, standalone operations, somewhat isolated from the business processes in much the same way the IT people once cloistered their operations in a glass-walled room. More recently, they have trended toward the practice of open innovation, which is partnering with universities and start-up companies to bring new technology to bear on the company's products and services. However, a significant challenge these labs face is how to take these new technologies and products to market.

CREATING INCUBATORS AS PART OF CORPORATE RESEARCH LABS

Two concepts have begun trending in CRL for the past few years. While initially conceived for start-ups, they serve their purpose as extensions of the CRL operations. One is the accelerator, which allows the CTO to green-light a project that needs immediate attention. The second and the one more pertinent to this discussion of the CRL's organic operations is the incubator, a more or less distinct mini CRL within the CRL. It, too, has its heritage. In its case, it was once known to the engineers at Lockheed as the skunkworks.

The intent is the same: allow a group of engineers bent on a dynamite idea to break free of the rest of the organization, go off to another place, and bring the idea to fruition as quickly as possible. The incubator team takes the concept to a finished product or service in such instances. In this respect, it sets an example for the larger, perhaps somewhat sluggish, CRL engineers accustomed to only working on the ideation and early innovation states and seeing how it is possible and desirable to participate in carrying it through the entire business value chain.

Typically, any large company will have a well-established go-to-market or sales channel. Either they will have a direct sales force with some salespeople and application engineers directly trying to market and sell their suite of products to customers. When you have a B2B business, the salespeople try to sell their products to leaders in other enterprise companies—e.g., if you have a CRM tool, you try to sell that to the sales teams of that company; if you have a CAD or simulation too, you try to sell the tool to the designers and analysts and engineers of the company. These tool purchases are approved by their sales manager or engineering manager and the CIO of the company. However, if a company is in a B2C business—selling directly to consumers, like selling a vacuum cleaner—they will create a channel like a retail store (Walmart) to sell the product to consumers.

So the challenge is the following: Suppose you are working for a company that makes servers and storage devices for large enterprises, and they are selling them to CIOs of large organizations. Suppose the central research lab of that company develops an interesting cloud-based software app targeted to consumers. In that case, there is no way for the sales team in the company to sell that technology no matter how disruptive it is. In such a case, the only way for this innovative product to be successfully sold to customers is to have a sales function dedicated to the central research lab to develop a sales and marketing approach for that product. This is the concept of incubating new businesses inside a corporate research lab.

While I was with HP Labs, one of the big bet projects we worked on was called BookPrep to allow anyone to publish any book using the cloud and get it sold to customers with a size of one unit. The HP sales team used to sell servers, storage, PCs, and printers and did not have the skill set to sell a product like BookPrep. So this business was incubated at HP Labs. We will discuss this concept of incubating new businesses in a large company in chapter 6.

Author's Personal Experience in Central Research Labs

From 2013 to 2015, Accenture, managing director of Global Technology Research and Development. In this role, I oversaw the Accenture Labs (www.accenture.com/technologylabs), the global technology R&D organization within Accenture, which explored new and emerging technologies. Accenture Labs was a global organization with more than two hundred researchers in five lab locations worldwide (San Jose; Washington, DC; Sophia, France; Beijing; and Bangalore). As part of directing Accenture Labs, I was responsible for research in five R&D groups: (1) infrastructure and systems, (2) software engineering, (3) cybersecurity, (4) big data analytics, (5) and digital experiences. I also directed Accenture's annual Technology Vision research, which looked at the future of enterprise IT. Finally, I was responsible for Accenture's open innovation program with start-up companies, corporate partners, and universities, which I also started.

From 2007 to 2012, Hewlett-Packard Company, senior vice president of research and director of HP Labs, the company's central research organization. In these roles, where I reported to the CEO, I helped chart technical strategies for the company and headed HP Labs. I managed a group of six hundred researchers in seven worldwide locations (Palo Alto, USA; Bristol, UK; Haifa, Israel; Beijing, China; Bangalore, India; St. Petersburg, Russia; and Singapore).

I was responsible for creating a comprehensive strategic plan for reorganizing and redirecting HP Labs to have the researchers work on fewer high-impact projects and focus on the impact on the businesses and customers. We reorganized HP Labs into eight labs: print and content delivery, mobile and immersive experiences, cloud and security, information analytics, networking, intelligent infrastructure, services and solutions, and sustainability. Collectively, the five hundred researchers work on twenty-five big bet research projects around these eight themes.

Successful technology transfers from HP Labs have included low-power servers in Project Moonshot, storage deduplication in the StoreOnce product, the IBRIX-Metabox data archival product, scalable cloud storage, optical backplanes for servers and switches, the Net Zero Data Center, the CeNSE sensor project for oil exploration, immersive 3D displays, commercial digital printing, Openet, and the Vayu Internet Device.

CHAPTER 6

How Large Companies Can Support Long-Term Disruptive Innovation

Interview: Mallik Tatipamula, CTO of Ericsson Silicon Valley, a multinational networking and telecommunications company head-quartered in Stockholm, Sweden

As a CTO at Ericsson Silicon Valley, Dr. Mallik Tatipamula leads the evolution of Ericsson's technology and champions the company's next phase of innovation and growth. Before Ericsson, he held several leadership positions at F5 Networks, Juniper Networks, Cisco, Motorola, Nortel, and Indian Institute of Technology (Chennai).

During his thirty years of professional career, he has played a unique leadership role in delivering the industry's most powerful innovations, standards contributions, products/solutions, early design implementation of real-world deployments by working with telecom operators, and also innovating for the future, working with academia, by anticipating what might happen next to accelerate the architectural transitions in the telecom industry.

He has identified strategic opportunities and implemented programs that have brought world-leading innovations to the telecom sector with a multibillion-dollar impact, launching over fifty products/solutions deployed in global telecom networks to enable these major networks to transition from 2G to 5G. Since 2011, he has been a visiting professor at King's College London. He is a fellow of the Canadian Academy of Engineering (CAE) and the Institution of Engineering and Technology (IET, UK). He received the University of California, Berkeley, Garwood Center for Corporate Innovation award in 2019, CTO of the year award by Total Telecom World Communications Awards (WCA) for the year 2020, IEEE Communications Society (ComSoc) Distinguished Industry Leader Award for the year 2020, and also the IET Achievement Medal in Telecommunications for the year 2020.

He has a PhD in information and communications engineering from the University of Tokyo, Japan, a masters in communication systems from the Indian Institutes of Technology, Chennai, India, and a bachelor's in electronics and communications engineering from NIT Warangal, India. He delivered lectures and taught courses at UC Berkeley, the University of Tokyo, Stanford, and other universities. He mentored over one hundred undergraduate and graduate students, delivered more than four hundred keynote/invited talks, tutorials, and lectures, coauthored two books and more than one hundred publications/patents, served on more than thirty IEEE conferences committees. He has been developing industry-academia partnerships in Canada, the US, the UK, and India for future technology innovations. He serves on several advisory boards, including Global Semiconductor Alliance, Gartner/ Evanta CIO Council, Digital India Initiative, and London Digital

Twin Research Centre, as chair for the Industry Advisory Board for Garwood Center for Corporate Innovation, and as adviser to Center for Growth Markets at the University of California, Berkeley.

INTERVIEWER. Mallik, thank you very much for agreeing to be interviewed for my book The Innovation Factory. Tell me about your personal and professional background.

INTERVIEWEE. Throughout my thirty-two-year career, I had the chance to perform a unique leadership role in delivering the industry's innovative products for telecommunication networks, working with global telecommunication operators and working with academia, innovating for the future. I have helped enable the telecommunication industry's major architectural transitions, translating innovations into standards and technology developments that created the foundation of our increasingly connected world and helped bridge the digital divide.

INTERVIEWER. Can you tell me about your company Ericsson? What does it do, and who are your customers and businesses? How many employees? What is your annual revenue?

INTERVIEWEE. Ericsson is one of the leading providers of information and communication technology (ICT) to service providers. We enable the total value of connectivity by creating game-changing technology and services that are easy to use, adapt, and scale, making our customers successful in a fully connected world. Our comprehensive portfolio ranges across networks, digital services, managed services, and emerging businesses, powered by 5G and IoT platforms. We are approximately one hundred thousand employees worldwide with $24 billion annual revenue in 2020.

INTERVIEWER. Can you provide an overview of Ericsson Research today (how many people and locations)?

INTERVIEWEE. Research and development (R&D) is at the heart of our business with approximately 26,000 employees. Ericsson engineers, researchers, and scientists around the world are working on what's the next big thing with technology in focus. With more than 57,000 granted patents, we have one of the industry's most robust intellectual property rights portfolios.

INTERVIEWER. How has the role of Ericsson Research changed over the past thirty years, since its inception?

INTERVIEWEE. In the beginning, we revolutionized analog communications with new switching techniques and technology. When the digital revolution came, we were first there too. When broadband was in its infancy, we were already working on the technology that would become 3G, and we were developing 4G long before the smartphone became ubiquitous.

Every innovation has a story of its own with many great people joining together to challenge traditional ways of thinking. Since the dawn of telecommunications, Ericsson has put enormous time and effort into collaborating with others to set the open standards that make global communications and connections possible.

Innovation is in our DNA; and we are pushing boundaries in 5G, IoT, and the cloud. The role of Ericsson research changed while working with academia, industrial IoT partners, customers (telcos and enterprise), and cloud providers in driving innovation across the intersection of various technologies and also multisector cocreation and innovation, enabling industry 4.0. Our ideas can become products, services, or business models. We pioneer disruptive technologies in augmented reality, artificial intelligence, or blockchain.

INTERVIEWER. What are some successful inventions or innovations or products that have come out of Ericsson?

INTERVIEWEE. We have 5G, IoT, and distributed cloud to name a few, the most successful innovations that have transformed the industry.

INTERVIEWER. How does Ericsson partner with research, internships, and talent hiring with universities?

INTERVIEWEE. As a part of public partnerships, we work with key stakeholders in government in establishing internship programs. For example, in Canada, we work with Mitacs (https://www.mitacs.ca), and we have established a formal relationship with Canadian universities by hiring eighty interns to work on AI for 5G networks. Similarly, when it comes to research, we have several mechanisms as follows to focus on a "particular problem within a technology area" or "founding member of a research center" or interdisciplinary, multi-university initiative through public-private partnerships.

1. Ericsson as a founding member of a research center, such as UC Berkeley RISELab, to work on a topic or technology of interest
2. Ericsson to professor to work on a particular problem within a technology area
3. Ericsson working with NSF or other research agencies to initiate a public-private partnership in emerging technology, such as 6G with NSF RINGS project (https://www.nsf.gov). This is a multi-university, interdisciplinary research effort.

We hire interns based on these approaches depending on the need and project scope.

INTERVIEWER. How does Ericsson partner with start-ups? Do you invest in start-ups?

INTERVIEWEE. We have D-15 Labs in Ericsson, where we engage with start-ups as follows:

1. Creating dialogue on what future problems that industry is facing to address
2. Cocreation of use cases to address industry problems
3. Investing in a start-up through corporate venture

INTERVIEWER. What are some of the critical research areas Ericsson's pursuing today?

INTERVIEWEE. We are leading our research across the following research areas to innovate for the next decade: Internet of Senses, connected intelligent machines, programmable world, Connected Sustainable World, extreme wireless, trustworthy systems, cognitive network, and network compute fabric.

INTERVIEWER. How are technologies invented at Ericsson Research transferred to businesses?

INTERVIEWEE. Innovations in communications technology have opened us up to new digital experiences. Through our creation of cellular standards, we have pioneered the technology that drives connectivity and continues to lead the way for advancements. Most of our innovations resulted in 3GPP and other telecom standards that guide the implementations in products deployed by our customers. So our inventions at Ericsson Research translate into telecom standards that get adopted into our businesses through products and deployments by our customers.

INTERVIEWER. Does Ericsson incubate new businesses?

INTERVIEWEE. Yes, we have incubated many businesses at Ericsson. We have listed several details on this topic on this website: https://www.ericsson.com.

Introduction

Our focus of interest in this book is that large companies are promising innovators in the short- and medium-term. Still, they often struggle with long-term innovation and its more complicated problem-solving. Partnering with academia is, by and large, a long-term relationship. Partnering with start-ups, which are more agile and precisely focused, can be effective when your program or project needs an energy boost. Both provide the highest return on value when working with your central research lab.

It may surprise you to learn that there are more incidents of innovation not converting into a marketable product than there are success stories. According to the most recent studies, the innovation failure rate is 60–80 percent. Over many years and innovations, Xerox PARC functioned more like an academic think tank than a corporate lab, inventing Ethernet, local-area networking, and the infamous mouse and graphical user interface (GUI). Although Alto was Xerox's attempt at commercializing its technology, outliers turned its most pervasive innovations into commercial products. PARC was not interested in partnering, and it was only by accident that Steve Jobs discovered its innovative research.

This chapter presents practical solutions for the large company wishing to develop and support long-term H3 innovation. Chapter 2 has introduced how long-term innovation is pursued in academia; however, most research does not make it into innovative products. Often, academic research is funded by governmental agencies and is discussed in more detail in the next chapter on funding models. Chapter 3 has detailed how start-ups funded by venture capitalists take disruptive ideas (sometimes developed by or with academia), then focus on building a product and selling it into a disruptive market.

How large companies pursue different horizons of innovation (H1, H2, or H3) with a portfolio of R&D investments have been introduced in chapter 4. Chapter 5 has explained how large companies manage a portfolio of R&D projects to drive innovation across many products in multiple divisions. That approach works well for H1 and H2 innovations and is an effective way to grow revenue profitably. Chapter 5 is concerned with how large companies successfully create a central research lab primarily to pursue H3 innovations. Chapter 6 brings all these ideas together to demonstrate how large companies can sharpen the focus on H3 innovation, support long-term R&D of a new product or service, and equally important, what it takes to sell the new product effectively to their customers.

INNOVATION: RISK AND REWARD

Businesspeople often talk about how visionary Steve Jobs was; how Apple is such an innovative company; and how it invented the iPhone, iPad, App Store, and Apple Music—genuinely disruptive innovations. Steve got Apple innovating when its only product was the Macintosh personal computer. The iPad was a truly disruptive product. It bridged the phone and computer with Wi-Fi connectivity, an on-screen keypad, and a large viewing window for greater access. Besides, the iPad developed markets on both the consumer and business sides—from writing shopping lists in the car to using it to pay for your morning croissants at the bakery. But these same businesspeople often confess they do not know how to innovate like Apple. Why is that? Perhaps they do not understand, as Steve did, that work in the innovation lab has to integrate into the business's value chain and ultimately connect with practical usefulness to the real world.

Steve understood that it was not enough to have a new or exciting concept or a clever device. It had to have a purpose with an appeal to a substantial market. Once he determined its intent and market potential, he unleashed all his efforts to make certain that happened. He understood that there were critical developmental spaces between an idea and the means of innovation and the result of the business process. He knew because he learned the hard way, such as the Lisa computer and the Newton MessagePad handheld device. He understood and grew more confident in his convictions, inspiring his innovators to follow suit. As an Apple commercial said, "People who think they are crazy enough to change the world are the ones who do."

Innovation solves business problems, but more importantly, it meets needs and solves problems for the consumer. The iPad made it possible for people to consume a wide array of media content on a portable reading device. That was its innovation reward. The risk was in what it might take in time, effort, and money to make the innovation happen, to develop a product the customer would not only desire but also afford. This was the outcome for the iPad during its heydays. But as everyone understands, most technology products have a life cycle simply because one innovation inevitably leads to another. The iPad led to dedicated e-readers, iPods, and large-screen phones.

While there is no single magical formula for successful innovation, the critical success factor is that the return must outweigh the risk. There is an inherent risk in creating disruptive innovation. This requires some rigid thinking, because the business landscape is constantly changing. Even with H3 innovations, innovation cycles have grown much shorter than even a decade ago. Competition has grown fiercer. The COVID-19 and Delta variant viruses have profoundly altered business models and assets. Thus, it becomes ever more critical for the innovator to be adaptive and to swiftly react when the risk is perceived based on new data. It is not a field of endeavor for the faint of heart.

Innovation strategists must envision both the innovation development and the business process before beginning a new project—knowing what problems may arise while building your product or service, evaluating how others have accomplished their innovation work, understanding what lessons can be learned from them, and mastering how to do it better this time. Elon Musk did not sleep on the Tesla factory floor night after night to rest. You have to think through the entire business life cycle.

How to Build H3 Innovation R&D Teams in Large Companies

While there are likely others—depending on intellectual resources, physical resources, or even deadlines—while serving as the CTO for several large companies, I have successfully practiced each of the three following approaches. I use the term *practice* here in the same manner as a doctor or a lawyer would. Innovation must be practiced for it to improve. It is the highest order of continuous improvement in which an enterprise can engage.

These are the three approaches for the practice of innovation to generate and develop ideation for long-term horizon 3 innovation: the central research lab, the side project, and the all-in team. In all innovation efforts, the central research lab should be the foundation for your company's innovation strategy and team approach. Figure 6.1 shows how a large company can organize its long-term disruptive innovation.

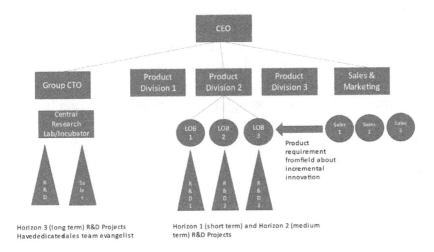

Figure 6.1. Organization structure for disruptive innovation in large companies

A company may have three product divisions or more; each of them could have three or more lines of business. The products from these LOBs are commonly sold by a central sales and marketing team. This works for H1 or H2 product innovation. But for long-term projects, you will need to create a dedicated incubation team working from the CTO's office to pursue H3 innovation successfully.

It will come as no surprise that either of the first two horizons, H1 and H2, allows for partnering with academia and start-ups, complementing the CRL's internal innovation projects. When such ad hoc incubation research is done and subsequently becomes a frequent activity, these group meetings are often termed innovation hubs. Like what was once referred to as skunkworks, they are usually situated at a regional office or a distanced LOB. When well-organized, they can become feeders for innovation projects at the CRL. But that said, the most productive H3 outcomes are almost always a result of team engagement with the corporate central research lab. Further, all three approaches offer value within open innovation, which is discussed in greater detail in the following chapter.

This organization structure is used at Alphabet, where start-up businesses, such as Waymo, the autonomous driving company, are kept entirely separate from the mother ship, Google, that has the core business of search and advertising. Most recently, the quantum computing group working on the Moonshot project under the Sandbox organization has been reported to be spun out as a separate company (https://www.datacenterdynamics.com).

Let us now examine the three approaches to innovation in detail: the CRL, the side project, and the all-in company. It makes sense to have the CTO guiding the project in any method.

THE CENTRAL RESEARCH LAB APPROACH

The key advantages to the CRL approach to guiding innovation projects are the following:

- The team is dedicated to working on long-term research problems.
- The team is trained to work with professors and graduate students.
- You have specific programs to hire such technical talent by leveraging the academic programs sponsored by the company.

Some of the disadvantages to the CRL approach are the following:

- Creating truly innovative ideas should not be restricted to only a tiny fraction of the overall R&D talent of a company.
- The researchers often become too specialized in certain areas or too academic and often find that they cannot contribute to building innovative products or services.
- It is usually challenging to find fresh talent to pursue new and emerging technology quickly.

For example, thirty years ago, HP Labs may have hired many engineers knowledgeable about the emerging inkjet printing technology. Today, with faster-moving, hot technical areas, to name but a few, are artificial intelligence / machine learning, virtual reality, and quantum computing. R&D people from the older generation trained in a single product, such as printer technologies, are ill-equipped to lead innovative R&D in fast-changing new fields. As discussed in chapter 5, the CRL is the best home for the full-time, dedicated team of researchers (about 5–10 percent of the total R&D head count), whose mission is to pursue long-term disruptive R&D.

Assuming a large company with about one thousand R&D people, a hundred—about 10 percent—work in a central lab. These individuals typically have PhDs in different technical areas relevant to the company's business objectives. In addition to pursuing long-term R&D, they attend conferences, publish in journals and academic papers for peer review, and may liaise with university professors and graduate students. These people are typically the deepest technical talent in the company and often rise to become fellows of the company. Such a five-to-ten R&D developers team is commonly handpicked and formed for twelve to thirty-six months. Assuming salaries of $150,000 per R&D developer, each R&D project needs funding of $1 to $5 million dollars.

THE SIDE PROJECT APPROACH

In this innovation ideation approach, everyone in the company is asked to work on long-term innovation about 20 percent, or one workday, of their time. This is often an effective way to identify the upcoming best and brightest. The company 3M may have been the first to employ this method to drive innovation, as did Google years later. Other examples of the side project approach include Gmail, Google Maps, Twitter, Slack, and Groupon. The advantages of the side project approach are the following:

- Introducing genuinely innovative ideas is no longer restricted to a small number of people working in a central research lab but rather to all employees in the company.
- It is an outstanding morale builder.

The disadvantages of the side project approach are the following:

- It implies that the R&D manager will allow anyone to work on creative ideas, even when they are not related to their assigned R&D projects, which is not likely to happen.
- Most employees are constantly working on deadlines and will, therefore, find it very hard to devote that 20 percent of the time to work on side projects, which may, unfortunately, mean that they are performing 100 percent on

their regular jobs plus an additional 20 percent on the side project.

- Since they can only give 20 percent of their time to the innovation project, it will likely take five times longer to complete.

The All-In Approach

This approach can generate a great deal of successful long-term innovation because all the employees are allowed to work on innovative ideas in a more unstructured, ad hoc manner and submit their ideas directly to the CTO's office. If an idea is selected, a team of five to ten people is typically funded for a three- to six-month time frame to work 100 perent of their time on the innovation project.

The advantages of the all-in approach are the following:

- The generation of truly innovative ideas is not restricted to a small number of people working in a central research lab. Still, it is on offer to all employees in the company.
- It is a good morale builder.

The disadvantages of the all-in approach concern disrupting the company management and workplace hierarchy and must be carefully administered:

- The CTO is expected to allow anyone and everyone to work on creative ideas, whether they are related to currently assigned R&D projects or not.
- Say the CEO (or CTO) decides to administer the innovation assignments and selects a team of R&D engineers for a three- to six-month-long project period. These engineers must be relieved from their current projects.

In all likelihood, you will use each of the three approaches—the CRL, the side, and the all-in—at one time or another or elements of one and another in a hybrid approach depending upon the project's importance and requirements. Each method has value. No technique works for every project and no approach that cannot be adapted to specific criteria or circumstances.

IDEASPARK PROGRAM AT CUBIC

Cubic Corporation, a public transportation and defense systems multinational, has an IdeaSpark program, which funds about ten to fifteen ideas initiated by the CEO in a given year. This program was discussed in detail in the interview with Brad Feldmann in chapter 4 (his response to the fourth question). Teams of three to four are selected for about twelve weeks at about $100,000 per project.

IdeaSpark was developed in 2014 to serve as a comprehensive innovation enablement platform that empowers organic, community-driven ideas and crowdsourced solutions to solve critical business challenges and maximize competitive advantage. IdeaSpark provides a reliable digital forum for employees to engage in creativity and offers Cubic employees direct opportunities to grow new solutions to support overall business strategy. Cubic uses community-driven ideas and bounty challenges with crowdsourced solutions as two distinct ways to capture creative input from the Cubic workforce. These methods allow users of various functional disciplines and experience levels to contribute ideas and improvements to reach innovation goals.

Cubic's primary ideation workflow is called community-driven ideation. This is a guided ideation workflow and bottom-up approach to creativity. Ideators can propose new products and process improvement ideas to the entire IdeaSpark community. To submit a funding proposal, an employee must answer two fundamental questions: One, what problem does your idea address. Two, how does your idea solve that problem? Once an idea is submitted, other users can use social features to vote, comment, and follow arguments. Using collaborative tools based on well-known social media paradigms, the combined innovation team and Business Unit Innovation Council members review and vote on the submitted ideas.

Suppose an idea is advanced to the seedling stage. In that case, the sponsoring Business Unit decides whether to fund the proposal effort for an assigned business development / capture lead and Cubic integrator to explore and validate the potential business case. This validation would include market analysis, user experience surveys, evaluation of current Cubic IP, and rapid development of a minimum viable prototype (MVP). Suppose the idea is validated at this Business Unit adjudication stage. In that case, the Business Unit sponsor will move the concept into one of four potential streams: customer-funded development, rapid prototype, product/technology roadmap, or future R&D project.

The second type of workflow implemented in IdeaSpark is a problem-based workflow called Bounties. Bounties are a top-down innovation approach that enables Business Unit stakeholders to narrow the topics for ideation and enlist the workforce to compete against one another and attempt to solve a customer pain point or offer a new approach for applying technology. Using gamification and discussion forums, the stakeholder can post a problem or challenge in the form of Bounty on IdeaSpark, outline a specific time limit for the challenge, and award points and a winner when the time expires. Using this social, crowdsourced format, all ideators can comment on and upvote/downvote on the submitted solutions for the stakeholders. Winning challenges leads to increased social status and points and a Bounty award for the winning submission. This cycle of gamified innovation then repeats as new problems are posted and new solutions are submitted.

The IdeaSpark community hub fosters Cubic's innovation culture with focused communication that speaks directly from and to our innovation community. To keep employees coming back and contributing to the ecosystem outside of idea submissions, IdeaSpark's community pages offer rich media blogs and video support. The R&D developers selected for funding get released from their regular R&D duties by their manager to work full-time on a disruptive innovation R&D project. Since the CEO sponsors this program, no R&D engineer realistically declines to work on the assigned project. However, being away from one's day job can create a workflow and interpersonal disruption between the R&D engineer and their manager.

Funding Big Bet Research Projects Just Like Start-Ups and VCs

Once an R&D innovation team is formed, it must be treated like any other start-up. A start-up receives seed funding of $1–$3 million to go from idea to prototype. Similarly, a large company funds a select team of five to ten people to create its disruptive product or service prototype. Each R&D project team needs the trust and assurance that comes from funding; on the other hand, it must be given performance milestones to demonstrate its metrics of success and, thereby, deserving of funding. Only when incremental milestone criteria are met will the office of the CTO approve the next phase of funding (e.g., Series A or Series B).

The process of R&D and long-term disruptive innovation design is risky. A CEO/CTO must support a culture of risk-taking in the company knowing well that only one idea in ten will be successful. Therefore, they must create a large funnel of innovative ideas for first-stage funding knowing that only 20 percent of these ideas will reach the next stage. This CEO/CTO may fund ten ideas at $1 million each in stage one, but only two will be approved for the next stage of, say, $5 million funding. This process is the innovation funnel and is graphically represented in figure 6.2.

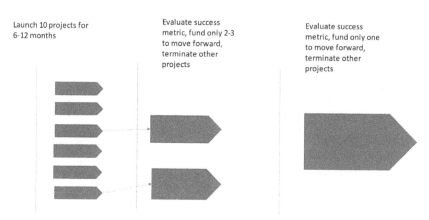

Launch 10 projects for 6-12 months

Evaluate success metric, fund only 2-3 to move forward, terminate other projects

Evaluate success metric, fund only one to move forward, terminate other projects

Figure 6.2. Innovation funnel. Start with a large number of small R&D projects. Evaluate success, select winners, and fund them to the next stage.

The metric for first-stage funding may be to build prototype hardware or software product. That is an acceptable milestone so long as the project proceeds on schedule and performance. But the checkpoints must also recognize when a project is stalling or has gotten stuck and if the metrics indicate that it ought to be terminated. The point here is that metrics can prove successful progress and signal when to stop funding a failure. VCs are ruthless in shutting down start-ups that are not succeeding. Large companies should apply the same metrics.

CENTRAL RESEARCH LAB, THE MOST SIGNIFICANT FUNDING VALUE-ADD

Whether the enterprise is a start-up, midsize, or already a large company, there is a strong value-add in establishing a CRL. However, the enterprise that stands to reap the most benefits from a CRL is the large parent company. This has been proven repeatedly, dating back to the life science labs in academia and commercial enterprise labs, such as General Electric Research Laboratory, Bell Labs, HP Labs, IBM Research, and Microsoft Research.

The CRL permits a more inclusive big bet ideation environment with either or both the side project and all-in approaches but extends outside the corporate environment to embrace academic and start-up partners. It can also engage business partners and suppliers and the board. But at its core, the CRL comprises of dedicated people primarily involved in long-term innovation. That is good since long-term innovation projects produce the greatest return on innovation investment.

PRACTICING OPEN INNOVATION WITH START-UPS AND ACADEMIA

It is understood that many of the innovative R&D engineers and thought leaders of the world do not work for your company. So how do you reach out to those innovative minds from universities, start-ups, and other companies to co-innovate with you? UC

Berkeley professor Henry Chesbrough wrote the book on this and titled it *Open Innovation*. Open innovation recognizes that all the creativity necessary for enterprise innovation cannot be found within the corporation itself; therefore, it is essential to have an inflow of stimuli from the outside world. This concept is illustrated in figure 9.1 and will be discussed in greater detail in chapter 9.

For various reasons, the central research lab team may not be able to develop all the creativity necessary for sustained innovation. Communicatie and ultimately partner with academia by discussing innovation with professors and students to learn about new technologies and to bring this creativity into the company. Academia is good at discovery but not good at building actual products or services, but they play an essential role in creativity and development and, therefore, a good partner in open innovation.

For example, when I was director of HP Labs, we were involved in an open innovation program, funding about eighty universities per year at around one hundred thousand dollars per school, supporting one PhD student at a time. HP's contract terms reserved the right to license codeveloped IP on a royalty-free, nonexclusive license or, alternately, a royalty-based, exclusive license, an acceptable quid pro quo. It was a productive partnership.

The universities saw their ideas become realities because of HP's ability to manufacture and market them, and we recognized that the academic perspective helped us build better products. It was a natural synergy between HP's researchers in our central labs and its academic partners, both professors and graduate students. Yet we noted that technology transfer from the academic bureaucracy to a private company could be difficult—for example, when negotiating IP contracts. Academia often does not understand the extent of the work to create a finished product or service. It is rare to find a university's think tank concepts already in a form that can be productized.

Tech transfer works best when

- hiring the graduate students to work for your company,
- funding a gift support to the professors, such as research grants or paid sabbaticals, or

- hiring the professors as consultants to partner in turning the results of their research into products. Each of these bypasses the process of negotiating IP contracts with the university.

Some R&D developers may do the actual work of technology transfer in the company's CRL under the guidance and even supervision of the professors. In contrast, the company's R&D engineers perform the implementation. For this to work effectively, though, one has to embrace the not-invented-here syndrome. No one solely owns an idea; all work together to express their opinion. The best collaborations and partnerships do not require recognition for the various individuals' contributions.

Two Case Studies: Partnering with Start-Ups to Take Innovative Products to Market

One option available to large companies is to partner with a start-up, which often has a clearer sense of innovating an idea through the business process and reaching the marketplace. Adidas and Google have both achieved very successful partnerships with smaller companies, each in a somewhat different manner.

Adidas. For over fifty years, Adidas was the premier shoe and footwear maker in the world. Suddenly, it found itself in dire competition with Nike and Reebok, both of whom were innovating the sports shoe. Adidas could not compete efficiently because its shoes were manufactured in factories with old technologies. Company executives knew they had to find innovative new technologies to make new shoes people would want to buy.

They discovered additive manufacturing / 3D printing. They thought that if they could 3D-print the footwear, they would be able to develop some exciting products quickly and less expensively. Adidas could have launched an internal group to pursue 3D printing with metals, binder jets, or plastics; but the learning curve would have taken too long. Instead, they looked around at a dozen 3D printing start-up companies. They found one, Carbon, which had developed a specific differentiated technology called digital light synthesis (DLS) that was just right for designing and manufacturing their footwear products.

Carbon worked with Adidas for several years to build the first 3D-printed shoes, then scaled them into production to manufacture millions of shoes. Their story is one of true open innovation. Each company brought what they were good at to the partnership, and by innovating together, they created a new and extraordinarily innovative shoe-manufacturing process. Adidas was once again a top-selling sports shoe.

Alphabet. Google is the flagship company owned by Alphabet through its 2015 diversification. Google is considered by many to be one of the most innovative companies in the US and perhaps the world. Google's search technology, developed by two Stanford grad students, is the company's core asset. Yet Google soon recognized that its search engine was a natural for serving website content and advertising. That evolved into developing various technologies to target the most relevant ads to specific consumers.

At the outset, the Google search tool was only available on desktop computers. When Google decided to move the search to mobile devices, like phones and tablets, in 2005, it acquired Andy Rubin's company, Android, and developed the open Android operating system. The Android OS is an open system platform that runs on more devices than any other, including the Apple iPhone, and is the leading OS for mobile devices. Google has found great success in building more open-system platforms, like Google Earth, YouTube, and its Chrome browser apps platform.

OPEN INNOVATION AT ACCENTURE

As global managing director of R&D at Accenture, I led the open innovation program with start-ups. We recognized that it is often difficult for a large company to raise internal awareness about business change, so it is almost always wise to partner with start-ups and academics. Start-ups are passionate and usually know how to launch a new product and business but may lack the depth of the technical experience or the insights into it. That is where the academic steps up even though they can rarely deliver the product or service. But that is the job of the commercial partners. They each have critical knowledge insights and technological perspectives to share.

Accenture saw all this and knew we could help create significant value by helping partner quickly moving start-ups with experienced companies who were receptive to innovating together. So we looked at a funnel of start-ups Accenture could partner with. Figure 6.3 shows the open innovation funnel at Accenture in 2015.

Example of Open Innovation with VCs and Startups at Accenture

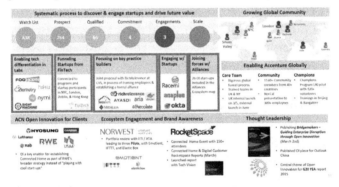

CHALLENGE: Innovation managers in large corporations identify startups and innovative ideas and nurture them, however the business units often do not leverage the opportunities and build them at scale

Figure 6.3. Open innovation funnel at Accenture during 2015 (courtesy of Accenture)

FOUR WAYS TO PARTNER WITH START-UPS

- Sales partnership (OEM relationship)—this means putting the start-up company's product or service on the large company's product sheet for its salespeople to sell. The benefit to the large company is streamlined access to new technology for their customers without investing organically in its development. The benefits for the start-up are more straightforward access funds, production, and an established sales channel. The issue is, if the sales staff can sell the new product or service. This is where the CTO and sales and marketing managers must all put their heads together to determine the best ways to train the salespeople and the best sales, marketing, and distribution channels for getting the product into customers' hands.

For example, Ansys had partnered with a start-up company called Dynardo GmbH in 2019. Ansys is a modeling and simulation company with many different physics solvers. Dinardo developed a tool called optiSLang, which allowed customers to use the Ansys solvers iteratively, running hundreds of design experiments to determine an optimal design. Ansys decided to form a partnership with Dynardo to sell optiSLang to its customers as part of a package of simulation solvers.

- *Invest in the start-up.* Start-ups always seem to require financing. Large companies often have investment arms and can take an equity stake in the start-up or accept either a board or an observer seat. The advantage for the large company is influencing the start-up's future product direction and the first rights of refusal in acquiring the young company, as discussed next. For example, the start-up I founded, AccelChip, received investment from Xilinx as part of the Series B investment; and in exchange, they received a board seat.

- *Acquire the start-up.* If the synergy seems to be there, the natural next step after executing a sales partnership or making an investment is to acquire the start-up company simply. The large company saves the expense of investing in organic R&D development and avoids the risk of creating a product for a new or emerging market. For example, Xilinx acquired AccelChip in 2006 for $25 million to bring the AccelFPGA technology into Xilinx customers to drive more Xilinx FPGA sales. Recently, General Motors acquired Cruise, and Ford acquired Argo to accelerate the development of their autonomous driving programs. The disadvantage is that the large company now has to pay to acquire the company (typically valued at ten to twenty times the revenue of the start-up). It can be expensive, so the earlier the large company makes its financial valuation, the better.

- *Integrate the start-up into your company.* Once the start-up company is acquired, it is essential to integrate its team, product, sales potential, and go-to-market activities with the large company. For example, after Ansys acquired Dynardo, the optiSLang product was included in the list of products from Ansys, and its optimization capability was integrated with other simulation products. The Dynardo business has grown significantly because of its access to Ansys's sales and marketing channels. Ansys considers this an excellent product synergy and sales synergy.

DISCOURAGING THE NOT-INVENTED-HERE (NIH) SYNDROME

Many people in large companies feel that to get credit for some innovation, the idea has to be entirely their own. That culture needs to be changed to the work of a scout, whose job is to identify technologies from universities that can be productized. Often, the most innovative products emerge from a team of people skilled in different technologies, who work together to solve problems and create a marketable solution.

A straightforward way to encourage more long-term innovation is for every CRL member to focus on developing new technologies organically and scouting for new technologies in development in universities and start-up companies and bring them into your company's fold. It is for the large company to assemble a solution or workflow built around its key technologies, then organically integrate it with the technologies developed outside.

An example is when Apple, too busy with the Mac to undertake a new product development project, assembled a team of outside entrepreneurs and start-ups to create a digital music player. The critical technology was hard disk storage, invented by Toshiba engineers. Still, each team member made a significant contribution, right down to branding it the iPod, a device that Steve Jobs described as putting "1,000 songs in your pocket."

CHALLENGES TO SUCCESSFUL RISK-TAKING INNOVATION IN LARGE COMPANIES

Challenges come in many shapes and colors and will not surprise the enlightened business leader. When it comes to achieving success with your company's innovation, a challenge may be either an opportunity or a threat, but none can be slighted or ignored for a single moment. They are the first stage of your rocket; without being factored in, you will not lift your innovation project successfully into its intended market. Carefully consider the challenges.

Talent challenges. One of the most challenging tasks for the CTO is finding and hiring great innovators. The GAFAM (Google, Apple, Facebook, Amazon, and Microsoft) companies can afford to pay handsomely for new talent while the well-funded start-ups are fighting for the same or even less talent. Take the time to develop a set of criteria for your talent search. Look for individuals who may not possess the deepest knowledge in their technology area yet have a passion and drive for building something new and exciting. Sometimes, you need to trust your instincts when interviewing them.

Forming academic partnerships. It is up to the large company to find the best university programs and professors with whom to partner. You may be fortunate enough to find one geographically near your company, which in less uncertain times usually produces a stronger bond. Yet even if that is not possible, identify at least five graduate-level professors and programs that hold promise, then conduct the equivalent of a job search and interviewing process to determine the best candidates.

Funding. Of course, you will need to budget your innovation development projects. Your company likely has at least five divisions, each with an average of twenty lines of business (LOBs). In many large companies, each line of business can have at least ten products targeted for innovation. So now we are talking about four hundred different products or services in a given company at various stages of innovation development. Not every project will be successful, nor will every project even be completed. Your role is to help identify those from the sharpest teams, having the high customer demand and sales potential that will contribute to the company's growth.

Access to customers. Innovators do not create products or services for the simple pleasure of it. There must be a clearly defined customer demographic and known, established sales and marketing channels to reach customers. This is where innovation becomes integrated into the value chain—in other words, where the critical touchpoints guide and build out the product or service toward marketing and sales.

Secrets of Successful Innovation Risk-Taking

Innovation must not—indeed, cannot—take place in a vacuum. You need to start not just as an innovation evangelist but as a business manager with a plan for the technology transfer, because this is how it will result in success. You have to sell the innovation to the people in your organization who are selling to the customer. The true excellence in a central research lab is when its work is embedded in the business value chain. So think about the process of coming up with a new product and the supporting business processes that will get it to market. It must be introduced, explained, and sold to the sales teams who take the orders, which produce revenue for the enterprise, or the innovation work is all for nothing.

Often, a what-if analysis is to reconfigure an H3 innovation project that may be going off the rails or when the CTO recognizes the need to take it in a new direction. Of course, this is less than desirable; so to avoid this, the following are the three most prevalent means of supporting and ultimately implementing successful innovation projects.

Once you have determined that the innovation project has sales and marketing legs, immediately begin planning its future. The best way to do this is to make the innovation a corporate-sponsored start-up, such as a spin-in or spin-up, a ring-fence, or a subsidiary integration for its established products.

- In a spin-in example, a CRL researcher, a professor, or a start-up founder with whom you are either currently working or interested in doing so has come up with the idea that has merit. Immediately launch an internal start-up and put her in charge.
- In the case of a spin-up, a team built on or from members of your CRL (and which may include others from your academic and start-up partners) has created not simply an innovative product but a platform that can be transformed into a distinct business entity. All that it may lack is funding and management support, which your backing can help facilitate
- Ring-fence the spin-up. Allow the new business to build and sell its products as a separate financial entity, which both protects its assets and insulates the large company against it in the event it incurs financial losses
- Integrate the business as a subsidiary. This benefits the large company because it owns the intellectual property and diversifies the parent's risk while the subsidiary remains a separate legal entity with its successes. For example, Hewlett-Packard spun off Hewlett Packard Labs and Hewlett Packard Enterprise, retaining HP Labs for Hewlett Packard Inc.

The Sales Force, Innovation's Other Partner

Selling a product is a complicated process. It involves personality, a knowledge of the principles of selling, and of course, extensive product understanding. At the outset, salespeople may not think they can sell something new and different. Of course, they can if they are brought into the process early enough and are thoroughly educated and trained.

At this point, the CTO must step up and become the evangelist. The innovation lab people create the product or service—for example, digital twin. The company's business value chain now takes over to make it viable. Next, the sales force gets involved with the product or service to market it to the customer. The company may have to hire fresh salespeople focused on selling a different kind of innovation. As its release nears, these sales and marketing teams must enter the value chain to become thoroughly familiar with the product or service. Training materials, especially videos, are essential. Let them handle and use prototypes if possible.

It is axiomatic. Innovators must share their expertise to partner with marketing and sales. Through a wide range of activities, they teach how to sell it. This is an aspect similar to the start-up ring-fenced organization. When large companies create this ring-fence group, everyone participates in disruptive innovation.

Determining Technical Milestones

When evaluating outcomes for an innovation project, here are some considerations.

- With pen and paper, thoughtfully describe in a few sentences the project's objectives, followed by columns enumerating the pluses and minuses of using each of the three horizon approaches. Then compare using a what-if analysis (at this point, a spreadsheet app becomes useful).

- Create a big bet ideation team, which may be internal or internal/external combined and may include team leaders from CRL product, tech, and design as well as finance and marketing and sales. Meet off-site for a day or until reaching consensus
- Fix the funding within a practicable time. Review other similar internal or external projects for size and budgeting. Build a spreadsheet projection of success.
- Know when to cut your losses. Terminate projects if or when it becomes clear they will not succeed or become too costly.
- Set and deliver the technical milestones (use project management software if that is practicable) and assure they are met. When a milestone is reached, test with go-to-market sales teams dedicated to the product's central purpose.

THE SPIN-IN MODEL: INCUBATING NEW BUSINESSES

Suppose large companies are truly serious about long-term disruptive innovation. In that case, they are wise to turn to their central research lab to create the spin-in models for their business relationships with others, especially for the start-ups. We live in an age when business innovation means partnering to lower risk and providing more opportunities for reward than trying to go it entirely on your own. To do otherwise means greater exposure to failure. But any innovation-building effort must be based on the core concept of the central research lab. Ideally, the CRL becomes the sole hub for your innovation business efforts and conveys to your partners that your company is serious about innovation—mainly H3, long-term disruptive innovation.

Cisco has supported the concept of spin-in incubators for a while. The former CEO John Chambers awarded a well-known group of four entrepreneurs dubbed MPLS (Mario Mazzola, Prem Jain, Luca Cafiero, Soni Jiandani) with more than $2.4 billion of investment dollars to start new companies. Each innovation team receiving funding from Cisco was ring-fenced from Cisco's HR and finance policies or procedures. None applied to these start-up incubator teams so they could hire whomever and spend money on whatever they wanted. The team leaders were only responsible for meeting the product milestones, precisely like a start-up company has to meet milestones for a VC's funding stages. Once the team demonstrated the value of the technology, it was acquired by Cisco. This organizational structure is shown in figure 6.7.

Here are some organizational approaches and principles.

- A spin-in is a highly unusual way to retain top talent.
- Adopt a form of R&D in which the large company is the sole investor in the start-up.
- Send a team of employees off to build an experimental product, then buy that start-up for a predetermined price.
- Fund the start-up only in the initial R&D mode to prove the business before they hire salespeople to scale it.
- Ring-fence the teams. Protect them from organizational constraints (HR, finance, IT, or travel policies) and give them needed support.

This model has been used successfully by Cisco. They have allowed ring-fenced teams to incubate new businesses and then repurchase them. Cisco has spent on average $763 million to acquire each spin-in these intrapreneurs have founded. For over twenty years, Cisco CEO John Chambers has funneled $2.38 billion to them and their teams.

But the most important thing to remember is that for this to succeed, you need the organizational structure shown in figure 6.4. And you need a talented team like Mario, Prem, Luca, and Soni, who have the skill sets to be intrapreneurial within a large company. Many a company have tried this spin-in model but failed since they did not have the innovative talent to lead these teams to success.

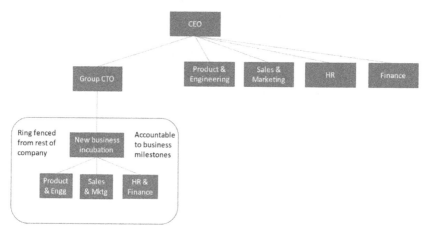

Figure 6.4. Organization structure of spin-in model

Kickstarting Your Innovation

An example from my own experience is Hewlett-Packard's HP Labs, which I regard as a role model for large companies wishing to take advantage of the innovation opportunities a CRL affords them. As senior vice president of research and director of HP Labs in Palo Alto, I manage six hundred brilliant researchers across seven CRL locations worldwide (Bristol, Haifa, Bangalore, Beijing, Singapore, and St. Petersburg) to tap into innovative talent.

When I joined HP Labs in 2007, the researchers were working on more than two hundred different projects, each with one to three team members. As part of a significant transformation, as mentioned earlier, we decided to focus the entire organization on twenty big bet projects with twenty-five to thirty team members per team.

For HP Labs, it was one thing to get fantastic results from creating innovative technology products, such as the first LED display or inkjet printing. It was quite another to involve an individual line of business in cocreating the technology under development in our central research lab. Often, these H3 projects had been in development for three to five years, so we worked closely with the LOBs to transfer the research results.

We accomplished this by establishing an HP Labs Technical Advisory Board, which consisted of members from HP Labs and the VPs/GMs and CTOs of the businesses. As the project in HP Labs made progress towards its milestones, the LOB would become enthusiastic, anticipating the technology transfer to happen. Our mantra was, "To create, identify, and develop novel technologies and experiences that delight customers and define the future of HP Inc." And we did just that.

Role of Mergers and Acquisitions to Drive Disruptive Innovation

In addition to this incubation model, a very important approach for larger companies to perform disruptive innovation is through mergers and acquisitions. Most companies have a strong corporate development organization, whose role is to identify other companies to acquire and to be brought under the fold of the larger company. The central R&D team can play a very important role in identifying which start-up companies to partner with and which start-up companies to acquire. The most innovative companies, like Google and Amazon, have been able to enter some new disruptive markets using acquisition. Google acquired YouTube to expand from search-based advertising to video-based advertising, and Amazon acquired Kiva to accelerate their logistics in distribution centers.

For example, Ansys was founded by John Swanson in 1970 as an engineering simulation company focused on finite element analysis of structural problems. Over the past fifty years, Ansys has acquired more than twenty-five companies (Fluent for fluid dynamics, Ansoft for electromagnetics, Apache for semiconductor, Esterel for embedded software, Granta for materials, LSTC for crash simulation, AGI for digital missions engineering, and Phoenix Integration for model-based system design) and brought a lot of disruptive innovation to their customers. In each of these areas, it would have taken Ansys at least three to five years and tens of millions of dollars to organically develop these capabilities. Hence, M&A is a very effective approach to grow a company's business. The revenue of Ansys was $100 million when the company went through an IPO in 1996, and it is $2 billion in 2022. Such revenue growth is a result of a combination of organic R&D and M&A. Figure 6.6 shows the M&A and partnership journey of Ansys in the past fifty years.

Figure 6.6. Mergers and acquisition and partnership
strategy of Ansys (courtesy of Ansys)

When exploring disruptive innovation using M&A of a start-up company, the leaders of a large company need to analyze the following:

1. Does the target company's product (or list of products) produce product synergies with the home company? This means that the target company's product(s) can be integrated with the home company's products and combined into a larger solution for the customer.

2. Does the target company's sales force or list of customers produce sales synergies with the home company? This means that the home company's products can be sold to the target company's customers using the target company's sales force, or the target company's products can

be sold by the home company's sales force to the home company's customers. The idea is that the total available market for the combined collection of products has to increase for the combination of the host company and the target company.

3. Is there cultural synergy between the employees of the home company and the target company? Because if there is a cultural conflict, the acquisition of the company will not be successful.

4. Is their business model synergy between the companies? If the home company sells hardware products and the target company sells software as a service, the business models are different, and it will be difficult to make the acquisition successful.

CONCLUSION

In summary, my key recommendations for large companies to get started with horizon 3 disruptive innovation are the following:

1. Create a central R&D arm like HP Labs or Microsoft Research to identify H3 areas to invest in. Expect that the central lab may not be able to build market-ready products.

2. In addition to the role of creating organic innovation, the role of the central research lab should be to scout for innovation outside the company and bring those innovations to the company.

3. Let the central R&D arm practice open innovation. Partner with academia and start-ups so they can develop external perspectives and ideas for innovation within.

4. As part of open innovation with academia, fund R&D programs at partner universities and hire students for joint R&D. Create a program to hire those students into the company. Note that technology transfer mainly happens with the people transfer through students and professors.

Universities rarely create working products and need the relationship with business for execution, just as much as business relies on the academic input.

5. As part of open innovation with start-ups, form partnerships in start-ups at different levels—technology partnerships, sales or OEM relationships, and investments. Create different stages of engagement as watch lists, prospect list, engage list, etc. If these OEM partnerships are successful, acquire the start-ups.

6. Use mergers and acquisitions of start-ups as an effective way to bring disruptive innovation to the large company.

7. Create a start-up incubator within the central research arm to market and sell the H3 products by creating your own sales force within the central R&D and not try to sell through the larger sales arm of the large company. Use a spin-in model like Cisco Systems does. Allow existing employees to create disruptive ideas. Fund those ideas. Ring-fence the team and allow them to build the products and sell them until reaching a certain scale, then integrate into the mother ship.

AUTHOR'S PERSONAL EXPERIENCE WITH LARGE COMPANIES

Below are the lessons I learned from my work in large companies—HP, ABB, Accenture, Schneider Electric, and Ansys.

From 2007 to 2012, Hewlett-Packard Company, senior vice president of research and director of HP Labs, the company's central research organization. In these roles, in which I reported to the CEO, I helped chart technical strategies for the company and head HP Labs. I managed a group of six hundred researchers in seven worldwide locations (Palo Alto, USA; Bristol, UK; Haifa, Israel; Beijing, China; Bangalore, India; St. Petersburg, Russia; and Singapore).

During my tenure, HP Labs created a comprehensive strategic plan for organizing HP Labs to have the researchers work on fewer high-impact projects and focus on the impact on the businesses and customers. We reorganized HP Labs into eight labs: print and content delivery, mobile and immersive experiences, cloud and security, information analytics, networking, intelligent infrastructure, services and solutions, and sustainability. Collectively, the five hundred researchers work on twenty-five big bet research projects around these eight themes.

Successful technology transfers from HP Labs included low-power servers in Project Moonshot, storage deduplication in the StoreOnce product, the IBRIX-Metabox data archival product, scalable cloud storage, optical backplanes for servers and switches, the Net Zero Data Center, the CeNSE sensor project for oil exploration, immersive 3D displays, commercial digital printing, Openet, and the Vayu Internet Device. Many of these projects successfully created new businesses for HP. HP Labs had a very successful open innovation program with more than eighty universities in the world. We will discuss open innovation in more detail in chapter 6.

From 2012 to 2013, ABB, executive vice president and chief technology officer. I was executive vice president, chief technology officer, and member of the executive committee of ABB, reporting to the CEO. In this role, I headed up the technology directions for both corporate and divisional technology, which included more than eight thousand scientists and engineers in seven ABB Corporate Research Centers around the world (China, India, Germany, Poland, Sweden, Switzerland, and the USA) and two Global Labs, Global Labs Power, and Global Labs Automation.

I was responsible for starting some new initiatives at ABB around long-term disruptive innovation involving large, multidisciplinary teams of researchers. Some example areas were big data for services; cloud automation; energy-efficient data centers; single-day robot integration; next-generation power grids; and smarter integration of motors, drives, and applications. We also started some new initiatives around university collaboration and further business incubation. Many of these research projects were transferred into new products for the ABB businesses. ABB practiced open innovation with more than one hundred universities worldwide.

From 2013 to 2015, Accenture, managing director of Global Technology Research and Development. In this role, I oversaw the Accenture Labs (www.accenture.com/technologylabs), the global technology R&D organization within Accenture, which explored new and emerging technologies. Accenture Labs was an international organization with more than two hundred researchers in five lab locations worldwide (San Jose; Washington, DC; Sophia, France; Beijing; and Bangalore). As part of directing Accenture Labs, I was responsible for research in five R&D groups: (1) infrastructure and systems, (2) software engineering, (3) cybersecurity, (4) big data analytics, and (5) digital experiences. I also directed Accenture's annual Technology Vision research, which looked at the future of enterprise IT (www.accenture.com/technologyvision). Finally, I was responsible for Accenture's open innovation program with start-up companies, corporate partners, and universities, which I also started. We will discuss open innovation in more detail in chapter 6.

From 2015 to 2017, Schneider Electric, executive vice president and chief technology officer. I was executive vice president, chief technology officer, and member of the executive committee of Schneider Electric, reporting to the chairman and the CEO. In this role, I was responsible for driving innovation and technology differentiation and coordinating the company's R&D activities across its five businesses with eight thousand R&D personnel and a 1.3 billion euro R&D investment. My CTO office had four pillars: (1) the five business CTOs through whom I coordinate the R&D across the divisions and lines of business, (2) central functions, like R&D governance, technology community, and open innovation with start-up companies, universities, and partners, (3) corporate research center, which is the central research arm, (4) and IOT and digitization, where we are building an IOT platform for Schneider Electric. I was also responsible for the development of the EcoStruxure IoT platform.

From 2018-current, Ansys, chief technology officer. In this role, I led the evolution of Ansys's technology and championed the company's next phase of innovation and growth. I was responsible for about $300 million in R&D activities and led two thousand R&D engineers across the seven businesses. I led the long-term technology strategy at Ansys around areas such as AI / machine learning, high-performance computing, multiphysics platforms, model-based systems engineering, and digital twins. We built high-growth solutions at Ansys around autonomy, electrification, 5G, IIoT, and health care. I was also responsible for driving Ansys's new and emerging business (having P/L responsibilities) in three initiatives: (1) AI/ML applied to simulation, (2) digital twins, (3) and simulation opportunities in health care. As part of my role, I worked with Ansys's large enterprise customers on aligning the Ansys long-term technology strategy with the customers' business priorities. We also participated in numerous long-term customer co-innovation projects.

CHAPTER 7
Funding Models for Innovation

Interview: Erwin Gianchandani, assistant director of the directorate for Technology, Innovation, and Partnerships (TIP), National Science Foundation

Dr. Erwin Gianchandani is the National Science Foundation (NSF) assistant director of the directorate for Technology, Innovation, and Partnerships (TIP). In this role, he contributes to all aspects of the management of the CISE directorate, including strategic and human capital planning, formulation and implementation of the directorate's more than $900 million annual budget, and oversight of day-to-day operations. In the last several years, he has led the development, launch, and implementation of several new NSF investment areas, including Smart and Connected Communities and Platforms for Advanced Wireless Research.

Previously, Dr. Gianchandani served as the deputy division director for the CISE Division of Computer and Network Systems (CNS). Before joining NSF in 2012, he was the inaugural director of the Computing Community Consortium (CCC), providing leadership to the computing research community in identifying and pursuing audacious, high-impact research directions. Prior to that, he was the director of innovation networking at the University of Virginia, reporting to the university's vice president for research. Dr. Gianchandani has published extensively and presented at numerous international conferences on the subject of computational systems modeling of biological networks with the goal of better understanding disease mechanisms and identifying therapeutic targets. He earned his PhD and MS in biomedical engineering and his BS in computer science from the University of Virginia.

INTERVIEWER. Erwin, thank you very much for agreeing to be interviewed for my book The Innovation Factory. Tell me about your background leading to your current role at NSF.

INTERVIEWEE. I have had the pleasure of serving at the National Science Foundation, or NSF, since September 2012. I started as the deputy division director for the Division of Computer and Network Systems, served almost six years as the deputy for our Computer and Information Science and Engineering (CISE) directorate, including a couple of stints as acting head of the directorate during periods of transition, and have been the senior adviser to the director for translation, innovation, and partnerships for the last fifteen months.

As an example of my work as the deputy for CISE, I was responsible for leading budget and science strategy for the directorate, including its $1 billion annual budget, human capital planning for a team of over 130, and oversight of day-to-day operations, including over eight thousand proposals in a given year. In that role, I led the development of new programs like the platforms for Advanced Wireless Research, Smart and Connected Communities, Civic Innovation Challenge, and National Artificial Intelligence

Research Institutes. Prior to NSF, I was the inaugural director of the Computing Community Consortium, an NSF-funded project that seeks to unite the computing and information research community around compelling research agendas, particularly in the context of national priorities, like health, climate, and equity.

I earned my BS in computer science with a minor in biomedical engineering, followed by an MS and PhD in biomedical engineering from the University of Virginia. My research interests have been in computational systems biology with a particular focus on novel computational approaches to integrate heterogeneous data and model biochemical networks, contributing to improved understanding of disease mechanisms and potential therapeutic targets.

INTERVIEWER. What is the mission of the National Science Foundation? What is the total amount of funding in 2021? How many directorates are there?

INTERVIEWEE. NSF was established by Congress in 1950 with the mission "to promote the progress of science; to advance the national health, prosperity, and welfare; and to secure the national defense." NSF is the only federal agency that supports fundamental research in all fields of science and engineering with the exception of the medical sciences, which are generally supported by the National Institutes of Health. Over the last seven decades, NSF's investments have given rise to new knowledge and innovations that have, in turn, transformed our lives. For example, NSF-funded research has resulted in the seminal breakthroughs leading to GPS technology, 3D printing, Doppler radars, and the modern Internet, among others. An NSF-funded project in the 1990s led to the page-rank algorithm that is the basis for the Google search engine.

NSF's budget in fiscal year (FY) 2021, which ended on September 30, 2021, was $8.5 billion. Unlike many other federal agencies, NSF's research portfolio is entirely extramural. In a typical year, about 93 percent of NSF's funds are awarded to colleges and universities, small businesses and start-ups, and nonprofits with the remainder supporting our operations. In recent FYs, NSF has been the funding source for approximately 27 percent of the total federal budget for basic research conducted at US colleges and universities. In many fields, such as mathematics, computer science, and the social sciences, NSF has been the major source of federal funding.

Beyond research, NSF also supports science and engineering education, from pre-K through graduate school and beyond. Our goal is to help grow domestic talent, particularly individuals skilled and available to work in new and emerging scientific, engineering, and technological fields, along with teachers capable of educating the next-generation workforce.

NSF also funds equipment that is needed by scientists and engineers but is often too expensive for any one group or researcher to afford. Examples of such major research equipment include giant optical and radio telescopes, Antarctic research sites, high-end computer facilities and ultra-high-speed network connections, ships for ocean research, sensitive detectors of very subtle physical phenomena, and gravitational wave observatories. In general, we like to say that NSF is "where discoveries begin."

At present, NSF has a total workforce of about 2,100 at its Alexandria, Virginia, headquarters, including approximately 1,400 career employees and 200 scientists from research institutions who are on temporary assignment to NSF. In addition to financial management, award processing and monitoring, legal affairs, outreach, and other functions, our staff is distributed across the following seven directorates that support science and engineering research and education: biological sciences; Computer and Information Science and Engineering; engineering; geosciences; mathematical and physical sciences; social, behavioral, and economic sciences; and education and human resources. Each directorate is headed by an assistant director, and each is further subdivided into divisions like materials research, ocean sciences, and behavioral and cognitive sciences.

INTERVIEWER. How does NSF facilitate technology transfer to industry? Can you speak about the NSF Industry-University Cooperative Research Centers?

INTERVIEWEE. NSF is proud to be a pioneer across the federal government when it comes to technology translation. For example, NSF was the first agency to establish the Small Business Innovation Research, or SBIR, program back in the late 1970s. Today, SBIR has been adopted by eleven other federal departments and agencies. Similarly, NSF led the establishment of the Innovation Corps, or I-Corps, program in 2011, providing entrepreneurial education, and several other agencies have followed suit.

Today, NSF offers five highly connected programs that collectively constitute the agency's Lab-to-Market Platform—Industry-University Cooperative Research Centers (IUCRC), Transition to Practice, Partnerships for Innovation, I-Corps, and SBIR and Small Business Technology Transfer. These programs allow the NSF research community to demonstrate initial results; form partnerships with others to start to translate those research results into practical settings; receive education and training about how to conduct market research; and validate results through novel products, services, and solutions.

For example, for over forty years, the NSF IUCRC program has sought to foster breakthrough research by enabling close and sustained engagement between industry innovators, world-class academic teams, and government agencies. NSF provides a relatively small investment and, more importantly, the structure that allows university researchers to partner with industry and other government agencies to motivate use-inspired research problems. Today, over seventy IUCRCs span nearly all the areas of science and engineering research that NSF supports—from the life sciences, to new materials design, and to emerging sensing and analytical platforms.

We invest about $20,000 in a planning grant leading to an IUCRC and then step IUCRCs through two phases totaling up to $300,000 in additional investment, trying to build in sustainability for the centers along the way. The return on investment is clear. For every $1 that NSF invests, companies and other agencies contribute, on average, $7 toward specific precompetitive research projects that align with their mission interests.

INTERVIEWER. What are some examples of successful inventions or innovations or products that have come out of research funded by the National Science Foundation?

INTERVIEWEE. NSF-funded research has laid the foundation for many of the groundbreaking discoveries and game-changing technologies that we rely upon today. Here are a few examples, taken from https://www.nsf.gov.

- *The Internet.* Drawing on DARPA's pioneering support for early computer networking projects and the development of Internet protocols, NSF funds catalyzed the creation of the commercial Internet that we know today. Starting with NSFNet in 1985, a high-speed network for the academic research community, NSF support created a major infrastructural backbone that would eventually link to smaller regional networks, spreading connectivity across the country and overseas. NSF leveraged public-private partnerships to broaden access to the network and to make it easier to navigate, including managing domain name creation and the development of one of the first Internet browsers: Mosaic. By 1995, successful commercial networking efforts led NSF to decommission NSFNet, allowing for public use of the Internet.
- *Google.* When the Internet first began, it had fewer than one hundred websites, but searching even this small number was not a straightforward task. Recognizing this need, NSF led the multiagency Digital Library Initiative (DLI). Two graduate students working on the project, Larry Page

and Sergey Brin, created a new way to search the web. They used a page-ranking system that was built on foundational, NSF-supported work in economics and sociology. In 1998, Page and Brin concluded their NSF-funded research project by launching an Internet search website that used that system called Google. Today, Google's parent company, Alphabet, is valued at hundreds of billions of dollars.

- *Smartphones.* From the liquid-crystal display and multitouch zoom to the lithium battery and the mapping software, including GPS, NSF supported research essential to the creation of many technologies contained in today's smartphones.

- *Spectrum auctions.* Spectrum licenses make communicating and connecting over the airwaves possible. To broadcast something across any portion of the electromagnetic spectrum, like television or telecommunications, companies need to purchase a license. When the federal government began selling portions of the telecommunications spectrum in 1994, it chose to auction them using rules based on auction theory research funded by NSF. Over the past two decades, the auctions have raised more than $100 billion for the US Treasury. Several other countries have also adapted the auction approach to spectrum allocation.

- *Kidney exchanges.* According to the National Kidney Foundation, more than one hundred thousand people are waiting for a kidney transplant at this moment, and about thirteen people die every day while on this waiting list. Many kidney patients who need a donation rely on a relatively small pool of potential donors among their friends and family. If the blood type of the patient and donor don't match, the transfer can't happen, further dwindling hope of a successful transplant. While game theory and market dynamics may seem unrelated to kidney transplants, they have become the backbone of a nationwide, lifesaving kidney match program. With NSF support, economist Alvin Roth and a team of researchers created software that matched kidney recipients to compatible donors regardless of whether they knew one another, significantly widening the donor pool. In 2012, Roth shared the Nobel Prize in economics for his research in game theory and market designs.

INTERVIEWER. Can you speak about NSF Engineering Research Centers, such as how many there are, and what the latest thinking is at NSF around innovation centers?

INTERVIEWEE. My colleagues in NSF's engineering directorate, Dr. José Zayas-Castro, the division director for the engineering education and centers division, can speak much more eloquently about the historic Engineering Research Centers, or ERCs, program. Briefly, ERCs are multidisciplinary, multi-institutional centers that join academia, industry, and government in partnership to produce transformational engineered systems, along with engineering graduates who are adept at innovation and primed for leadership in the global economy.

At each ERC, academic and industry researchers collaborate in the pursuit of advances in complex engineered systems and systems-level technologies that could spawn whole new industries or radically transform the product lines, practices, and processes of current industries. The ERC program was created in 1984; today, we have about eighteen active centers and a number that have graduated.

Beyond the ERCs, NSF also supports other center-scale projects, like the Science and Technology Centers, which provide a means to undertake significant investigations at the interfaces of disciplines or fresh approaches within disciplines. More recently, NSF has launched center-scale activities in key technology areas, like the National Artificial Intelligence Research Institutes and Quantum Leap Challenge Institute. A key focus across our portfolio of center-scale programs and projects is broadening participation, including the full range of institution types and the nation's geography.

INTERVIEWER. Let us speak about your own TIP directorate that is being proposed.

INTERVIEWEE. As you well know, there have been a number of broad calls over the past couple of years for a new directorate at NSF. For example, the US Senate has passed the US Innovation and Competition Act, or USICA, which authorizes the establishment of a new Directorate for Science, Technology, and Innovation, focused on strengthening US leadership in critical technologies through basic research in key technology focus areas, such as artificial intelligence, high-performance computing, and advanced manufacturing, and the commercialization of those technologies to businesses in the US.

Likewise, the US House of Representatives has passed the NSF for the Future Act, authorizing the establishment of a new directorate for Science and Engineering Solutions to advance research and development solutions to address societal and national challenges. And this past May, the Biden-Harris administration issued its FY 2022 President's Budget Request, seeking a new Technology, Innovation, and Partnerships, or TIP, directorate.

Our view of TIP is that this is a once-in-a-generation opportunity to transform the nation's research and innovation ecosystem through an intentional focus on use-inspired research and translational research. We must bring together teams of researchers not only from academia but also from private industry, government, including at the state and local levels, nonprofits and philanthropies, civil society, and communities of practice to inspire research questions derived from pressing real-world challenges, catalyze iterative codesign and cocreation, and pilot and prototype research results in the very same settings where the problems framing the original research questions emerged.

Our goal is to advance critical technologies, like advanced manufacturing, advanced materials, advanced wireless, artificial intelligence, biotechnology, quantum information science, and semiconductors and microelectronics, and to address pressing societal challenges, such as climate change, equity, and critical and resilient infrastructure. Indeed, we feel strongly about the bidirectional nature of critical technologies and societal challenges. Our climate change challenges prompt new artificial intelligence techniques, for example, just as advances in artificial intelligence offer new lenses for thinking about how to mitigate climate change.

A focal point for us in TIP is to much more fully and equitably harness the geography of innovation that exists across the country. We must find ways to engage everyone in science, technology, engineering, and mathematics regardless of background, organizational affiliation, or geographic location. And indeed, many of today's problems are inspired by unique challenges in different parts of our country, and they benefit from diverse perspectives. It is high time for us to engage the full breadth of civil society and communities of practice in motivating and shaping research and in translating research results to society.

Along the way, we would like to positively impact the research enterprise as well, encouraging (i) flexible cross-organization and cross-sector appointments with seamless transitions (e.g., professors of practice) and comentoring of students by academia and industry and others, (ii) workforce development at all levels, giving rise not only to future researchers but also practitioners and entrepreneurs, and (iii) increased connection between researchers and the broader civil society in their communities and regions. Ultimately, our ambition in TIP is to engender a paradigm shift. Rather than an emphasis on pushing research results, including new technologies, out of the laboratory and out to the market and society, we would like to encourage the market to inspire research questions and specifically draw out research results. That is, this market pull dynamic will enable the beneficiaries of research to motivate that work and, thus, become invested in seeing it translated and realized in society.

Introduction

This chapter focuses on the funding models for innovation in academia, start-up companies, and large companies. As discussed throughout this book, large companies excel at incremental improvements to their current products (H1) and usually perform well with medium-term innovation on the adjacencies (H2); they are often less successful when creating highly disruptive, innovative products or services. Academia typically excels in long-term R&D and H3 innovation. Start-up companies usually excel in H3 disruptive innovation. Academic innovation described in chapter 2 is primarily funded by government agencies. Start-up companies described in chapter 3 are mainly financed through venture capitalists. Large company innovation is financed mainly by the company, determined by its R&D budget, or in some instances by initiatives sponsored by the CEO or the board. In this chapter, we will review how these three types of innovation are funded and how the funding environment is transforming.

A Brief History of Funding Innovation

Governments and academia have long funded basic and applied research innovation projects. It is unlikely that Isaac Newton (1642–1726) could have had the time or resources needed to discover the nature of optics, celestial mechanics, or gravity had it not been for the support of the British Royal Society and several universities. Before 1948, the US government funded research and development primarily in the defense and energy labs. In 1945, Vannevar Bush, director of the Office of Scientific Research and Development, presented a report entitled "Science, the Endless Frontier" to President Dwight Eisenhower. The National Science Foundation (NSF) was created in 1950 in response to his report. NSF today is the US's most crucial long-term innovation funding body.

ESTABLISHMENT OF THE NATIONAL SCIENCE FOUNDATION

Realizing the need for advancing the country's scientific interests, Bush's report redefined the relationship between government funding, industrial funding, and academic research. Congress established the National Science Foundation (NSF) with the National Science Foundation Act of 1950 "to promote the progress of science; to advance the national health, prosperity, and welfare; to secure the national defense; and for other purposes." The NSF's support recognized scientific R&D as a primary driver of the US economy, which enhanced the nation's security while advancing knowledge to sustain global leadership.

Since its founding, the NSF has grown ever more critical with an annual budget in FY 2019 of $8.1 billion. It supports national discovery, learning, innovation, and research infrastructure to boost US leadership in all aspects of science, technology, engineering, and mathematics (the STEM initiative). In contrast, other federal agencies support research focused on more specific missions, such as health, energy, or defense.

NSF vision and goals. The NSF Strategic Plan for 2018–2022—"Building the Future: Investing in Discovery and Innovation"—states that its goal is to make the United States "a nation that is the global leader in research and innovation." The plan sets three strategic objectives.

1. Expand knowledge in science, engineering, and learning
2. Advance the capability of the nation to meet current and future challenges
3. Enhance NSF's performance of its mission

Research and education priorities. NSF supports basic research and education in all scientific and engineering disciplines. NSF is the funding source for approximately 27 percent of the total federal budget for basic research conducted at US colleges and universities. NSF invests in transformational research to catalyze breakthroughs in national priorities, including clean energy, robotics, nanotechnology, and cybersecurity. NSF's educational programs reflect its long-standing commitment to developing a highly capable and diverse science and engineering workforce prepared to drive discovery and innovation and provide global leadership in the years ahead.

Results. Through the merit review process, NSF funds the best ideas and best people in science and engineering. NSF-supported advances include Doppler radar, the Internet, web browsers, barcodes, magnetic resonance imaging, inkjet printers, computer-aided design systems, artificial retinas, tissue engineering, and other technology-based innovations that spur economic activity and improve the quality of life of all Americans. NSF's accomplishments include the following:

- In FY 2017, more than 350,000 people (researchers, postdoctoral fellows, trainees, teachers, and students) were supported directly by NSF programs.
- As of 2021, 253 Nobel Prize winners, including two 2018 Nobel laureates in chemistry, one in physics, and two in economics, received NSF support at some point in their careers.

Research infrastructure. NSF supports a research infrastructure that provides multiusers with advanced capabilities for measuring, observing, manipulating, and experimenting across the broad science and engineering enterprise. Its portfolio, developed and managed in cooperation with US and international partners, includes research vessels, astronomical observatories, particle accelerators, seismic observatories, US research stations in the Antarctic, unique ecological research sites, large datasets, including long-term survey data, and advanced cyberinfrastructure, including cutting-edge computational and communications networking capabilities.

NSF funding. Considering its sizable budget allocation, the US government certainly takes funding the NSF seriously. Most graduate-level faculty in academia in science and engineering receive their research funding from the NSF. Its funding disbursements in 2020 totaled about $7.8 billion and funded about 8,100 new research grants. It is interesting to note the distribution of NSF funding across the country.

- California (with UC Berkeley, UCLA, UCSD, Stanford, and Caltech): $1 billion
- Massachusetts (with MIT, Harvard, Boston University, and the University of Massachusetts)
- New York (with Columbia, NYU, SUNY, and Cornell): $500 million
- Texas (with UT Austin and Texas A&M): $400 million
- Maryland (with University of Maryland and Johns Hopkins): $400 million.

NSF funding is targeted at states with top research universities and medical schools. There is a direct correlation between the states that receive significant basic research funding to where innovation occurs. Basic research funding (from agencies like the NSF and NIH) together with venture capital funding, which we will review later, make Silicon Valley, Boston, and Austin the innovation hubs in the US.

TRENDS IN R&D FUNDING IN THE US

The United States, through concerted effort, became a global leader in R&D in the twentieth century. Figure 7.1 shows the total US R&D expenditures growth from 1955 to 2019 in current dollars. However, accelerated funding efforts by other nations intent on growing their R&D reduced the US share of global R&D to approximately 29.9 percent in 2019.

Two sectors—business and the federal government—have together accounted for more than 90 percent of US R&D funding since 1955. Federal R&D expenditures as a share of total US R&D expenditures peaked in 1964 at 66.8 percent. Between 1964 and 2000, the federal government's share fell while the business's share rose. In 2000, business accounted for 69.4 percent of US R&D expenditures and the federal government just 25.1 percent. This shift in the composition of R&D funding resulted not from a reduction in federal government R&D expenditures but rather from faster development and growth of business R&D expenditures. From 2000 to 2010, business R&D's share declined from 69.4 percent to 61.0 percent and has risen each year since, reaching an all-time high of 70.7 percent in 2019. From 2010 to 2019, the federal share declined from 31.1 percent to 21.2 percent.

Figure 1. U.S. R&D Expenditures by Source of Funding, 1955-2019
Current dollars, in billions

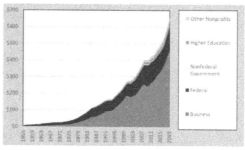

Source: CRS analysis of National Science Foundation, *National Patterns of R&D Resources: 2018–19 Data Update,* NSF 21-325, Table 6, April 9, 2021, https://ncses.nsf.gov/pubs/nsf21325.

Figure 7.1. US R&D expenditures by sources of funding, 1955–2019

TRENDS IN FEDERALLY FUNDED R&D IN THE US

In current dollars, federal funding for R&D grew from $3.5 billion in 1955 to $138.9 billion in 2019, a compound annual growth rate (CAGR) of 5.9 percent. In constant dollars, federal R&D grew by a 2.6 percent CAGR. Figure 7.2 shows federal R&D funding by budget function in constant dollars from 1955 to 2020.

Figure 3. Federal R&D Funding by Budget Function, 1955-2020
Current dollars, in billions

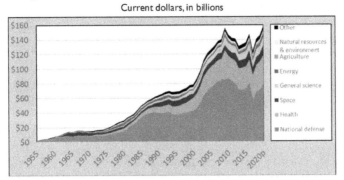

Source: CRS analysis of data from National Science Foundation, *Federal R&D Funding, by Budget Function: Fiscal Years 2019–21*, (NSF 21-315), Table 23, February 22, 2021, https://ncses.nsf.gov/pubs/nsf21315.

Figure 7.2. Federal R&D funding by function from 1955 to 2020

US FEDERAL R&D BUDGET BY FUNCTIONS

The US federal R&D budget for FY 2019 was approximately $139 billion, concentrated in a few departments and agencies (https://trumpwhitehouse.archives.gov). Eight agencies accounted for 97.2 percent.

- Department of Defense (DOD): 40.1 percent with a budget of $55.8 billion (a small part of it is for basic research at DARPA)
- Health and Human Services (HHS): 27.7 percent with a budget of $38.6 billion (NIH is part of this)
- Department of Energy (DOE): 12.8 percent with a budget of $17.8 billion
- National Aeronautics and Space Administration (NASA): 7.7 percent with a budget of $10.7 billion
- National Science Foundation (NSF): 4.5 percent with a budget of $6.3 billion
- Department of Agriculture: 1.9 percent with a budget of $2.7 billion

- Department of Commerce (NIST is part of this): 1.5 percent with a budget of $2.2 billion
- Department of Transportation (DOT): 0.8 percent with a budget of $1.1 billion (FAA is part of this)

BASIC RESEARCH, APPLIED RESEARCH, ADVANCED DEVELOPMENTAL RESEARCH

R&D funding can be understood better by the nature of the work it supports—basic research, applied research, and development.

- Basic research is defined as experimental or theoretical work undertaken primarily to acquire new knowledge of the underlying foundations of phenomena and observable facts without any particular application or use in view.
- Applied research is defined as original investigation undertaken to acquire new knowledge, directed primarily, however, toward a specific, practical aim or objective.
- Developmental research is defined as systematic work, drawing on knowledge gained from research and practical experience, producing additional knowledge directed toward creating new products or processes or improving existing products or processes.

Total estimated US R&D expenditures, which includes federal, state, venture, and corporate funding, in 2019 were $656.0 billion. Broken down, this amount went to the following:

- Basic research: $107.8 billion (16.4 percent)
- Applied research: $124.8 billion (19.0 percent)
- Developmental research: $423.4 billion (64.5 percent)

Table 7.1 shows the distribution of federal, nonfederal, business, and university funding in the US in 2019 across the three categories. The table shows total US R&D expenditures in 2019 by funding sector and nature or character. Notably, federal R&D funding accounts for the largest share of basic research (40.7 percent) while business accounts for the most significant shares of both the applied (55.0 percent) and developmental research (85.5 percent).

Sector	Basic Research		Applied Research		Development		Total	
	Dollars	Percent	Dollars	Percent	Dollars	Percent	Dollars	Percent
Federal Government	$43.9 billion	40.70%	$41.8 billion	33.50%	$53.2 billion	12.60%	$138.9 billion	21.20%
Nonfederal Government	$2.6 billion	2.40%	$1.7 billion	1.40%	$0.6 billion	0.20%	$5.0 billion	0.80%
Business	$33.0 billion	30.60%	$68.7 billion	55.00%	$362.1 billion	85.50%	$463.7 billion	70.70%
Higher Education	$13.6 billion	12.60%	$5.9 billion	4.70%	$2.3 billion	0.50%	$21.8 billion	3.30%
Other Nonprofit	$14.7 billion	13.60%	$6.8 billion	5.50%	$5.1 billion	1.20%	$26.7 billion	4.10%
Total	$107.b billion	100.00%	$124.9 billion	100.00%	$423.4 billion	100%	$656 billion	100.00%

Table 7.1. 2019 distribution of R&D funding in the US in terms of basic, applied, and development

While agencies like the NSF or NIH fund basic research in academia, the US government invests in applied research and development in government labs. In the past, government R&D was funded for defense applications. For example, in the early twentieth century, both the United States and the Soviet Union realized the potential of rocketry as a military weapon and began a variety of experimental programs. The United States started a program with high-altitude atmospheric sounding rockets, one of Robert H. Goddard's early ideas while a professor at Clark University. Later, Goddard was funded by the Smithsonian Institution and other scientific organizations while he experimented with liquid fuel propellants. His work produced a variety of medium- and long-range intercontinental ballistic missiles, which became the starting point for the US space program. Missiles such as the Redstone, Atlas, and Titan would eventually launch astronauts into space.

On October 4, 1957, the world was stunned by the news of an earth-orbiting satellite launched by the Soviet Union. Called Sputnik

I, it was the first successful entry in a race for space between the two superpower nations. Less than a month later, the Soviets followed with the launch of another satellite, carrying a dog named Laika on board. The US realized it needed to aggressively fund space research to contain any threat Russia could commandeer the skies and attack the US with, such as missiles and satellites. A few months after the first Sputnik, the United States followed the Soviet Union with a satellite of its own. Explorer I was launched by the US Army on January 31, 1958. In October of that year, the United States formally organized its space program by creating the National Aeronautics and Space Administration (NASA).

An example of recent R&D funding by NASA is the Space Launch System (SLS), a replacement for the Space Shuttle, which is a super heavy-lift expendable launch vehicle that has been in development since 2011. It replaced the Ares I, Ares V, and Jupiter planned launch vehicles, all canceled while still in development because they were already obsolete. Like those proposals, it is a design derived from the components and technology of the earlier Space Shuttle. The SLS has been funded from 2011 to 2021 at about $1.5 billion per year to about $2.25 billion in 2021 for $18 billion. Boeing is the prime contractor for the SLS system with subcontractors being Pratt & Whitney, Teledyne, and others. The $2.35 billion allocated to the SLS program is about 10 percent of NASA's total budget for fiscal year (FY) 2021, which is $23.3 billion.

TECHNOLOGY READINESS LEVELS IN GOVERNMENT R&D FUNDING

US government labs have created a formal definition of technology readiness levels. Faculty in academia are typically funded by TRL levels 1 and 2 in funding from the US government from agencies like the NSF or NASA. It is the responsibility of government labs, such as NASA Jet Propulsion Lab or the Oak Ridge National Lab, or the Air Force Research Lab, to lead work in TRLs 3–8. Typically, researchers in these government labs interact with faculty in academia on TRLs 1–2 (https://esto.nasa.gov).

- *TRL 1, basic principles observed and reported.* Transition from scientific to applied research. Essential characteristics and behaviors of systems and architectures. Descriptive tools are mathematical formulations or algorithms.
- *TRL 2, technology concept and application formulated.* Applied research. Theory and scientific principles are focused on a specific application area to define the concept. Characteristics of the application are described. Analytical tools are developed for simulation or analysis of the application.
- *TRL 3, analytical and experimental critical function and characteristic proof of concept.* Proof of concept validation. Active research and development (R&D) is initiated with analytical and laboratory studies. Demonstrate technical feasibility using breadboard or brassboard implementations exercised with representative data.
- *TRL 4, component/subsystem validation in a laboratory environment.* Standalone prototyping implementation and test. Integration of technology elements. Experiments with full-scale problems or data sets.
- *TRL 5, system/subsystem/component validation in the appropriate environment.* Thorough prototyping testing in a representative environment. Essential technology elements integrated with reasonably realistic supporting elements. Prototyping implementations conform to the target environment and interfaces.
- *TRL 6, system/subsystem model or prototyping demonstration in a relevant end-to-end environment (ground or space).* Prototyping implementations on full-scale realistic problems. It is partially integrated with existing systems. Limited documentation is available. Engineering feasibility is fully demonstrated in actual system applications.

- *TRL 7, system prototyping demonstration in an operational environment (ground or space).* System prototyping demonstration in a working environment. The system is at or near the scale of the operating system with most functions available for demonstration and test. It is well-integrated with collateral and ancillary systems. Limited documentation is available.

- *TRL 8, actual system completed and mission qualified through test and demonstration in an operational environment (ground or space).* End of system development. They were fully integrated with functional hardware and software systems. Most user documentation, training documentation, and maintenance documentation were completed. All functionality tested in simulated and operational scenarios. Verification and validation (V&V) completed.

- *TRL 9, actual system mission proven through successful mission operations (ground or space).* Fully integrated with operational hardware/software systems. The actual system has been thoroughly demonstrated and tested in its operating environment. All documentation completed. Successful operational experience. Sustaining engineering support in place.

For example, for a space program like the Space Shuttle, Apollo mission, or moon landing, NASA provides R&D funding over ten years. The early work on TRLs 1 and 2 is funded in academia, but most of the funding is invested in TRLs 3 through 8. These funds are disbursed to companies like Boeing, Northrop Grumman, or General Dynamics, who build the rockets for space missions.

In recent years, much of the R&D funding for space missions has been spent by private companies, such as SpaceX (Elon Musk's company), Virgin Galactic (Richard Branson's company), and Blue Origin (Jeff Bezos's company). These companies are leveraging the large amounts of basic R&D funding invested by NASA from over the past two decades and are now investing themselves in commercial space travel. Yet companies like these spawn innovation in many directions, which leads to more start-ups providing the needed technologies.

GOVERNMENT PROGRAMS TO FUND
START-UPS: SBIR AND STTR

While most start-up companies get their funding from seed investors and venture capitalists, the US government has programs such as Small Business Innovation Research (SBIR) and Small Business Technology Transfer (STTR). The Small Business Innovation Research (or SBIR) program is a US government program coordinated by the Small Business Administration intended to help certain small businesses conduct research and development (R&D). Funding takes the form of contracts or grants. A recipient's projects' commercial potential must meet specific US government R&D needs.

The SBIR program was created to "support scientific excellence and technological innovation through the investment of federal research funds in critical American priorities to build a strong national economy...one business at a time." In the words of program founder Roland Tibbetts, "To provide funding for some of the best early-stage innovation ideas—ideas that, however promising, are still too high risk for private investors, including venture capital firms." For the SBIR program, the term "small business" is defined as a for-profit business with fewer than five hundred employees and owned by one or more individuals who are citizens of or permanent resident aliens in the US.

Funds are obtained by allocating a certain percentage of the total extramural (R&D) budgets of the eleven federal agencies with over $100 million in research budgets. Approximately $2.5 billion is awarded through this program each year. The DoD is the largest agency in this program, administering roughly $1 billion in SBIR grants annually. Over half of the DoD awards are to firms with fewer than twenty-five people, and a third are to firms with fewer than ten. One-fifth is minority or women-owned businesses. Historically, a quarter of the companies receiving grants are first-time recipients. Besides the DoD, similar programs are administered by the National Institutes of Health, the National Science Foundation, the Department of Agriculture, and others.

Small Business Technology Transfer (STTR) is an essential small business program that expands federal innovation research and development funding opportunities. Central to the program is extending the public/private sector partnership to include joint venture opportunities for small businesses and the nation's premier nonprofit research institutions, namely universities. STTR's most important role is to foster the innovation necessary to meet the nation's scientific and technological challenges in the twenty-first century.

There is, therefore, a continuum of R&D funding from the federal government (with agencies such as the NSF, NIH, and DARPA) to universities and government labs supporting basic research to the SBIR and STTR programs to fund the start-up companies that can take these basic research prototypes from academia into commercial products and innovation. These start-ups often raise future funding through venture capitalists, which will be explained in a later section.

FUNDING TO SUPPORT INNOVATION AND TECHNOLOGY TRANSFER

It is well-known that there seems to be a valley of death from the basic research in academia and the R&D needed to build actual hardware and software products in the industry. While funding exists at NSF and NASA for the basic R&D (TRL levels 1 and 2) that university professors apply for funding, these R&D funds result in very preliminary prototypes of hardware and software products. The professor and graduate students often require two to three years of more work to take that prototype into a product. Funding agencies like NSF or NIH have typically not funded such technology transfer work.

Venture capitalists fund development work in start-ups but do not fund long-term R&D. VCs want the start-up founder to have built some hardware or software prototypes of their product before investing in the start-up. This is the funding gap that innovation leaders have been discussing recently. This point was highlighted in a recent National Academy of Engineering workshop held in June 2021 on the future of teaching, research, and innovation in the US.

NSF Engineering Research Centers

The National Science Foundation had a program called Engineering Research Centers (https://nsf.gov). The NSF Engineering Research Center (ERC) program supports convergent research, education, and technology translation at US universities that lead to substantial societal impacts. Each ERC has interacting foundational components beyond the research project, including engineering workforce development at all participant stages, a culture of diversity and inclusion where all participants gain the mutual benefit, and value creation within an innovation ecosystem that will outlast the lifetime of the ERC.

Since the program's start in 1985, NSF has funded seventy-five ERCs throughout the United States. NSF supports each center for up to ten years. This investment has led to many successes.

- more than 200 spinoff companies
- more than 850 patents
- more than 13,500 total bachelors, masters, and doctoral degrees to ERC students
- numerous research outcomes enabling new technologies

Over the years, the ERC program has adapted to meet the nation's future workforce and technological needs. In late fiscal year (FY) 2020, NSF launched the fourth generation of centers, known as Gen-4 ERCs. NSF has created the Industry-University Cooperative Research Centers (IUCRC) to encourage more breakthrough research by enabling close and sustained engagement between industry innovators, world-class academic teams, and government agencies.

Most recently, NSF has started discussing creating innovation centers in areas such as future of Wireless for 5G and 6G. A workshop managed by NSF and the National Academy of Engineering (NAE) in June 2021 discussed these concepts. Such a global R&D center will bring together university professors and graduate students with industry leaders and entrepreneurs. Professors will develop new intellectual property on a technology platform like 6G, and entrepreneurs will try to establish businesses out of the technology.

R&D Funding in the Large Companies

Business funding of R&D, measured in current dollars, has grown nearly every year since 1955. In current dollars, business-funded R&D grew from $2.2 billion in 1955 to $463.7 billion in 2019 for a compound annual growth rate of 8.5 percent. In constant dollars, business-funded R&D grew by a 5.1% CAGR.

Research and development investments in large public companies are paid by the CEO and the board of those companies. When one looks at the financial results of any company, one can find the R&D investment. The R&D investment of large computer companies, like HP, Dell, or IBM, or automotive companies, like Ford or GM, or aerospace companies, like Boeing or Airbus, is about 2–5 percent of revenue. This is because their R&D leverages that of their suppliers. An example is when Ford/GM assembles a car with ten thousand parts that are sourced from hundreds of OEM suppliers (brakes, radios, wheels, etc.), such as Bosch, Continental, Delphi, or Aptiv, who themselves invest in their own R&D. An aircraft company like Boeing gets their jet engines from GE, Rolls-Royce, or Pratt & Whitney. Hence, they are leveraging the R&D of these suppliers.

On the other hand, the R&D investment of software companies as a percentage of revenue is much higher. For example, as CTO of Ansys, the company invested about $300 million in R&D in 2020 on revenue of about $2 billion (about 15 percent of revenue). Other software companies, like Microsoft, Oracle, SAP, and Adobe, invest about 15–20 percent of their revenue in R&D.

Similarly, semiconductor chip companies, like Intel, Nvidia, Qualcomm, and Broadcom, invest about 20 percent of their revenue in R&D because they manufacture the chips themselves and, therefore, are not leveraging the R&D of their suppliers. For example, a chip company like Nvidia may include IP from a soft-core from ARM on a system or processor chip. When this occurs, they will leverage their R&D investment against the supplier who provided the IP. Both companies benefit from this leveraging.

European Union Funding

The European Union (EU) offered support to R&D projects during the 2014–2020 funding period in the form of its Framework Programme for Research and Innovation, Horizon 2020. With a budget of more than €77 billion, Horizon 2020 is the world's largest funding program for research and innovation. Horizon 2020 support is usually provided to R&D projects operating on a transnational level with at least three project partners from different European countries. Support is allocated in the form of grants covering 100 percent of the R&D project expenditures and 70 percent of the innovation project expenditures plus a 25 percent flat fee for indirect project costs (https://ec.europa.eu).

Horizon 2020 funds were available in the following areas: agriculture and forestry, bio-based industries, biotechnology, energy, environment and climate action, food and healthy diet, health, ICT research and innovation, international cooperation, key enabling technologies, oceans and seas, plastics, raw materials, research infrastructures, security, SMEs, social sciences and humanities, society, space, European research era, and Transport.

Horizon Europe, the world's largest multinational research and innovation program, has issued its first call for grant applications in March 2021. Over the next seven years (2021–2027), the European Union's giant research-spending scheme will distribute a record €95.5 billion (US$116 billion), including €5.4 billion from a COVID-19 recovery fund, to basic science projects and cross-border research collaborations to be carried out by tens of thousands of researchers across twenty-seven member states and more than a dozen other countries. The fifteen older EU countries (EU-15) consisted of countries such as United Kingdom, Germany, France, Spain, Denmark, Italy, Belgium, and Sweden and dominated collaborated research projects in Horizon 2020. But now they are combined with the thirteen newer EU countries (EU-13), which consisted of countries such as Bulgaria, Estonia, Slovenia, Slovakia, Poland, and Hungary, as well as countries that are not members of the EU, such as Switzerland and Israel.

Horizon Europe is an evolution of the EU's previous research programs. Like its predecessor, Horizon 2020, which ran from 2014 to 2020, it is a mixed bag of funding schemes. It includes grants for individual scientists in all fields and for large multinational collaborations covering grand societal challenges, such as health, climate change, and the digital revolution. But Horizon Europe also includes new elements that reflect increasing attention to open science, equality, interdisciplinary research, and practical applications. Here, *Nature* takes a look at some of the major changes.

The most anticipated change in Horizon Europe is the introduction of heavily financed, high-priority missions. About EUR 4.5 billion is earmarked for five areas: climate change; cancer; oceans and other bodies of water; smart cities; and soil and food.

In both scope and ambition, the missions go far beyond normal research collaboration, and will incorporate tools and resources from flanking EU programs such as the Common Agricultural Policy, which administers farming subsidies, and EU initiatives for developing infrastructure in poorer regions. The idea is to get researchers, businesses and governments to pool their skills towards a common goal, selected with input from the public.

The missions replace the European Flagships EUR 1-billion programs that focused on particular areas of research, such as graphene or the human brain. The European Commission says that missions will mirror the spirit of the European Green Deal plan for a sustainable economy, Europe's Beating Cancer Plan or the United Nations Sustainable Development Goals. But many of the details remain to be determined. Over the next few months, mission boards appointed by the commission must lay out specific goals, research needs and indicators for measuring impact. First calls for proposals are expected by the end of this year.

Although much attention has been focused on the introduction of missions, they are only a relatively small part of the new program. Basic science will continue to be a centrepiece of European research. Between 2021 and 2027, the EU's premier funding agency for basic research, the European Research Council (ERC), will divide EUR 16 billion among researchers at various career levels, an increase of more than 20% compared to Horizon 2020. Non-EU countries associated to Horizon Europe are expected to contribute an extra roughly EUR 4 billion, depending on their level of participation. Associates include research-intensive nations such as Israel, Switzerland and the United Kingdom—which left the bloc at the beginning of 2021, but has signed a deal to allow its scientists, research organizations and companies to participate in Horizon Europe.

The ERC issued its first round of calls for starting grants under Horizon Europe on March 1, 202. Competition for ERC grants—which assign up to EUR 2.5 million for 5 years to an individual investigator—has historically been tough, with an acceptance rate of around 12%, but the larger pot of money could mean that more scientists get funded. Another important change is that researchers at international organizations headquartered in the European Union will now be able to apply for these grants. Around 80 such organizations were previously excluded from the scheme.

Horizon Europe will also aim to strengthen support for applied research with economic benefits. To this end, the European Commission has established the European Innovation Council (EIC), a new funding agency aimed at facilitating the transfer of inventions and research into goods and services.

Around EUR 10 billion is earmarked for the EIC, to be divided between three types of grant. In an early "pathfinder" phase, researchers can get support to develop ideas that have commercial potential. A second, "fast track to innovation" phase will support the transition of promising results to market.

Finally, after market launch, entrepreneurs will be able to request EIC "accelerator" support—including grants, loans and coaching services—to expand their businesses. (The accelerator programme was excluded from the UK-EU trade deal, so UK-based researchers will not be eligible.)

The idea is that recipients of ERC proof-of-concept grants will also be able to apply for EIC support. "Combining support from the two agencies is a wonderful opportunity to unlock commercial potential of basic science," says Fischer.

Horizon Europe is expected to mandate that grant recipients publish their results according to the principles of open science. In particular, immediate open-access publishing will become mandatory for all recipients of Horizon Europe research grants, including those from the ERC. Scientists will be required to post an accepted, peer-reviewed version of their papers online at a trusted repository. Grants will cover publishing costs for pure open-access journals, but not for hybrid publications. Authors must also retain intellectual-property rights for their papers.

The commission will encourage EU-funded scientists to post their papers on Open Research Europe, an open-access platform that will formally launch in March. Works submitted on the platform, run by the London-based open-science publisher F1000 Research, will be posted immediately and cannot be published elsewhere. Articles will be subject to open peer review, meaning that the reviews and reviewers' names will be openly available, and the commission will cover publication costs.

Scientists will also need to make sure that any research data they generate are preserved and made available for reuse by others. Horizon Europe will require participants to submit a data-management plan, in line with the FAIR principles (findability, accessibility, interoperability and reusability), within six months of completing a research project, although exceptions may be granted where business secrets or sensitive personal data are involved. A partnership of research and data-service organizations across Europe is developing the European Open Science Cloud, a freely accessible virtual repository for data from all research that is publicly funded, whether by a participating state or by the EU.

GLOBAL R&D FUNDING

Since the creation of the National Science Foundation and basic research funding in the USA, other countries followed suit, and many countries now have strong government funding programs for research and development. While the US used to be the largest investor in R&D in the world until a few years ago, China has now taken the lead. Typically, countries that invest a large share of their

GDP in R&D do so to support more innovation. Among the top ten countries, South Korea has the highest R&D investment percentage of GDP.

Table 7.2 shows the R&D funding by countries and its relationship to the gross domestic product (GDP). Here are a few points to note.

- China spends $621 billion in R&D (2 percent of GDP), the highest total R&D.
- US spends $598 billion in R&D (2.9 percent of GDP).
- Japan spends $182 billion in R&D (3.5 percent of GDP).
- Germany spends $127 billion in R&D (2.84 percent of GDP).
- India spends $93 billion in R&D (0.86 percent of GDP).
- South Korea spends $91 billion in R&D (4.35 percent), highest percent of GDP.

Top Ten	Country	GDP PPP USD Billion	R&D % of GDP	2020 Estimated GERD PPP USD Billion	GDP PPP USD Billion	2021 Forecast R&D % of GDP	GERD PPP USD Billion
1	China	29,010	1.98%	574	31,389	1.98%	621
2	US	20,145	2.88%	580	20,789	2.88%	598
3	Japan	5,174	3.50%	181	5,210	3.50%	182
4	Germany	4,283	2.84%	121	4,480	2.84%	127
5	India	9,991	0.86%	85	10,870	0.86%	93
6	South Korea	2,002	4.35%	87	2,102	4.35%	91
7	France	2,864	2.25%	64	2,979	2.25%	67
8	Russia	3,927	1.50%	58	4,037	1.50%	60
9	United Kingdom	2,876	1.73%	49	2,983	1.73%	51
10	Brazil	3,199	1.16%	37	3,288	1.16%	38

Table 7.2. Annual research and development funding around the world

The world spends $2.5 trillion in R&D across all industries: high-tech, $440 billion; health care, $240 billion; automotive,

$170 billion; aerospace and defense, $32 billion. This is shown in figure 7.3.

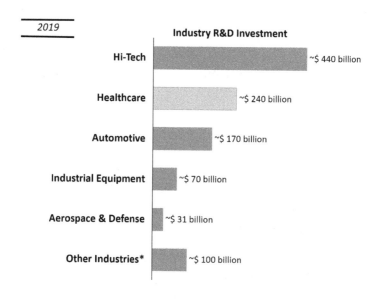

Figure 7.3. Global R&D spending by verticals

ENGINEERING R&D FUNDING BY LARGE COMPANIES AROUND THE WORLD

Zinnov published a report in 2021 on the total amount of engineering research and development funding by large companies across all industries during 2019–2023 (www.zinnov.com). The total R&D funding was about $1,466 billion in 2019 and is expected to grow to $1,928 billion by 2023. The interesting point to note in this study is that the legacy engineering R&D spent was about $997 billion in 2019, growing to $1,017 billion by 2023. However, digital engineering spending will increase from $469 billion to $911 billion. We will discuss digital technologies (AI/ML, IoT, Cloud, Analytics, etc.) to drive product innovation in chapter 8.

Let us look in detail at the digital engineering spend in different industries. For example, manufacturing of automotive, industrial, and pharmaceutical products are investing in digital R&D areas, such as connected vehicles, wearables, industry 4.0 and IoT technologies, autonomous driving, remote patient monitoring, and intelligent services. High-tech industries, such as software, telecommunications, and consumer electronics, invest in digital R&D areas, such as AI/ML, 5G, IoT, cybersecurity, software-defined networking, and data centers. Service-led verticals, such as banking and financial services, retail, and health care, invest in digital R&D areas, such as robotic advisory, contactless payment, fraud detection, and augmented reality / virtual reality.

The distribution of the $1,928 billion in R&D spending in companies in 2023 across the world is interesting. The North American R&D spend the largest with about $972 billion, of which $576 billion is expected to be in digital engineering spend and $395 billion will be on legacy R&D spend. The European R&D spend is expected to be about $467 billion (digital engineering will be $148 billion, and legacy spending will be $319 billion). Finally, the Asia-Pacific R&D spend is expected to be about $471 billion (with the digital engineering spend of $180 billion and legacy R&D spend of $290 billion). These numbers should point to where there are opportunities for digital technologies and product innovation in the world. These digital technologies will be described in chapter 8.

FUNDING FOR START-UP COMPANIES

As discussed in chapter 3, start-up companies are funded by three types of investors in different stages of investment: seed or angel investors, venture capitalists, and large companies (sometimes mitigated because of trade-offs in investments by strategic investors or conflict with exit target price).

A start-up business presents a higher risk investment than a mature business. The mature business has assets for collateral and a known cash flow, allowing investors and lenders to assess business risk with more caution and attention to performance. By its nature, the risk profile of a start-up business is much more difficult to determine. The importance of focusing on early-stage and expansion-stage financing as well as the various risk/reward phases within each stage is to understand the unique business and financing characteristics that determine the success or failure of the investment.

The seed phase, also known as the precommercialization stage, is the proof-of-concept stage in which a business idea is tested for its viability. The basic research may have been completed, but the commercial potential is still unproven. The following is to review the discussion in chapter 3: The prelaunch phase occurs after the decision has been made to move forward with the business's creation. In this phase, all the foundational aspects and characteristics of the business are created.

During the start-up phase (Series A), also known as the launch phase, production is initiated, and sales occur. It is characterized by hiring employees and establishing the products in the marketplace. First-stage financing (Series B), also known as the ramp-up phase, is the final phase in early-stage financing. It is characterized by ramping up production and sales. Ramping up the business by increasing sales is an indication of success because the company's business model is being validated.

Second-stage financing (Series C) follows first-stage financing and provides working capital for the initial expansion of a business producing and shipping products and has growing accounts receivable and inventories. Although the company has made progress, there are instances in which it may not yet be profitable. Third-stage financing, or mezzanine stage (Series D), is provided for significant expansion of a company with an increased sales volume and is profitable. These funds are used for further plant expansion, marketing, working capital, or improved product development. The company reaches profitability and is ready for exit. Exit strategies take on different forms, but investors will want to know this. While they are rooting for and supporting your business, they are also looking for a return on their investment.

Table 7.3 shows an example start-up business plan for an enterprise software start-up that will grow its revenue to $100 million over five years. The business plan for the start-up with three stages of investment—$5 million, $10 million, and $20 million and growing to $100 million in revenue in five years—is shown. The head count growth for the company is planned to grow from fifteen employees in year one to two hundred in year five. Figure 7.4 shows the business plan.

	Year 1	Year 2	Year 3	Year 4	Year 5
Units					
Software Product 1 SAAS	10	20	100	300	800
Software Product 2 SAAS		10	20	150	300
Software Product 3 SAAS		10	30	100	250
Unit Pricing					
Software Product 1 SAAS	$100,000	$100,000	$100,000	$100,000	$100,000
Software Product 2 SAAS	$50,000	$50,000	$50,000	$50,000	$50,000
Software Product 3 SAAS	$20,000	$20,000	$20,000	$20,000	$20,000
Revenue					
Software Product 1 SAAS	$1,000,000	$2,000,000	$10,000,000	$30,000,000	$80,000,000
Software Product 2 SAAS	$0	$500,000	$1,000,000	$7,500,000	$15,000,000
Software Product 3 SAAS	$0	$200,000	$600,000	$2,000,000	$5,000,000
Total Revenue	$1,000,000	$2,700,000	$11,600,000	$39,500,000	$100,000,000
Head Count	Year 1	Year 2	Year 3	Year 4	Year 5
Head Count—Management	4	6	7	8	10
Head Count—Employees	11	34	53	122	190
Total Head Count	15	40	60	130	200
	Year 1	Year 2	Year 3	Year 4	Year 5
Revenues and Other Income	$1,031,107	$2,792,719	$11,682,139	$40,419,984	$101,242,437
Expenses	$1,321,439	$12,176,912	$18,602,685	$31,206,921	$52,114,460
Equity Capital	$5,000,000	$10,000,000	$20,000,000	$0	$0
Ending Cash Balance	$4,699,323	$5,320,232	$18,399,686	$24,848,749	$59,238,727

Table 7.3. Sample start-up business plan

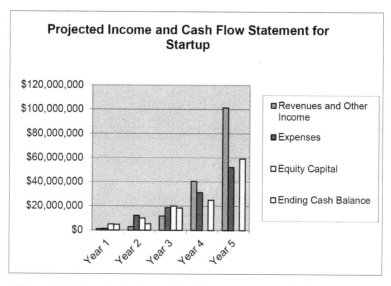

Figure 7.4. Sample business plan for a start-up with three stages of investment—Series A, $5 million; Series B, $10 million; and Series C, $20 million—and growing to $100 million in revenue in five years. The head count grows from fifteen to two hundred people in over five years.

GLOBAL VENTURE FUNDING FOR START-UP COMPANIES

Global venture capital (VC) funding is about $300 billion per year. Global VC funding hit an all-time high in the first half of 2021 with about $288 billion. Global VC investments are tracked by organizations such as Crunchbase (www.crunchbase.com). Some recent data has shown that the global venture funding in the first half of 2021 surged by 61 percent compared to the prior peak of $179 billion in the second half of 2020. That was up 95 percent compared with the first half of 2020, when VC investors deployed $148 billion globally. Table 7.4 shows the global VC funding trend over the past few years, including the distribution by late-stage and early-stage investments.

Stages of VC Funding	H1 2017	H2 2017	H1 2018	H2 2018	H1 2019	H2 2019	H1 2020	H2 2020	H1 2021
Angel/Seed (Billion)	10	14	15	17	15	15	15	18	29
Early-Stage (Billion)	35	49	53	60	53	53	52	63	101
Late-Stage (Billion)	40	56	60	68	60	61	59	72	115
Technology Growth (Billion)	15	21	23	26	23	23	22	27	43
Total (Billion)	100	140	150	170	150	152	148	179	288

Table 7.4. Global venture funding trends from 2017–2021 with angel/seed, early-stage, late-stage, and growth funding distribution (courtesy of www.crunchbase.com)

A more significant number of those venture-backed companies have gone public, valued above $10 billion in the first half of 2021, just halfway in, than in 2020. And already, by H1 of 2021, another 250 companies joined the Crunchbase Unicorn Board compared to the 161 new unicorns for the whole of 2020 (a unicorn is defined as a company with a valuation of at least $1 billion).

FUTURE FUNDING MODELS

In the past, the federal government funded universities and government labs, CEOs and the boards supported large companies' R&D, and venture capitalists invested in start-up companies. In the future, we will see all kinds of cross-relationship funding between government, private enterprise, and VCs. This is shown in figure 7.5.

R&D Ecosystem

FUNDING: R&D is funded by three groups
- Federal government, e.g. US spends $6 billion in Basic Research at National Science Foundation, Department of Defense, EU
- Venture Capitalists, providing Series A funding to startup companies.e.g. Kleiner Perkins, Norwest Ventures
- CEOs and Boards of Companies as Corporate R&D to fund growth, CUBIC, Cray, HP, ABB, etc.

TALENT: R&D is performed by four groups
- Academia, professors and graduate students at universities like MIT, Berkeley, Stanford, Illinois, ETH
- Researchers at the government National Labs, e.g. Lawrence Livermore National Labs, Argonne National Labs, Sandia Labs
- Entrepreneurs working for startup companies
- R&D engineers working for larger establishes companies like CUBIC, Cray, HP, ABB, Schneider Electric

OPEN INNOVATION encourages collaboration between different groups (NSF ICURC Funding, DOD SBIR Grants)

Figure 7.5. Funding models in the past and future
for academia, start-ups, and large companies

INNOVATIVE FUNDING MODELS FOR LARGE COMPANIES IN THE TWENTY-FIRST CENTURY

In the past, large companies commonly funded research in all three horizons. Many of them had a central research lab, as described in chapter 4. These CRLs would fund work conducted in academia, where they had strong research ties. Such companies funded with the intent of facilitating a technology transfer to make commercial products and services. But more recently, owing to increased pressure on corporate profit margins and the push for short-term benefits from innovation work, many companies have had to reduce funding for their CRLs.

That has resulted in the formation of research consortia that pool resources among multiple companies in a common development area, which then funds one or more universities to pursue the research. Two examples of successful consortia-based research programs are the Semiconductor Research Corporation (SRC) and SEMATECH, which were discussed in chapter 7.

Semiconductor Research Corporation

SRC was founded in 1982 in the North Carolina Research Triangle. It is the world's leading nonprofit, three-point industry/government/academia microelectronics research consortium funding academic research tasks selected and directed by 20 semiconductor industry companies, three government agencies, and over 100 universities. Its three program concentrations have elicited 55 research topics and over 500 research projects conducted by 1,200 SRC-sponsored undergraduate and graduate students. By pooling, the SRC research model accelerates growth into new markets and new product technologies by pooling industry and government funds to create much larger and more effective research programs than could be done alone.

SRC graduates possess a clear competitive edge in high-tech hiring markets because they have worked to solve some of the deepest technical challenges—for example, nanosheets for GAA transistors, high-k dielectrics, copper interconnects, FinFET, scalable flash memory, MRAM, EDA design, simulation, verification tools, and millimeter-wave CMOS circuit design. SRC has a rich history of success. Since 1982, SRC has funded over $2 billion of research, has built a semiconductor workforce by sponsoring over 12,000 graduate students, and has provided over 700 patents to member companies.

Sematech

SEMATECH (Semiconductor Manufacturing Technology) is a nonprofit consortium that performs research and development to advance chip manufacturing. SEMATECH has broad engagement with various sectors of the R&D community, including chipmakers, equipment and material suppliers, universities, research institutes, and government partners. The group is funded by member dues. SEMATECH was conceived in 1986, formed in 1987, and began operating in Austin, Texas, in 1988 as a partnership between the US government and fourteen US-based semiconductor manufacturers to solve common manufacturing problems and regain competitiveness for the US semiconductor industry, which had been surpassed by Japanese industry in the mid-1980s. SEMATECH was funded over five years by public subsidies coming from the US Department of Defense via the Defense Advanced Research Projects Agency (DARPA) for a total of $500 million.

SEMATECH conducts research on the technical challenges and costs associated with developing new materials, processes, and equipment for semiconductor manufacturing. Advanced technology programs focus on EUV lithography, including photomask blank and photoresist development, materials and emerging technologies for device structures, metrology, manufacturing, and environment and safety issues.

CONCLUSION

This chapter addressed the critical funding issues for innovation. The most basic research or discovery happens in academia and is funded by the government. While government funding for innovation used to be most prevalent, there has been a substantial rise in businesses supporting their own R&D. Also strengthening is R&D funding around the world, as China, India, and South Korea are becoming more innovative in their businesses. It will come as no surprise that VC funding trends around the world usually begin in the US. What remains a constant is a need for new ideas and start-up companies, which have obtained their funding most often from seed and angel investors and venture capitalists. However, government small business funding agencies and large companies looking for strategic investments are on the rise.

We tried to answer some questions in this chapter.

1. *If I am an entrepreneur, how can I learn about government programs for funding my innovation?* We saw that the primary funding source for start-ups is venture capitalists and large strategic investors. By 2021, the amount of VC fund-

ing for start-ups globally was about $300 billion. However, there are programs like the SBIR or STTR from the US government for early-stage start-ups with about $3 billion per year available for entrepreneurs.

2. *If I am a program manager at NSF or DARPA, how can I encourage more innovation?* Program managers at NSF and DARPA can encourage their academic partners to see the research end with publications and patents and see if they can transfer the results of their research into larger companies or start-ups. They can connect these researchers to potential SBIR and STTR programs.

3. *How do I partner with governmental agencies if I am a large company?* Many large funding agencies, like NSF, NASA, and DARPA, are encouraging more technology transfers to companies. These program managers can facilitate the researchers in academia to work with larger companies so that their technologies are transferred.

AUTHOR'S PERSONAL EXPERIENCE WITH FUNDING IN ACADEMIA, START-UPS, AND LARGE COMPANIES

The following is Prith's personal journey with funding in academia, start-ups, and the corporate world.

When I was a PhD student at the University of Illinois from 1982 to 1984, my PhD research was funded by the SRC and by an IBM graduate fellowship. When I subsequently became a professor at the University of Illinois, my research was funded by the SRC from 1985 to 1996.

When I was a professor, department chairman, and dean at the University of Illinois Urbana-Champaign (1985–1996), Northwestern University (1996–2004), and University of Illinois Chicago (2004–2007), I received more than $20 million of research funding from government agencies, such as the National Science Foundation, NASA, DARPA, Office of Naval Research, and Air Force Research Lab, and from industry, such as Semiconductor

Research Corporation, Intel, IBM, and HP. This research funding allowed me to support more than fifty graduate students for their PhD and MS theses and resulted in more than 350 publications in journals and conferences.

When I founded AccelChip in 2000, I received about $2.3 million of Series A funding from Arch Venture Partners and seed investors, $5 million of Series B funding from Interwest and Greylock Partners in 2003, and $6 million of Series C funding from Interwest and Greylock Partners as well in 2005. This VC funding allowed me to hire more than thirty employees and grow the company to about $5 million in revenue. AccelChip was acquired by Xilinx in 2006.

When I founded Binachip in 2006, I received SBIR and STTR funding from the National Science Foundation, NASA, and DARPA. Binachip was acquired by Quickstream in 2011.

When I was SVP and director of HP Labs during 2007–2012, the annual revenue of HP (the parent company) was about $120 billion, and the R&D investment was about $3.2 billion (about 3 percent of revenue). I managed a team of about six hundred researchers in HP Labs with an annual budget of about $150 million. When I was EVP and CTO of ABB during 2013–2014, the total company revenue in 2013 was about $40 billion, and the R&D investment was $2 billion (about 5 percent of revenue). As CTO, I was responsible for setting the technical direction of about eight thousand engineers in the company with an annual R&D budget of about $2 billion.

When I was EVP and CTO of Schneider Electric during 2015–2017, the total revenue was $25 billion, and the R&D investment was $1.3 billion (about 5 percent of revenue). As CTO, I was responsible for setting the technical direction of about 11,000 engineers in the company with an annual R&D budget of $1.3 billion.

I have been CTO of Ansys since 2018. The revenue of Ansys is about $2 billion in 2021 with an R&D investment of $300 million (about 15 percent of revenue). As CTO I am responsible for setting the technical direction of two thousand engineers with an annual R&D budget of $300 million.

CHAPTER 8

Digital Technologies to Drive Product Innovation

Interview: Gamiel Gran, Mayfield, creator of CXO podcasts

Gamiel has a unique passion for helping drive corporate innovation and grow Mayfield's early-stage portfolio. He runs the business development function for Mayfield and focuses specifically on accelerating product-market fit and early customer adoption for Mayfield's investments. He and his team have built a global network of CXOs called the Mayfield Innovation Network, which is made up of CIOs, CTOs, CISOs, and business leaders from across all industries who need access to new ideas to compete in their markets. This is a highly engaged global network whose members join CXO Insight forums and CXO of the Future podcasts and provide CXO Priorities informal reports.

Gamiel brings more than twenty-five years of operational and venture capital experience to the Mayfield team. He previously served as chief strategy officer for SOASTA (acquired by Akamai). He was responsible for ongoing operational improvements in sales, marketing channels, and strategic partnerships, corporate development, and investment support. Gamiel was also a partner at Sierra Ventures, responsible for leading the Sierra CIO summit attended by over 150 global CIOs for eight years. He has also held executive leadership roles at IBM, Oracle, BEA (acquired by Oracle), Appcelerator (developed by Axway), and Cassatt (acquired by CA). Gamiel is a California native, father of three, and husband of more than thirty years. He loves to give back as a volunteer, focusing on education. He is currently leading an effort as chair of the Career Services Advisory Council at Cal Poly.

INTERVIEWER. Gamiel, thank you very much for agreeing to interview for my book *The Innovation Factory*. Can you provide a quick overview of Mayfield, the size of its funds, what verticals you are investing in these days, and some example portfolio companies?

INTERVIEWEE. Mayfield is a venture capital firm with a fifty-year track record of investing at the inception stage in iconic enterprise, consumer, and engineering biology companies. We're guided by our people first philosophy and are proud to have served as early investors to over 500 companies, leading to 119 IPOs and over 200 M&As.

At Mayfield, our motto is people first. Our investment team operates from a shared set of beliefs and partners with entrepreneurs pursuing big ideas at the founding stage. We are former operators who invest at the inception stage of companies (seed and Series A with check sizes ranging from $500,000–$3 million for seed and $4–$12 million for Series A) with selective investments in companies at Series B and beyond. We are currently investing out of our sixteenth early-stage fund, the $475 million Mayfield XVI for inception stage companies, and our Select funds—the $400 million Select and Select II funds for companies at Series B and beyond. We currently have $2.2 billion under management.

INTERVIEWER. How has the role of venture capitalists changed in the past decade? Have angel investors and seed investors created new expectations for Series A and Series B and Series C VCs? How about investment from firms such as SoftBank? What is the current state of the outlook of VC funding in 2021? Is it increasing, decreasing, or flat?

INTERVIEWEE. The venture capital market is facing some of the most significant changes in its model ever. Some fifty-plus years ago, when Mayfield started, there were fewer VC firms with minimal funds and allocations to start-ups. Funding rounds were $500,000 to $3 million in size, and VC firms' overall funds were in the sub-$100 million range. Fast-forward to today, there are thousands of VC firms and many who raise multibillion-dollar funds. The returns from VC funds that typically return two to four times the financial returns compared to treasury bonds, real estate, or public equities are why more funding continues to be allocated to venture. This has caused new entrants to join the VC market, such as sovereign wealth funds, private equity funds, corporate venture funds, and private family offices. Therefore, there are more dollars chasing deals today than ever. It's an excellent time for an entrepreneur. Mayfield remains focused on early-stage investing, both seed and Series A, and across the enterprise, SaaS, consumer, and health/biology sectors.

INTERVIEWER. I will be interviewing you for chapter 8 in my book, dealing with some key technology trends that will drive product and process innovation in the twenty-first century. These technologies include semiconductors and nanotechnology, photonics and optical interconnects, quantum computing, wireless communications, additive manufacturing, virtual reality / augmented reality, blockchains, cybersecurity, high-performance computing, cloud computing, AI / machine learning, Internet of Things (IoT), and platforms. Do you agree with these technology trends? What are some top three to five technology trends you are personally excited about? Are there some other technology trends we should add to this list?

INTERVIEWEE. You have a great list, and I agree that these are pretty relevant topics. I would add that business application, provided as SaaS offerings that support sales, marketing, finance, HR, support, etc., evolve to no-code solutions. And lastly, the B2B software market has witnessed a wholesale evolution in how products are sold. The term PLG, or product-led growth, is the standard expectation for a sold product. This is the outcome of years of open-source, developer-friendly tools adopted virally into an organization as free or freemium products. The products are designed to sell themselves, whereby limited sales or marketing resources are needed to drive user adoption. Still, instead, the out-of-the-box experience for the user is elegant and impactful.

INTERVIEWER. Can you speak about some of your portfolio companies in Mayfield related to AI / machine learning?

INTERVIEWEE. We believe AI is an enabling technology that can augment manual, human tasks and drive breakthrough productivity improvements. We believe in the science of new algorithms, purpose-built to solve complex problems, and that leveraging extensive data sets is the best way to view the AI/ML market. We have invested in solutions that leverage AI in this form across many markets. Here below are some examples.

- Balbix—automate cybersecurity posture, continuously analyzes threat surface risk
- Barbie—develops ID verification software that automates data collection to spot fraud instantly

- BigPanda—event correlation and automation, powered by AIOps
- Mirvie—liquid biopsy to predict and prevent pregnancy complications for mom and baby
- Securiti.ai—AI-powered cybersecurity and data protection infrastructure for PrivacyOps to automate privacy compliance, enabling enterprises to give rights to people on their data, be responsible custodians of people's data, comply with global privacy regulations, and bolster their brand
- Qventus—the leader in AI-powered health care operations, optimizes operational decisions in hospitals in real-time.
- SeekOut—AI-enabled Talent 360 platform to provide recruiters/talent teams with a competitive advantage in recruiting hard-to-find and diverse talent.
- ShiftLeft—delivers a new model for protecting cloud or data center hosted software by understanding the Secure DNA of each new version of any application or microservice and limiting its attack surface at runtime

INTERVIEWER. Can you speak about some of your portfolio companies in Mayfield related to platforms? Every company, like GE, ABB, and Schneider Electric, is creating a platform to drive their business. Is this a new trend?

INTERVIEWEE. The definition of a platform is often misused. It should include technologies that others can build on top of or leverage for extended use cases, providing the core function for the business need. Platform companies can create new markets but must be designed to allow others to contribute with open tools, APIs, etc. Here are some examples from our portfolio.

- Alchemy.io—blockchain developer platform, the AWS for blockchain, DeFi developers
- Dynamics—develop therapeutics to directly target the heart using an authentic human cardiac organoid discovery engine
- Forum—open-source community enabling platform

- Fungible—hyperscale infrastructure for all, Fungible DPU, the datapath hub, connected all servers called TrueFabric.
- HashiCorp—the leader in infrastructure automation for multi-cloud environments with open-source offerings, such as Terraform, Vault, Consul, etc., to deliver consistent workflows to provision, secure, connect, and run any infrastructure for any application.
- InfluxData—the creator of InfluxDB, the open-source time series database purpose-built to handle the massive volumes of time-stamped data produced by IoT devices, applications, networks, containers, and computers
- Mammoth Bio—leading CRISPR platform company, Intel/Microsoft of bioengineering
- Outreach—integrated sales engagement platform that helps sales reps and leaders increase productivity, world's number one sales engagement platform
- WorkSpan—ecosystem business management platform to manage indirect revenue by connecting partners on a live network with cross-company business applications to build, market, and sell together

INTERVIEWER. Can you speak about some of your portfolio companies in Mayfield related to blockchains? Is this a future, or is it a hype?

INTERVIEWEE. It is real. Initial-use cases around cryptocurrencies will evolve into markets for Ethereum-based applications and NFT for content. Platforms to support these new models at an enterprise scale will create investment opportunities for tools, media, and enabling solutions. Some examples are Alchemy.io and FTX, a cryptocurrency exchange built by traders for traders.

INTERVIEWER. Can you speak about some of your portfolio companies in Mayfield related to augmented reality / virtual reality? Companies like Facebook and Microsoft are talking about the metaverse that will leverage AR/VR technologies. Is this a new trend?

INTERVIEWEE. VR/AR is nearly ten years old since Facebook acquired Oculus. Early deployments have disappointed uses and investors. Web 3.0 or metaverse remains an idea, but the technologies to support the use cases are better than ever. The killer app remains elusive. Here's an example from Mayfield: TRIPP, an XR platform designed to address mental and emotional well-being.

INTERVIEWER. Some start-up founders get too focused on digital technology (like AI/ML or blockchain) rather than the business outcome driven by digital technology. What advice do you have for founders to focus on the business?

INTERVIEWEE. PMF, or product-market fit, is not a technology problem but a business impact question. We often see founders leading with the technology, but the business use case is more about change and operationalizing the change. Therefore, a start-up needs to become a deep-use case domain expert; and while their technology is the enabler and maybe the game changer, they need to offer a solution that impacts the business, to appreciate the change management to evolve to a new use of technology, and to allow for a stepped increase in business impact for the user (i.e., a customer journey).

INTERVIEWER. How important is it for a start-up company to get strategic investors to complement VC investment from funds such as Mayfield?

INTERVIEWEE. The needs for a start-up are significantly more than money. They require support in hiring an effective team and leading an organization through the ups and downs of market issues and risks. Therefore, a start-up should look for a VC firm that can bring a lot more than capital to the equation and offer a proven set of resources to support the long-term journey from seed to iconic outcome.

Introduction

The first Industrial Revolution (1760–1820) was marked by a transition from hand production methods to machines through steam power and water power. Implementing new technologies took a long time. Textile manufacturing was the first to experience its effects; but the changes rippled forward into the iron industry, agriculture, and mining. But it was felt the most in society, creating an ever stronger middle class.

The second Industrial Revolution (1871–1914) resulted from building the extensive railroad and telegraph networks, which made for faster transfer of people and their ideas and electricity. Increasing electrification replaced gaslights in homes, making them safer and allowing manufacturers to develop the modern production line. It was a period of significant economic growth and increased productivity, even as it caused a surge in unemployment, as machines replaced many factory workers.

The third Industrial Revolution, also known as the Digital Revolution (1969–2000), resulted from a slowdown in industrialization and technological advancement compared to previous periods. The advent of the stored-program digital computer (the 1940s), which used binary floating point numbers and Boolean logic, was only the beginning of continuous advances in digital computing. Significantly, computational machinery began to nullify the need for human control. The fourth Industrial Revolution, also called Industry 4.0, originated around 2015 from a high-tech German strategy project conceived by Klaus Schwab to computerize manufacturing. It led to the industrial Internet of Things (IoT).

We are now in the fifth Industrial Revolution, or Industry 5.0. Like Industry 4.0, which focused on using artificial intelligence (AI), big data, and the IoT, Industry 5.0 embodies these advanced technologies and systems and incorporates greater human intelligence. This is the main—and very important—difference. Rather than humans competing with or losing the job to robots for employment, as was feared with the arrival of Industry 4.0, humans are now envisioned collaborating with them. These cobots—collaborative robots—are designed to be integrated into industrial processes for more repetitive and mundane tasks, providing humans with more significant opportunities to use their creative flair.

While we have discussed the process of innovation in the previous seven chapters, at this point, it is essential to review some of the critical technology trends that are and will drive product and process innovation in the twenty-first century. This chapter explores the following technologies:

- CAD/CAE simulation-driven product innovation
- semiconductors and nanotechnology
- photonics and optical interconnects
- quantum computing
- wireless communications
- additive manufacturing
- virtual reality / augmented reality
- blockchains
- cybersecurity
- high-performance computing
- cloud computing
- AI / machine learning
- Internet of Things (IoT)
- platforms

Table 8.1 lists these digital technologies, their market size, large companies, and start-ups in each technology.

Digital Technology	2030 Market size	Key Large Company Players	Start-Ups
CAD/CAE Simulation-Based Product Innovation	$30 billion	Ansys, Dassault, Siemens, Cadence, Synopsys, PTC, Autodesk	SimScale, OnScale, Onshape, Cascade, Neural Concept
Semiconductor and Nanotechnology	$1,300 billion	Intel, IBM, Qualcomm, Broadcomm, Samsung	Graphcore

Photonics and Optics	$20 billion	Intel, Cisco, Broadcom, KLA-Tencor	Xanadu, GenXComm, Rockley Photonics
Quantum Computing	$3.7 billion	IBM, Google, Honeywell, Intel, D-Wave, Microsoft	Rigetti, IonQ, Zapata, Cambridge Quantum Computing, Quantum Biosystems
Wireless Communications	$1,700 billion	Apple, Nokia, Ericsson, AT&T, T-Mobile, Verizon, Intel, Huawei, LG, and Cisco	Macrometa, viAct, Movanti, GenXComm, Ligado, Polte
Additive Manufacturing	$17 billion	3D Systems, Stratasys, HP, Carbon, GE, and EOS	Form Labs, Desktop Metal, Ultimaker Nanoscribe, and Markforged
Augmented Reality / Virtual Reality	$300 billion	Microsoft Hololens, Facebook Oculus Rift, Apple, and Google Glass	ScienceSoft, Niantic, Santa, Next/Now, 4Experience, CitrusBits, VironIT, GrooveJones, FundamentalVR, ValenceGroup, Gravity Jack, and TechSee
Blockchain	$40 billion	IBM, Oracle, Microsoft, SAP, Bitcoin, and Coinbase	ScienceSoft, Ripple Labs, LeewayHertz, Blockchangers, Techracers, Openledger, Extech, Limechain, Chain, and Intellectsoft
Cybersecurity	$345 billion	IBM, Microsoft, Norton, and Symantec	Arctic Wolf, Darktrace, Crowdstrike, Fireye, Netscout, and Extrahop
High-Performance Computing	$38 billion	IBM, HPE, Cray, Fujitsu, Dell	Cerebral, Samba Nova Systems
Cloud Computing	$835 billion	Amazon AWS, Microsoft Azure, Google GCP, Alibaba, IBM, Oracle	Aporia, Codescene, Filebase, Iterative, Goliath
AI / Machine Learning	$52 billion	Google, Microsoft, Amazon, Alibaba, Baidu, Nvidia, and Salesforce	Blue River Technologies, Bright machines, Brighteiron, H2O, AEye, Automation Anywhere, Orbital Insight, and People.ai

Internet of Things	$761 billion	Cisco, Broadcom, Amazon AWS, Microsoft Azure, Siemens, ABB, Schneider Electric, Rockwell Automation, Verizon, AT&T, Vodafone, Airtel, IBM, SAP, Oracle, and Texas Instruments	Macrometa, viAct, Movanti, GenXComm, Ligado, Polte, Fog Horn, and Sight Machine
Platforms	$45 billion	Apple, Google, Amazon, Salesforce, Microsoft, Netflix, Oracle, Pegasystems, and Facebook	Magic Software Enterprises, AgilePoint, OutSystems, Appian, Zoho, Quick Base, LANSA (US), Netcall, WaveMaker, and K2

Table 8.1. Digital technologies, the size of the
market, the key players, and start-ups

CAD/CAE Simulation Driven Product Innovation

In the past, designers of innovative products, such as airplanes, automobiles, high-tech semiconductor chips, mobile devices, energy, and consumer goods, used to create innovative products by building a hardware prototype of the product, testing the prototype under different operating conditions, refining the prototype, and finally, manufacturing the product at scale. For example, when an aerospace company designed a new airplane, they would create a clay model of the airplane and put in inside a wind tunnel and pass air over the wing at six hundred miles per hour to see if the airflow over the wing created the right lift so that the airplane would fly or at what angle of the wing the airplane would stall. If the airplane model did not fly, the designers would go back to the drawing board and design a modified airplane with a different wing shape. That process was long, costly, and error-prone.

Increasingly, designers of innovative products are using computer-aided design (CAD) and computer-aided engineering (CAE) simulation to build software prototypes of the product and performing virtual validation. This is being enabled by accurate, three-dimensional physical modeling of products. The world around us is governed by the laws of physics, which are modeled by second-order partial differential equations, such as Euler equations for structural mechanics, Navier-Stokes equations for fluid dynamics, Maxwell's equations for electromagnetics, and Kirchhoff's laws for electronic chips. These equations can be solved by CAE simulation tools using numerical methods, such as finite element analysis, finite volume methods, finite difference methods, and others.

In the past, the computational power of computers was not high enough; so even while the physics was known, it was not possible to accurately simulate the physics of a product in a reasonable amount of time. However, these days, with the power of high-performance computing enabled by the cloud, it is possible to simulate complex products with the most complex multiphysics interactions accurately in a few hours. Therefore, the need for building physical prototypes of products has been eliminated. This is the concept of simulation-based product innovation.

There are many stages involved in the product manufacturing cycle. The first is, of course, the concept of the product. Let us take the example of a simple product, like a cup. Cups come in different sizes and shapes. Manufacturers always attempt to come up with attractive and innovative designs. An artist then comes up with a new design using appropriate CAD software, like PTC Creo, CATIA, Solidworks, etc. However, it is a different ball game altogether to translate the design into a utilitarian product. This is where CAE comes in.

After the designing team hands over the CAD drawings to the engineering team, they assess the design from an engineering perspective. A cup is utilized to consume hot or cold liquids. It must, therefore, be able to withstand temperature fluctuations. The handle should be engineered in such a way that it is able to withstand the weight of the liquid without breaking. Furthermore, the entire weight of the cup and the liquid inside must be optimum so that the user has no difficulty lifting the cup. As you can see, CAD and CAE play different roles in manufacturing, even for a simple object like a cup. Simply put, CAD is the basic step in the manufacturing of an object, followed by the second step, which is the engineering analysis or CAE.

When it comes to designing complex objects or parts, the differences between CAD and CAE are more obvious. Many times, what designers feel is aesthetic may not be feasible functionally. When it comes to producing objects, like an airplane, this difference is glaringly obvious. While it is relatively easy to conceptualize an airplane using CAD, it is more difficult to make it really fly, and this is where CAE is useful. In such cases, both the design and the engineering teams need to proceed iteratively till they reach an optimum balance between what the designers want and what the engineering team can achieve. CAD allows designers to express their designs by drawing, building, and describing a model and its characteristics while CAE enables engineers to analyze, test, and improve that model.

Of the two, CAE is the more intricate, as it involves many engineering principles. While CAD simply involves design, CAE involves actually simulating the product's behavior in real life. CAD is used to help the users create and modify the graphic properties of a design using either 2D or 3D drawing, defining parameters like tolerances and dimensions. CAE tests the model for parameters like temperature, pressure, component interactions, and applied forces. That said, both CAD and CAE require a lot of practical training before it can be put to use. Typical software used for CAE simulation includes Ansys Mechanical, HFSS, Fluent, Altair HyperWorks, Dassault Abaqus, and Siemens STAR-CCM+, among others. Simply put, a major difference between CAD and CAE is that CAD software designs while CAE software analyzes. Another difference between CAD and CAE is that CAD models must aim to represent a design lucidly and in detail while CAE strives to solve the engineering problem determined by the boundary and load conditions set on a model.

Figure 8.1 shows the process of CAD/CAE based product innovation and the value of simulation. Simulation used to be used in the past by engineering analysts, but increasingly, simulation is also being used in the ideation phase by designers in the front end of the design and in the manufacturing phase and the operational phases. Simulation-based product innovation allows customers to support more rapid innovation, lower the cycle time to design new products, grow top-line revenue by allowing customers to offer more products, launch the right products, and faster time to market.

Simulation based product innovation

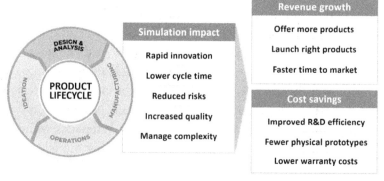

Figure 8.1. Simulation-based product innovation (courtesy of Ansys)

CAD involves 2D or 3D rendering of an object or a component while CAE simulation involves engineering analysis of it, which involves the following:

1. Static and dynamic analysis
2. Buckling analysis
3. Thermal analysis
4. Fatigue analysis
5. Optimization
6. CFD analysis
7. Crash analysis

Since CAE inherently involves simulation and prototype creation of a real-life model, it saves everyone time and money, as modern CAE software, like Ansys, Altair HyperWorks, and Abaqus, has the capability to validate the authenticity of the CAD drawings of that model. In the past, the engineering models were not accurate enough to be effective. However, these days, with the power of high-performance computing with millions of CPUs and GPUs available on the cloud, we are solving some really large, complex models accurately and fast. Furthermore, we are using artificial intelligence, machine learning, and deep learning to accelerate our simulation solvers by factors of one hundred times.

In addition, AI/ML is allowing our customers to use generative design and topology optimization to very rapidly and automatically explore thousands of designs to choose the optimal one. Finally, with the world of connected products and IoT, it is possible to get feedback about how a product is operating in the field and use that data to build digital twins of the product and improve the next version of the product. Innovators are working on hybrid digital twins to combine physics-based simulation and data analytics / AI.

Some of the future technology directions in simulation-based product innovation include new directions in numerical methods, such as finite element and finite difference methods and implicit and explicit solvers; innovations in meshing and preprocessing prior to the actual solvers using methods such as conformal and nonconformal meshing; new methods of visualization using augmented reality and virtual reality; innovations in multiphysics, multidomain, multiscale simulation platforms; use of AI / machine learning in accelerating simulation; use of high-performance computing to accelerate simulation; use of cloud for simulation and collaboration; model-based systems design to support rapid prototyping and virtual validation; digital twins; integrated computational materials engineering and additive manufacturing; and solutions for autonomy, electrification, IoT, and health care.

The future of product innovation in the connected world is very exciting in industries that are diverse and high-tech—semiconductors, aerospace and defense, automotive, industrial, and energy. The global market for CAD/CAE-driven product innovation is about $30 billion by 2025. The leading companies in the CAD space are Autodesk, PTC, Dassault, Altair, Siemens, Cadence, and Synopsys. The leading companies in CAE simulation are Ansys, Dassault, Altair, COMSOL, MathWorks, Siemens, Cadence, and Synopsys. Some of the exciting start-up companies in CAD/CAE are Onshape, SimScale, OnScale, Neural Concept, MStar, and Cascade.

SEMICONDUCTOR AND NANOTECHNOLOGY

Semiconductor and nanotechnology researchers have consistently kept pace with Moore's law (Gordon Moore, 1965), which stated that the number of transistors on a chip would double every two years. Figure 8.1 shows the advances in Moore's law over the years. Some believe the law will be obsolete by 2036. Others think we've already exceeded it, as we see chips with more than a billion transistors on a chip in 2021.

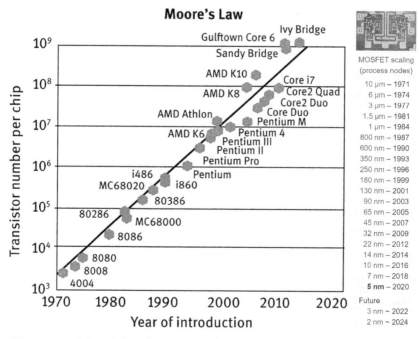

Figure 8.2. Moore's law for semiconductors and scaling of process nodes

Figure 8.2 also shows how the CMOS semiconductor technology has scaled down from ten micron minimum mask resolution in 1971 to ten nanometer (nm) in 2016 and continues to scale down to 7 nm and 5 nm today and 3 nm and 2 nm in 2022 and 2024. In 2021, IBM announced a 2 nm chip with some components smaller than human DNA. Technologies such as FinFET, gate-all-around, silicon nanosheets are being developed by foundries such as IBM, Intel, Samsung, and TSMC to manufacture semiconductor chips at these nanoscales. Most experts agree that silicon transistors are likely to stop shrinking at Moore's law scale around 2021.

Chipmakers are finding other ways to increase power. For example, germanium, different III-V compound semiconductor technologies, such as gallium arsenide or indium phosphide, and at some point, carbon nanotubes provide new ways of increasing power. Companies are exploring technologies such as extreme ultraviolet and self-directed assembly techniques. Manufacturers have experimented with other semiconductor materials: tin oxide, high-power gallium nitride, antimonide-based and bismuthide-based materials, graphene, and pyrite. All these are types of innovations that will take place in the semiconductor industry in the twenty-first century.

Technological advancements and their rapid integration into new digital ecosystems have impacted the semiconductor industry. Demand for the integration of maximum functionalities on systems on a chip (SOCs) has grown, increasing the number of semiconductor intellectual property (IP) cores. Furthermore, demands for high-performance memory systems have powerfully impacted semiconductor memory IP. The market demand for faster and more efficient memory solutions is driving the development of increasingly complex semiconductors capable of facilitating intense memory operations. Overall, dependence on IP core solutions providers is growing, driving considerable investments in the market.

The semiconductor industry is poised for solid growth throughout the 2020 decade. IDC predicts the semiconductor market could reach $1,300 billion by 2030, representing a CAGR of 5.3 percent through the forecast period. Some of the key players in the semiconductor industry include chipmakers such as IBM, Intel, ARM, AMD, Nvidia, Qualcomm, Broadcom, and Samsung and semiconductor manufacturing foundries such as Samsung, Intel, IBM, TSMC, and Global Foundries. IBM and Intel once designed and manufactured their chips in custom foundry services. Still, recently, they have decided to subcontract with other chip companies to better compete with TSMC and Global Foundries.

As semiconductor chips grow more and more complex, electronic design automation tools become more sophisticated. Semiconductor electronic design automation companies driving these innovations include Synopsys, Cadence, Mentor Graphics, and Ansys. Leading start-up companies in semiconductor chip design include Cerebral Systems, Samba Nova Systems, and Graphcore. Most are designing complex large chips to solve AI problems. In April 2021, Cerebral Systems unveiled its Wafer Scale Engine 2, its successor chip to the world's largest computer chip, the WSE. The new 7 nm chip boasts 2.6 trillion transistors and 850,000 AI-optimized cores and consumes fifteen kilowatts of power. This chip holds the world record regarding the most significant number of transistors on a chip. It represents the type of innovation we will see in the semiconductor industry in the twenty-first century.

PHOTONICS AND OPTICAL INTERCONNECTS

A third area where there will be a great deal of innovation is in photonics and optical interconnects. While semiconductor circuits operate near the speed of electrons, the bandwidth within and between electronic circuits is necessarily limited—for example, between a computer's graphics chip and its processor. This speed can be significantly increased by replacing wires with photons or light and optics. In the coming era of big data and IoT, data networks with an extremely high speed and capacity will undoubtedly be implemented everywhere. The broad bandwidth and long reach offered by light, advanced optical interconnect technologies will play an ever more critical role in scaling up the performance of various network segments, ranging from long-distance datacenter interconnections to short-reach, rack-to-rack communications and even onboard chip-to-chip links.

Extremely compact, highly energy efficient, low-cost, and densely integrated optical components are the fundamental vital enablers to satisfy the intrasystems' and intersystems' ever-growing bandwidth requirements of future data centers and high-performance computers. For both the inter-boards and inter-chip connects, man-ufacturers have explored high energy-efficient and low-cost VCSELs (vertical-cavity surface-emitting lasers) in the last few years and, thus, significantly improved the energy-per-bit consumption of integrated laser sources. The development of silicon photonics technology also opens up new opportunities for high-bandwidth, low-power, and low-cost chip-to-chip links. We know that the silicon-based optical components should meet these demands: high stability, ultracom-pact, high energy efficiency, low cost, and high integration. Over the last decade, silicon photonics has experienced phenomenal growth and development transformations toward these goals.

To tightly integrate optics with computing hardware, particu-larly in the context of CMOS-compatible silicon photonics, optical printed circuit (PC) boards using polymer waveguides are consid-ered a formidable platform. A low-cost, single-mode new polymer waveguide technology has recently been used as the optical interface between silicon photonics chips and single-mode polymer wave-guides. These efforts and advances continue to expand the horizons of optical interconnect, resulting in more high-performance func-tionality and low-cost systems, resulting in high-capacity output and lower operating power.

The optical interconnect market can be looked at by product category, such as cable assemblies, connectors, free-space optics, fiber, waveguides, optical engines, optical transceivers, pic-based interconnects, and silicon photonics. Based on interconnect level, the market can be studied across board to board, rack-level optical interconnect, chip-and-board-level optical interconnect, and metro and long-haul optical interconnect. The market can be segmented across multimode fiber and single-mode fiber based on fiber mode. The multimode fiber is further studied across graded-index multi-mode fiber and step-index multimode fiber.

Based on data rate, the market can be subdivided across 10 Gbps to 40 Gbps, 41 Gbps to 100 Gbps, and less than 10 Gbps and more than 100 Gbps. Based on distance, the market can be studied across 1 km to 10 km, 11 km to 100 km, and less than 1 km and more than 100 km. Based on application, the market can be looked at across data communication and telecommunication. Data communication is further studied across data centers and high-performance computing. Based on these categories, the Global Optical Interconnect Market was estimated at $12 billion in 2020 and is expected to reach $20 billion by 2026. There is a lot of product innovation that will be enabled by optical interconnects and photonics in each of these categories.

Some of the key players in the photonics and optical interconnect market include Cisco, Intel, Broadcom, KLA-Tencor, Finisar, Mellanox Technologies, Molex, Sumitomo Electric Industries, TE Connectivity, Juniper Networks, Fujitsu, Infinera Corporation, 3M Company, Acacia Communication, Dow Corning, Huawei, and Infineon Technologies. Some tool companies include Lumerical, Zemax, Keysight, and Ansys SPEOS. Some of the exciting start-up companies in the space include Xanadu, Lightmatter, GenXComm, Rockley Photonics, and SiLC Technologies.

Quantum Computing

A fourth area where there will be a lot of innovations is in quantum computing. Quantum computing harnesses the collective properties of quantum states, such as superposition, interference, and entanglement, to perform calculations. They are believed to solve specific computational problems, such as integer factorization, which underlies RSA encryption, substantially faster than classical computers. Until recently, quantum computing was largely theoretical. Today, the use of quantum physics to increase computational power has moved beyond speculation.

There are two broad approaches to building quantum computers, the first using universal quantum gates and the other using quantum annealing. The first approach, known as the gate model, expresses the interactions between qubits as quantum gates. Classical computers can also be described in terms of gate functions—for example, AND gates and OR gates. It turns out that quantum gates, for reasons of quantum physics, have to function a little differently, and there is no AND gate or OR gate in a gate model quantum computer. Instead, there are Hadamard gates and Toffoli gates.

Unlike many classical logic gates, quantum logic gates are reversible. Several hardware companies, such as Google, Honeywell, IBM, and Intel, have built gate model quantum computers, which are now available in the marketplace. These devices must function at very low temperatures using superconducting qubits, requiring expensive refrigeration technology. It turns out that it is very challenging to build reliable qubits and very difficult to incorporate them into chips. These companies are working to scale up their machines.

The second approach, quantum annealing, originated from some theoretical work done in the 1980s and 1990s. Quantum annealing seeks to utilize effects known as quantum fluctuations to find the best possible solution for the user's problem. Rather than expressing concern about quantum gates, the user defines the problem as one of optimization, and the quantum annealing computer seeks the best solution. One company, D-Wave Systems, has a quantum annealing computer publicly available today for $10 million.

One way to understand the difference between the two types of quantum computers is that quantum computers' gate model requires problems to be expressed in terms of quantum gates. The quantum annealing computer needs problems to be expressed in operations research language. Likely, software tools will eventually emerge to convert the types of problems one into the other so gate model users won't have to understand the gates deeply. We expect such software products to appear over the next several years, making it easier to compare the performance between machines.

IBM, Google, and their quantum competitors are racing to build the most effective, universal gate quantum computers. D-Wave builds quantum annealing computers but has plans to build hybrids using both gate and annealing technologies. Advantage is the third upgrade to D-Wave's pioneering quantum annealer and is powered by five thousand qubits. Los Alamos National Laboratory plans to use the quantum annealer to support national security efforts launched next year.

In October 2019, Google announced a paper published in *Nature* entitled "Quantum Supremacy Using a Programmable

Superconducting Processor." The promise is that quantum computers are exponentially faster than conventional machines. A fundamental challenge is to build a high-fidelity processor capable of running quantum algorithms in an exponentially large computational space. Google researchers reported using a processor with programmable superconducting qubits in the *Nature* paper. To create quantum states on 53 qubits, corresponding to a computational state space of dimension 2^{53} (about 10^{16}). Measurements from repeated experiments sample the resulting probability distribution, which they verified using classical simulations. Google's Sycamore processor took about two hundred seconds to test one instance of a quantum circuit a million times; their benchmarks currently indicate that the equivalent task for a state-of-the-art classical supercomputer would take approximately ten thousand years. This dramatic increase in speed compared to all known classical algorithms is an experimental realization of quantum supremacy for this specific computational task, heralding a much-anticipated computing paradigm. This is the kind of digital innovation being performed in the twenty-first century.

Major companies, start-ups, research teams, and governments are creeping toward quantum. Arguably, the implications of the technology are most important, not the coveted title of quantum supremacy. Quantum computing will transform R&D in every possible field, providing the power needed to answer previously unanswerable questions. As we enter the age of quantum computing, education and understanding will dictate engagement and investment. For the present, though, quantum enthusiasts must communicate the tangible benefits of quantum rather than fueling hype.

The global quantum computing market was about $487 million in 2021 and is expected to reach $3.7 billion by 2030 at a CAGR of 25 percent over the forecast 2021–2030 period. Many advances in product innovation will happen with quantum computing. Some of the key players include Microsoft, Intel, IBM, Google, Honeywell, Toshiba, and Alibaba. Some of the critical start-ups in quantum computing include D-Wave, Rigetti, IonQ, Post-Quantum, Cambridge Quantum Computing, and Quantum Biosystems.

WIRELESS COMMUNICATIONS

A fifth area where there will be a lot of innovations is in wireless communications. The fifth-generation (5G) wireless technology standard for broadband cellular networks, which cellular phone companies began deploying worldwide in 2019, is the planned successor to 4G networks, which currently provide connectivity to most cellphones. Like its predecessors, 5G networks are cellular networks, in which the service area is divided into small geographical areas called cells. All 5G wireless devices in a cell are connected to the Internet and telephone network by radio waves through a local antenna. The main advantage of the new networks is that they will have greater bandwidth, delivering higher download speeds, eventually up to ten gigabits per second (Gbit/s).

Because of the increased bandwidth, it is expected that these networks will increasingly be used as general Internet service providers for laptops and desktop computers, competing with existing ISPs, such as cable Internet, and will also make possible new applications for the Internet of Things (IoT) and machine-to-machine (M2M) areas. Different opportunities for 5G include smart cities, industrial IoT, augmented reality / virtual reality, autonomous vehicles, health care, power grid design, and commercial mobile. 5G will enable different levels of innovation around devices, networks, and the data center using the edge and the cloud.

6G is the sixth-generation standard and is currently developing wireless communications technologies supporting cellular data networks. The plan is to deploy 6G around the year 2030. The planned successor to 5G will likely be fifty times faster. Several companies (Nokia, Ericsson, Huawei, Samsung, LG, Apple, and Xiaomi) and several countries (India, China, Japan, and Singapore) have shown interest in 6G networks. 6G networks are expected to exhibit even more heterogeneity (be even more diverse) than their predecessors and are likely to support applications beyond current mobile use scenarios, such as virtual and augmented reality (VR/AR), ubiquitous instant communications, pervasive intelligence, and the Internet of Things (IoT).

It is expected that mobile network operators will adopt increasingly flexible, decentralized business models for 6G with local spectrum licensing, spectrum sharing, infrastructure sharing, and intelligent automated management underpinned by mobile edge computing, artificial intelligence, short-packet communication, and blockchain technologies. Currently, the focus for 6G is limited to research and development, which is why most of the companies, such as smartphone manufacturers, semiconductor vendors, smart technology vendors, and other critical technology-oriented companies, are focusing on developing applications for the 6G spectrum. These applications include smart cities, edge devices, autonomous vehicles, holographic communication, satellite communication, IoT, and blockchain.

The competitive landscape of the 6G market consists of different strategies undertaken by major players across the telecommunication and electronics industries to gain an early market presence. Among all the processes in play, partnerships, collaborations, and joint ventures have been the most prominent and readily adopted by telecommunication and electronics providers. For instance, in January 2021, Google Cloud and Nokia partnered to work together on the cloud-native 5G core and codevelop the network edge as a business services platform for enterprises.

The global 6G market is expected to reach $1,773 billion by 2035. The market of 6G is yet to start, as NTT DoCoMo has announced 2030 as the launch year for 6G. The key 5G and 6G players include Apple, Nokia, Ericsson, AT&T, T-Mobile, Verizon, Intel, Huawei, LG, Cisco, and NTT DoCoMo. Some example start-ups in the 5G/6G space include Macrometa, viAct, Movanti, GenXComm, Ligado, and Polte.

Additive Manufacturing

Additive manufacturing (AM) is a sixth area where many innovations are expected. Also commonly known as 3D printing, it is the construction of a three-dimensional object from a CAD or digital 3D model. The term "3D printing" refers to various processes in which material is deposited, joined, or solidified under computer control to create a three-dimensional object with multiple materials combined, such as plastics, liquids, or powder grains, fused typically by layer. One of the key advantages of 3D printing is producing complex shapes or geometries that would otherwise be impossible to construct by hand, including hollow parts or parts with internal truss structures to reduce weight.

Let us now review how a 3D object is printed on a 3D printer. First, a virtual 3D representation of the object is rendered using computer-aided design (CAD) or another 3D software design app. Then the model is sliced into horizontal layers to convert the design into an STL (standard tessellation language) file readable by the 3D printer. Once this data is transferred to the printer, its print settings are defined. The final object is produced one layer, commonly with plastic or metal filament, each layer bonding and building upon the previous layer.

Because of the ability to produce very complex shapes and structures with high precision and repeatability from various materials, 3D printing is used in aerospace, automotive, construction, fashion, food, jewelry, manufacturing, and medical sectors. Numerous techniques exist to 3D-print objects with different mechanical, thermal, and chemical properties from materials in molten, liquid, or powder states. The many different additive manufacturing processes can be identified in seven categories.

- Vat photopolymerization
- Material jetting
- Binder jetting
- Powder bed fusion
- Material extrusion
- Directed energy deposition
- Sheet lamination

The main differences between these processes are the raw fabrication material and how layers are deposited to create the product. Each method has its advantages and drawbacks, so some companies choose construction materials, such as powder or polymer. Some printers can use standard, off-the-shelf business paper as the build material to produce a durable prototype. The primary considerations in choosing a machine are speed, cost of the 3D printer, cost of the printed prototype, choice and price of the materials, and color capabilities. Printers that work directly with metals are generally expensive; however, less costly printers can be used to make a mold, then used to make metal parts.

The overall additive manufacturing market for metal and polymer material is valued at $8.2 billion with a projected growth of CAGR 20.0 percent until 2025. The industrial polymer market is about 2.5 times greater than its metal equivalent. While system sales revenues in both markets are at a similar growth level, material and part manufacturing services are much more developed for polymers, resulting in a larger share of the revenue. The metal AM market alone is valued at $2.3 billion in 2020 with an expected CAGR of 29.2 percent until 2025 while the polymer market will continue growth by 15.4 percent annually, starting at $6 billion in 2020.

Large companies in additive manufacturing are 3D Systems, Stratasys, HP, Carbon, GE, and EOS. Some representative start-ups are Formlabs, Desktop Metal, Ultimaker Nanoscribe, Markforged, and MilliporeSigma.

Augmented Reality, Virtual Reality, and Metaverse

A fascinating digital technology in which many innovations will happen in the twenty-first century is focused on augmented reality, virtual reality, and the metaverse, which are being hyped by companies such as Facebook and Microsoft. Augmented reality (AR) is an interactive experience of a replicated real-world environment where objects are enhanced by computer-generated perceptual information, sometimes across multiple sensory modalities, including visual, auditory, haptic, somatosensory, and olfactory.

AR can be defined as a system incorporating three primary features: a combination of real and virtual worlds, real-time interaction, and accurate 3D representation of virtual and real objects. The over-laid sensory information can be constructive (i.e., augmenting the natural environment) or destructive (i.e., masking or misrepresenting the natural environment). This experience is seamlessly interwoven with the physical world such that it is perceived as an immersive but real environment. In this way, augmented reality alters one's ongoing perception of a real-world environment, whereas virtual reality completely replaces the user's real-world environment with a simulated one.

Augmented reality is related to two essentially synonymous terms: mixed reality and computer-mediated reality. The primary value of augmented reality is how components of the digital world blend into a person's perception of the natural world not as a simple display of data but through the integration of immersive sensations, which are perceived as biological aspects of the perceived environment. The earliest functional AR systems presenting immersive, mixed reality experiences for users were invented in the early 1990s, starting with the virtual fixtures system developed at the US Air Force's Armstrong Laboratory in 1992. Commercial augmented reality experiences were first introduced in the entertainment and gaming businesses. Subsequently, augmented reality applications have spanned commercial industries, such as education, communications, medicine, and entertainment. In education, content may be accessed by scanning or viewing an image with a mobile device or markerless AR techniques.

Augmented reality enhances natural environments or situations and offers perceptually enriched experiences. With the help of advanced AR technologies (e.g., adding computer vision, incorporating AR cameras into smartphone applications, and object recognition), the information about the user's external real world becomes interactive and digitally manipulated. Information-based representations of the environment and its objects are overlaid in the real world. This information can be virtual. Augmented reality is an artificial experience that adds value to existing reality. For example, it visualizes other genuine sensed or measured information, such as electromagnetic radio waves overlaid in exact alignment with where they are in space. Augmented reality also has a lot of potential in gathering and sharing tacit knowledge. Augmentation techniques are performed in real-time and semantic contexts with environmental elements. Immersive perceptual information is sometimes combined with supplemental information, like musical scores over a live video feed of a sporting event. This combines the benefits of both augmented reality technology and heads-up display technology (HUD).

Virtual reality (VR) as a simulated experience can be similar to or entirely distinct from the real world. Applications of virtual reality include entertainment (e.g., video games), education (e.g., medical or military training), and business (e.g., virtual meetings where avatars represent real individuals). Other distinct types of VR-style technology include augmented reality and mixed reality, sometimes referred to as extended reality or XR. One may distinguish between two types of VR: immersive VR and text-based network VR (also known as cyberspace). The immersive VR changes the user's view when the head moves. Both VRs are appropriate for training. The main focus is on immersive VR, although cyberspace is preferred for distance learning. In some cases, these two aspects can be implemented together.

Standard VR systems commonly use virtual reality headsets or multiprojected environments to generate realistic images, sounds, and other sensations to simulate a user's physical presence in a virtual environment. A person using virtual reality equipment can look around the artificial world, move around in it, and interact with virtual features or items. The effect is commonly created by VR headsets consisting of a head-mounted display with a small screen in front of the eyes but can also be made through specially designed rooms with multiple large screens. Virtual reality typically incorporates auditory and video feedback but may also allow other sensory perceptions, such as tactile force feedback, through haptic technology.

The global augmented reality (AR), virtual reality (VR), and mixed reality (MR) market is forecast to reach $30.7 billion in 2021, rising to close to $300 billion by 2024. AR/VR technology makes use of sensory devices to either virtually modify a user's environment or completely immerse them in a simulated environment. Virtual reality devices typically consist of specially designed headsets that offer complete visual immersion in the simulated environment. In contrast, augmented reality relies on headsets that add virtual elements to a user's actual environment. In 2020, AR/VR headsets sales were projected to reach 5.5 million units. When it comes to VR/AR device sales by vendor, Sony's PlayStation VR and Facebook's Oculus VR headsets are the major VR headset-based products on the market.

One primary use of VR headsets is for gaming, and as such, they give gamers a fully immersive experience, be it a fantasy land or the driver's seat of a racing car. There are different VR gaming headsets, including headsets for PC, console, premium mobile devices, and standalone play devices. In 2019, of the overall VR gaming device shipments, 2.8 million units of standalone VR gaming headsets were shipped worldwide. VR headsets are increasingly popular among gamers and are considered by 37 percent of surveyed global game developers to be an essential platform for future growth. The key players in AR/VR are Microsoft (Hololens), Facebook (Oculus), Apple (Glass), and Google (Glass). Some example start-ups in AR/VR are ScienceSoft, Niantic, Santa, Next/Now, 4Experience, CitrusBits, VironIT, GrooveJones, FundamentalVR, ValenceGroup, Gravity Jack, and TechSee.

Microsoft and Facebook have established major initiatives leveraging AR/VR around the metaverse. The metaverse envisions a virtual environment to interact with other humans and bots, play games, conduct business, socialize, and shop. That's the metaverse of the future. Today, the metaverse is a grab bag of hardware, software, and unrelated experiences. There is no connective tissue to bring all these components together yet. For example, Facebook's Horizon Workrooms are an example of mixed reality. The user joins a virtual office space with Oculus Quest 2 and can see their hands and keyboard. Also, colleagues not joining the meeting via a VR headset can join via a video feed that shows up in the virtual world, just as it would in a live conference room.

Companies and military trainers use VR and AR for training as well. Penske Truck Leasing uses the XRMentor training platform to train technicians and support them in the field. Instructors livestream classes to students, who can then use assisted-reality devices to refer to training documents when working on vehicles. It is possible to buy real estate in virtual worlds, such as Decentraland and Cryptovoxels, although those are definitely for early adopters.

The difference between these experiences and the full-on metaverse is the physical sensation of being in another place and sharing it with others. For most of these experiences, interaction with the online world is through a controller or similar piece of hardware. Although VR worlds are immersive, the headsets are still awkward, defining the entire experience like something ordinary. Some leaders see the metaverse as a fully immersive, partially real-life, and somewhat digital experience that parallels the physical world. Some tech leaders imagine a very different metaverse when discussing it. The metaverse currently under development would be next to reality and always on. It would have its currency and objects and would be interoperable. There are implications to this, which we have yet to comprehend fully.

BLOCKCHAIN TECHNOLOGY

Another exciting digital technology of the twenty-first century is blockchain. A blockchain is a growing list of records, called blocks, linked together using cryptography. Each block contains a cryptographic hash of the previous block, a time stamp, and a transaction data. The time stamp proves that the transaction data existed when the block was published to get into its hash. Each block contains information about the previous block. Together, they form a chain with each additional block reinforcing those before it. Blockchains resist modification and are secure because once recorded, the data in any given block cannot be altered retroactively without altering all subsequent blocks.

A peer-to-peer network typically manages blockchains as a publicly distributed ledger, where nodes collectively adhere to a protocol to communicate and validate new blocks. Although blockchain records are not unalterable forms, they are secure by design and exemplify a distributed computing system with high Byzantine fault tolerance.

The blockchain was popularized by a person using the name Satoshi Nakamoto in 2008 to serve as the public transaction ledger of the cryptocurrency Bitcoin, based on work by Stuart Haber, W. Scott Stornetta, and Dave Bayer. The identity of Satoshi Nakamoto remains unknown to date. The invention of the blockchain for Bitcoin made it the first digital currency to solve the double-spending problem without needing a trusted authority or central server. The Bitcoin design has inspired other applications and blockchains that are readable by the public and are widely used by cryptocurrencies. The blockchain is considered a type of payment rail. Private blockchains have been proposed for business use. Some have argued that if carefully designed, permission blockchains may be more decentralized and, therefore, more secure in practice than permissionless ones.

Blockchain is often mentioned in connection with Bitcoin and other cryptocurrencies. It is a decentralized technological system in which the transactions made in digital currencies are recorded and kept in linked computers. It manages a growing list of a record called blocks, is linked with cryptography and functions as a distributed ledger, works across a peer-to-peer network, is connected to a protocol for inter-node communication, and is capable of building new blocks.

Blockchain has been in existence as a concept in computer science even before it was used in cryptocurrency. The initial form of blockchain was known as the hash tree or Merkle tree, patented by Ralph Merkle in 1979. It functioned by verifying and handling data between computer systems. In 1991, the Merkle tree was used to create a secured chain of blocks of several data, connected in a chain one after the other. The newest record in the chain contains the history of the entire chain and, therefore, is how a blockchain is defined and formed. The peer-to-peer version of this electronic cash transaction is what we term Bitcoin and how the blockchain came about.

Let us review how a blockchain works. The blockchain records and maintains all the data exchanges. This record is known as a ledger, and the exchange data recorded in it are referred to as transactions. When a transaction is verified, it is added to the ledger as a block, and a peer-to-peer network of nodes is verified using a distributed system. When a new transaction is verified, it is added to the blockchain and never be altered. It connects through so many computers known as nodes, and each has a copy of the blockchain. The nodes ensure that the transactions are not changed by inspecting the hash. A transaction is written into the block only if approved by a more significant number of nodes. Each block refers to the previous one and together forms the blockchain. The blockchain updates itself every ten minutes.

The technology industry has discovered many applications of blockchain in finance and other vital sectors. Blockchain distributed ledger technology can increase transparency in data management and reduce fraud. It allows all customers to access a cloud-based solution; to build, host, and use their blockchain apps, smart contracts, and other functions on the blockchain system while the blockchain company manages all the activities involved in maintaining the transactional processes.

The global blockchain market size is expected to grow from $3.0 billion in 2020 to $39.7 billion by 2025 at an impressive CAGR of 67.3 percent during 2020–2025. The ever-increasing need to simplify business processes and supply chain management applications, all of which can be integrated with blockchain technology, will drive the overall blockchain market (https://www.marketsandmarkets. com). The key blockchain players include IBM, Oracle, Microsoft, SAP, Bitcoin, and Coinbase. Some vital blockchain start-ups include ScienceSoft, Ripple Labs, LeewayHertz, Blockchangers, Techracers, Openledger, Extech, Limechain, Chain, and Intellectsoft.

CYBERSECURITY

One of the most critical areas of innovation in the twenty-first century will be cybersecurity. The attack surface grows much more significant as the world gets more connections between people and machines using IoT. Hence, innovations in cybersecurity are becoming significantly more important.

Cybersecurity is the protection of computer systems and networks from information disclosure, theft of, or damage to hardware, software, or electronic data, as well as from the disruption or misdirection of the services they provide. Cybersecurity is becoming increasingly critical because of the continuously expanding reliance on computer systems, the Internet, and wireless network standards, such as Bluetooth and Wi-Fi, and because of the growth of smart devices, including smartphones, televisions, and the various devices that constitute the Internet of things. Cybersecurity is also one of the significant challenges in the contemporary world because of its complexity, both in terms of political usage and technology and the widening scope of cyber criminality.

To secure a computer/information system, it is essential to understand the nature of attacks. Cyber threats can typically be classified into one of these following categories:

- *Backdoor.* A backdoor in a computer system, a cryptosystem, or an algorithm is any secret method of bypassing standard authentication or security controls. They may exist for many reasons, including original design or poor configuration. An authorized party may have added them to allow some legitimate access (a fail-safe way of regaining access, for example, if a password is lost) or by an attacker for malicious reasons. But regardless of the motives for their existence, they represent a vulnerability. Backdoors can be challenging to detect and are usually discovered by someone who has access to application source code or intimate knowledge of the computer's operating system.
- *Denial service attacks (DoS).* This makes a machine or network resource unavailable to its intended users. Attackers can block access to individual victims by deliberately entering a wrong password enough times to cause the victim's account to be locked, or they may overload the capabilities of a machine or network and block all users at once. While a network attack from a single IP address can be blocked by adding a new firewall rule, many forms of distributed

denial of service (DDoS) attacks are possible. When a DoS attack comes from many points, defending is more complicated.

- *Direct-access attack.* An unauthorized user gaining physical access to a computer may copy data at will. This type of intrusion compromises fundamental system security by permitting operating system modifications or installing software worms, keyloggers, and covert listening/recording devices. Disk encryption and trusted platform module technology are intended to prevent these attacks.

- *Eavesdropping.* This is the act of secretly listening to private computer communication, typically between hosts on a network. Even machines that operate as a closed system can be eavesdropped upon via monitoring the faint electromagnetic transmissions generated by the hardware.

- *Multivector, polymorphic attack.* A new class of multivector, polymorphic cyber threats combine several types of attacks and can change their form to avoid cybersecurity controls as they spread.

- *Phishing.* This attempts to access sensitive information, such as usernames, passwords, and credit card or bank account data, directly from users by various forms of deception. Phishing is typically carried with email spoofing or instant messaging and often directs users to enter details at a fake website that appears almost identical to the legitimate one.

- *Privilege escalation.* This describes a situation where an attacker with some level of restricted access can, without authorization, elevate their privileges or access level.

- *Reverse engineering.* This is the process by which a man-made object is deconstructed to reveal its design, code, or architecture or extract IP; it is similar to scientific research, but instead of concerning a natural phenomenon, its intent is theft.

- *Side-channel attack.* Any computational system affects its environment in some manner. This includes a wide range of criteria, which can range from electromagnetic radiation to, for example, specific residual impacts on random access memory cells, which, as a consequence, make a cold boot attack possible, or to hardware implementation faults that allow for access or guessing of other values that generally should be inaccessible.

- *Social engineering.* In the context of computer security, this aims to convince a user to disclose secrets, such as passwords, card numbers, etc., or grant physical access by, for example, impersonating a senior executive, bank, contractor, or a customer. This generally involves exploiting peoples' trust and relying on their cognitive biases.

- *Spoofing.* This is the act of masquerading as a valid entity or individual through falsifying data, such as an IP address or username, to gain access to information or resources that one is otherwise unauthorized to access.

- *Tampering.* This describes a malicious modification or alteration of data. Examples are so-called evil maid attacks and security services planting surveillance capability into routers.

- *Malware.* Malicious software (malware) installed on a computer can leak personal information or give control of the system to the attacker, who can permanently delete data.

There are many ways information systems can be compromised. With each passing day, a new type of cyberattack occurs. Numerous companies provide innovative cybersecurity solutions. For example, in May 2021, Colonial Pipeline suffered a ransomware cyberattack that impacted computerized equipment managing the pipeline. In response, Colonial had to halt all pipeline operations. With the assistance of the FBI, Colonial paid the requested ransom (75 Bitcoin, or $4.4 million) several hours after the attack. The hackers sent a software application to restore the network. In June 2021, the Department of Justice, working with private cybersecurity companies, announced it had recovered 63.7 Bitcoin ($2.3 million), about half the ransom paid to the Russian hackers. It demonstrated that Bitcoin and cyberattacks can be traced.

The global cybersecurity market size will grow to $345.4 billion by 2026. The key players in cybersecurity are IBM, Microsoft, Norton, Symantec, MacAfee, and Palo Alto Networks. Examples of cybersecurity start-ups are Arctic Wolf, Darktrace, Crowdstrike, Fireye, Netscout, Infoblox, and Extrahop.

HIGH-PERFORMANCE COMPUTING

Another area where there will be a lot of innovations is in high-performance computing. High-performance computing, or HPC, enables scientists and engineers to push the edge of what is possible in science and innovation. Using HPC-based modeling and simulation, they can study systems that otherwise would be impractical or impossible to investigate in the real world because of their complexity, size, fleeting nature, or the danger they might pose.

A supercomputer was designed for a high level of performance compared to a general-purpose, business-purpose computer. The ability to perform numerical calculations at high speed made it applicable to the scientific community. Companies like Control Data and Cray Research developed these machines specializing in floating-point operations to recognize the need for specialized architectures. The performance of a supercomputer is commonly measured in floating-point operations per second (FLOPS) instead of million instructions per second (MIPS). Since 2017, supercomputers have performed over 10^{17} FLOPS (a hundred quadrillion FLOPS, 100 petaflops). Supercomputers play an essential role in the field of computational science. They are used for a wide range of computationally intensive tasks in various areas, including quantum mechanics, weather forecasting, climate research, oil and gas exploration, molecular modeling (computing the structures and properties of chemical compounds, biological macromolecules, polymers, and crystals), and physical simulations (such as simulations of the early moments of the universe, airplane and spacecraft aerodynamics, the detonation of nuclear weapons, and nuclear fusion).

Let us review how the supercomputing industry has evolved over the past three decades. As the number of processor families continued to shrink because of economics of scale, the Intel x86 family of processors grew in popularity, primarily because of the desktop personal computer (PC) revolution. In 1986, Intel began developing Pentium Pro processors designed for servers that lowered the cost of delivering FLOPS. Like early supercomputers, servers often had two or more processors working together and using shared memory, often called symmetric multiprocessing, or simply SMP, systems.

At the time, there were many SMP server options, such as those from Sun, IBM, HP, DEC, and others, each with their homegrown processor. These big players also offered large-scale SMP systems to perform many HPC tasks. The operating system of choice for supercomputing and SMP servers is Linux, an open-source version of UNIX. The ability to standardize on an open and freely available UNIX clone led to low-cost clusters of x86 workstations and servers. By using the message passing interface (MPI) library, clusters could run many of the supercomputing applications written for the larger, more powerful machines.

The performance of these first systems, often called Beowulf clusters (named for the NASA project that developed and used these systems), came close to that of large UNIX SMP systems and even many supercomputers of the day. The Beowulf systems were initially connected with Fast Ethernet, which turned out to be, in some cases, a bottleneck to performance. Other high-performance interconnects were developed, and eventually, the market settled on InfiniBand as the de facto HPC interconnect.

Instead of making processors faster, HPC vendors started to put more of them on a single processor substrate. The era of multicore began with dual CPU modules (cores) sharing the resources of a single processor socket. As should be evident, the new dual-core chips essentially doubled the number of CPU core elements in a cluster. More cores were added to each new generation of processors, taking advantage of Moore's law. The increase in computing density allowed the number of HPC jobs (the capacity) and the size of HPC jobs (the capabilities) to increase.

As the number of cores increased, another technology migrated into HPC, accelerating performance for many applications. These systems were based on commodity graphics processing units (GPUs) that contained hundreds to thousands of small, efficient cores working in unison. This new many-core approach essentially offloaded certain operations from the processor onto a GPU chip or cluster. Like those rendering graphics, these operations allowed processors to perform what is known as single instruction, multiple data (SIMD) parallel processing. As the switch to multicore, not all applications could take advantage of the new hardware resources, but those that could show a remarkable increase in speed, often twenty to thirty times faster.

In summary, there are three broad classes of high-performance supercomputing today.

- Shared-memory multiprocessors (SMP), programmed with languages such as pthreads
- OpenMP distributed memory multiprocessors programmed using message-passing libraries such as MPI
- Fine-grained data-parallel machines, such as graphics processor units (GPUs), programmed in languages such as CUDA or OpenGL.

The TOP500 ranks and details the five hundred most powerful computer systems globally. Table 8.2 shows the list of the top ten supercomputers globally as of June 2021. It shows that

- the number of cores varies from 450,000 to 10 million,
- the amount of memory goes from 350,000 GB (350 terabyte) to 5 million GB (petabyte),
- the LINPACK performance goes from 23.5 petaflops to 442.2 petaflops, and
- the theoretical peak performance ranges from 38.7 petaflops to 537.2 petaflops.

Rank	Name	Vendor	Processor and Network Architecture	Cores	Memory (GB)	LINPACK Peak Performance (Petaflops)	Theoretical Peak Performance (Petaflops)
1	Fugaku	Fujitsu	ARM A64FX 48C 2.2GHz, Tofu interconnect D	7,630,848	5,087,232	442.2	537.2
2	Summit	IBM	IBM Power System AC922, IBM POWER9 22C 3.07GHz, Nvidia Volta GV100, Dual-rail Mellanox EDR Infiniband,	2,414,592	2,801,664	148.6	200.7
3	Sierra	IBM/ Nvidia / Mellanox	IBM Power System AC922, IBM POWER9 22C 3.1GHz, Nvidia Volta GV100, Dual-rail Mellanox EDR Infiniband, IBM / Nvidia / Mellanox	1,572,480	1,382,400	94.6	125.7
4	Sunway	NRCPC	Sunway MPP, Sunway SW26010 260C 1.45GHz, Sunway	10,649,600	1,310,720	93	125.4
5	Perlmutter	HOPE	HPE Cray EX235n, AMD EPYC 7763 64C 2.45GHz, Nvidia A100 SXM4 40 GB, Slingshot-10, HPE	706,304	390,176	64.6	89.7
6	Selene	Nvidia	Nvidia DGX A100, AMD EPYC 7742 64C 2.25GHz, Nvidia A100, Mellanox HDR Infiniband, Nvidia	555,520	1,120,000	63.5	79.2
7	Tianhe 2A	NUDE	TH-IVB-FEP Cluster, Intel Xeon E5-2692v2 12C 2.2GHz, TH Express-2, Matrix-2000	4,981,760	2,277,376	61.4	100.6
8	JEWELS	Atos/Bull	Bull Sequana XH2000, AMD EPYC 7402 24C 2.8GHz, Nvidia A100, Mellanox HDR InfiniBand/ParTec ParaStation ClusterSuite	449,280	628,992	44.1	70.9
9	HPC5	Dell/ EMC	PowerEdge C4140, Xeon Gold 6252 24C 2.1GHz, Nvidia Tesla V100, Mellanox HDR Infiniband	669,760	349,440	35.4	51.7
10	Frontera	Dell/ EMC	Dell C6420, Xeon Platinum 8280 28C 2.7GHz, Mellanox InfiniBand HDR, Dell EMC	448,448	1,537,536	23.5	38.7

Table 8.2. List of top ten HPC supercomputers
in the world as of June 2021

The Japanese supercomputer Fugaku held the top spot with an HPL benchmark score of 442 petaflops. The machine is based on Fujitsu's custom ARM A64FX processor. In single precision, which is often used in machine learning and AI, Fugaku's peak performance is actually above an exaflop. This achievement has caused some to introduce this machine as the first exascale supercomputer. Fugaku already demonstrated this new level of performance on the new HPL-AI benchmark with 2 exaflops. Exascale computing can perform a billion billion (10^{18}), or a quintillion, computing operations per second. Crossing the exascale technology threshold will open new pathways of discovery and enable breakthrough solutions.

Let us now review the progression of the high-performance computing node architectures over the years. The early generations had a single processor per memory per node. Future generations have had multiple cores per node. In the future, each node will have multiple GPUs and multiple cores per node (called fat nodes). The Exascale Computing Project is building three computing machines with hundreds of thousands of fat nodes, such as the El Capitan machine at Lawrence Livermore National Lab, the Frontier machine at Oak Ridge National Lab, and the Aurora machine Argonne National Lab. This is the kind of innovation in the high-performance computing industry.

The HPC market size is expected to grow from $37.8 billion in 2020 to $49.4 billion by 2025 at a CAGR of 5.5 percent during the forecast period. The key players in HPC are IBM, HPE/Cray, Dell, Intel, AMD, Nvidia, Fujitsu, and NEC. Some example start-up companies in HPC are Cerebrus Systems and Samba Nova Systems.

Cloud Computing

Another area experiencing a lot of innovation is cloud computing. Cloud computing is the on-demand availability of computational and information resources, particularly data storage and computing power, without the user's direct active ownership or management. Large clouds often have functions distributed over multiple locations, each a data center. Cloud computing relies on sharing resources to achieve coherence and economies of scale, typically using a pay-as-you-go model, which can reduce capital expenses but may also lead to unexpected operating expenses, even service interruptions, for unaware users.

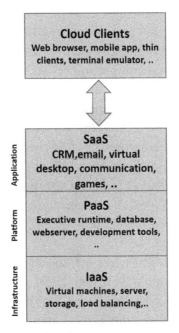

Figure 8.3. Cloud computing service models
as different layers of the stack

There are three service models in cloud computing.

- infrastructure as a service (IaaS)
- platform as a service (PaaS)
- software as a service (SaaS)

Infrastructure as a service (IaaS) refers to online services providing high-level application programming interfaces (APIs), which abstracts various low-level details of underlying network infrastructure like physical computing resources, location, data partitioning, scaling, security, backup, etc. Platform as a service (PaaS) is the capability provided to the consumer to deploy onto the cloud infrastructure consumer-created or acquired applications created using programming languages, libraries, services, and tools supported by the provider. Software as a service (SaaS) provides the consumer with the provider's applications—for example, Microsoft Office running on a cloud infrastructure. The applications are accessible from various client devices through either a thin client interface, such as a web browser (e.g., web-based email) or a program interface. Figure 8.3 shows the different cloud computing service layers.

Another way to categorize cloud computing is how customers access the cloud infrastructure: private, public, and hybrid cloud.

Private cloud. This is a cloud infrastructure operated solely for a single organization, whether managed internally or by a third party and hosted either internally or externally. Self-run data centers are generally capital intensive. They have a significant physical footprint, requiring allocations of space, hardware, and environmental controls. These assets have to be refreshed periodically, resulting in additional capital expenditures.

Public cloud. Cloud services are considered public when they are delivered over the public Internet. These services may be offered by a paid subscription or free of charge. Architecturally, there are few differences between public and private cloud services, but security concerns increase substantially when multiple customers share services (applications, storage, and other resources). Most public cloud providers offer direct connection services that allow customers to link their legacy data centers to their cloud-resident applications securely.

Hybrid cloud. This is a composite of public and private cloud environments, such as private or on-premises storage resources. They remain distinct entities but are bound together, offering the benefits of multiple deployment models. Hybrid cloud can also mean connecting collocation, managed, and dedicated services, all with cloud resources.

The global cloud computing market will grow from $371 billion (2021) to $832 billion by 2025. There are five major cloud providers of infrastructure as a service. As of this writing, in 2021, Amazon Web Services (AWS) has the most significant market share, about 31 percent. Microsoft Azure Cloud Services is second with about 22 percent, and Google Cloud Platform is third with about 8 percent. Other leading cloud providers include Alibaba Cloud, IBM

Cloud, and Oracle Cloud. Each provides a complete technology stack (data management for structured data, unstructured data, AI/machine learning, and APIs to access services) for any software company wishing to develop new software and other innovative products.

The key players in US cloud computing are Amazon AWS, Microsoft Azure, Google GCP, Alibaba, IBM, and Oracle. Emerging start-ups are Rescale, Nimbix, Aporia, Codescene, Filebase, Iterative, and Goliath.

Artificial Intelligence / Machine Learning (AI/ML)

The most exciting and impactful digital technologies to mature in the twenty-first century are artificial intelligence and machine learning. AI/ML, as attributed to computer pioneer Arthur Samuel in 1959, was defined as "a field of study that gives computers the ability to learn without being explicitly programmed."

Artificial intelligence (AI) describes programs to learn and reason similarly to humans. Although some have regarded the two words used together as an oxymoron, AI has been studied and practiced in computer science for as long as humans have tried to offload their work on a machine. Academic research began at Dartmouth College in the 1950s as students attempted to teach computers to play chess. By the next decade, the DoD had expressed interest as well. Around this time, Joseph Weizenbaum, a professor in MIT's Artificial Intelligence Laboratory, wrote a program called ELIZA to challenge the Turing test, intended to discern if a computer could express human thought.

Machine learning (ML) is a subset of artificial intelligence. ML is the study of computer algorithms that can self-improve automatically through experience and using (and reusing) data. It is regarded as an aspect of artificial intelligence. Machine learning algorithms build a model based on training data to make predictions or decisions without being intentionally programmed. Machine learning algorithms are used in a wide variety of applications, such as medicine, email filtering, speech recognition, and computer vision, areas in which it is difficult or unfeasible to develop conventional algorithms to perform needed tasks. Machine learning deals with algorithms that deal with programs that can learn without being explicitly programmed. Deep learning is a subset of machine learning in which artificial neural networks automatically adapt and learn from vast amounts of data.

AI and ML have been pursued for more than fifty years. They have been applied to a wide variety of applications, including sniffing out credit card fraud, like recommendation engines for Netflix and Amazon, for automatic identification of images and videos, virtual assistants for customer service, and natural language understanding and translation (ELIZA). Some of the application areas where AI/ML has been shown to be successful include: virtual assistants using intelligent agents and natural language processing; social media using sentiment analysis and spam filtering; transportation using safety monitoring and air traffic control; financial services using algorithmic trading and portfolio management; health care using drug discovery and robotic surgery; and e-commerce using customer support, product recommendation, and advertising.

What has made AI/ML relevant today is the confluence of three trends in computing.

- Vast amounts of cloud-based compute capabilities to run large neural networks and by leveraging architectures such as graphics processing units (GPUs)
- Access to vast amounts of training data and access to highly cheap data storage technologies, also on the cloud
- Availability of open-source software, such as TensorFlow, PyTorch, or Café, allowed any data scientist or software engineer to quickly implement a machine-learning framework with training data on the cloud.

Today, cloud service providers provide access to AI/ML technology stacks as part of their cloud services—for example, Microsoft's Azure Machine Learning stack, Amazon's AWS machines stack, or the Vertex AI stack on the Google Cloud Platform. Machine learning involves complex data preparation, transformation, training, tuning, deployment, and inference workflow. Besides the integrated development environments (IDEs), Jupyter Notebooks are used by data scientists and ML engineering for all workflow phases. A typical AI/ML workflow available on most cloud platforms involves the stages of (1) preparing the data, (2) training the model, (3) packing the model, (4) validating the model, (5) deploying the model, and (6) monitoring the model. It is relatively easy for innovators to apply AI/ML to a problem domain by leveraging an AI/ML technology stack on the cloud. There are many more innovations occurring at each level of the AI/ML technology stack and, in particular, workflow phases.

The global AI/ML market is expected to grow from $51 billion estimates in 2021 at a CAGR of 28.4 percent per annum. The key players in AI/ML are Google, Microsoft, Amazon, Alibaba, Baidu, Nvidia, and Salesforce. For example, Google uses AI to analyze earthquake tremors and alert the population, Amazon uses AI to match customer-purchasing preferences, and Alibaba uses AI to optimize its supply chain to develop personalized new product lines. Representative start-ups in AI/ML are Blue River Technologies, Bright Machines, Brighteiron, H2O, AEye, Automation Anywhere, Orbital Insight, and People.ai.

INTERNET OF THINGS (IOT)

The initial impetus for the Internet of Things (IoT) originated at Carnegie Mellon University regarding whether the drinks in a Coca-Cola vending machine were cold or not. IoT describes physical objects (or groups of such objects) embedded with sensors, processing ability, software, and other technologies connecting and exchanging data with other devices and systems over the Internet or other communications networks.

The IoT field has evolved because of the convergence of multiple technologies, including ubiquitous computing, commodity sensors, increasingly powerful embedded systems, and machine learning. Traditional areas of embedded systems, wireless sensor networks, control systems, automation, including home and building automation, independently and collectively enable the Internet of Things.

In the consumer market, IoT technology is most synonymous with products about the concept of the smart home, including devices and appliances, such as lighting fixtures, thermostats, home security systems and cameras, and other home appliances, that support one or more common ecosystems. It can be controlled via other devices associated with that ecosystem, such as smartphones and smart speakers at home or remotely. The IoT can also be used in health care systems.

IoT system architecture consists of devices, the edge gateway, and the cloud. Devices include networked controllers or peripherals, such as the sensors and actuators found in IoT equipment, particularly those that use Modbus, Bluetooth, Zigbee, or proprietary protocols, to connect to an edge gateway.

The edge gateway tier consists of eponymous sensor data aggregation systems that provide functionality, such as preprocessing the data, securing connectivity to the cloud, and using techniques, such as WebSockets, the event hub, and even in some cases, edge analytics or fog computing. This tier is also required to give a standard view of the devices at the upper layers to facilitate easier management.

The cloud itself is the final tier and includes the cloud application built for IoT using the microservices architecture. It contains various database systems that store sensor data, such as time series databases or asset stores using back end data storage systems (e.g., Cassandra, PostgreSQL). The cloud tier in most cloud-based IoT systems features an event queuing and messaging system to handle communication transpiring at all levels.

Some experts classify these three IoT tiers as edge, platform, and enterprise and say they are connected by proximity, access, and service networks respectively. Many technologies are enabling IoT. The network used to communicate between devices in an IoT installation is crucial to the field, which requires several wireless or wired technologies. These include the following:

- *Short-range wireless.* Bluetooth mesh networking, light fidelity (Li-Fi), near-field communication (NFC), radio-frequency identification (RFID), Wi-Fi technology for local area networking, Zigbee, and Z-Wave

- *Medium-range wireless.* LTE-advanced high-speed communication for mobile networks, 5G wireless networks capable of the high communication requirements of IoT and connecting a large number of IoT devices, even when they are moving
- *Long-distance wireless.* Low-power, wide-area networks (LPWAN), tiny aperture terminal (VSAT) with satellite communications using small dish antennae for narrowband and broadband data
- *Wired.* Ethernet general-purpose networking standard for twisted pair and fiber optic links in conjunction with hubs and switches, power line communication (PLC), and communication using electrical wiring to carry both power and data

Many innovations occur in the layers of the IoT stack and the different communication technologies. Industrial companies, such as GE, ABB, and Schneider Electric, are all creating platforms to tap into IoT platform innovation. Figure 8.4 shows some examples of IoT platforms from GE Predix, ABB Ability, Schneider Electric, and EcoStruxure.

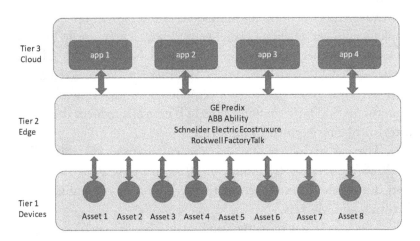

Figure 8.4. IoT platforms from industrial companies

These companies manufacture a lot of high-value assets, such as transformers, switchgear, UBS systems, drives, etc. In the past, when these assets failed in the field, it created business downtime and disruptions. With the Industrial Internet of Things (IIOT) growth, all these assets are connected using sensors and wired or wireless networks to a platform that runs on a cloud. These companies now can build applications on the platform, creating valuable services, such as predictive maintenance, predictive analytics, asset performance management, etc. Some of these apps are created by the companies themselves. Partners and third-party developers create other apps by leveraging application programming interfaces (API) on the cloud-based platform.

When I was CTO of ABB, I led teams to create the Ability IoT Platform and helped work with developers in the ecosystem to build apps on it. As CTO of Schneider Electric, I led teams to develop the EcoStruxure IoT platform and supported the same app development. We will discuss platforms in the next section.

A recent example of IoT innovation was Bahrain partnering with Nokia in a digital transformation of the country's water and electricity infrastructure. Bahrain's Electricity and Water Authority uses Nokia technology to modernize its water distribution network. In the first phase, the project covers the Al-Muharraq island city. A private LTE network for industrial connectivity has also been implemented to facilitate intelligent services and an IoT infrastructure. Another example is the Shanghai Public Health Clinical Center (SPHCC), which used the California-based connected health start-up VivaLNK's continuous temperature measuring device to monitor COVID-19 patients. This IoT network reduces the risk of caregivers being exposed to the virus.

The global IoT market is expected to reach $1,386 billion by 2026, up from $761 billion in 2020 at a CAGR of 10.53 percent during the forecast period (2021–2026), report published by Research and Markets.

The key large-company vendors in the IoT market include Cisco, Broadcom, Amazon AWS, Microsoft Azure, Siemens, ABB, Schneider Electric, Rockwell Automation, Verizon, AT&T, Vodafone,

Airtel, IBM, SAP, Oracle, and Texas Instruments. Some active start-ups in the IoT market include Samsara, Macrometa, Movanti, GenXComm, Ligado, Polte, Fog Horn, and Sight Machine.

The IoT node and gateway market was valued at $387.1 billion in 2020 and is projected to reach $566.4 billion by 2027; it is expected to grow at a CAGR of 6.7 percent from 2021 to 2027. Connectivity IC segment to account for the largest share of IoT node and gateway market during the forecast period. Consumer application to account for the largest share of IoT node and gateway market during the forecast period. APAC is expected to register the highest growth of IoT node and gateway market during the forecast period.

Major players operating in the IoT node and gateway market are Intel Corporation, Huawei Technologies Co. Ltd., NXP Semiconductor NV, Texas Instruments Incorporated, Cisco Systems Inc., Hewlett Packard Enterprise, TE Connectivity Ltd., Advantech Co. Ltd., Dell Technologies, Microchip Technology Inc., Notion, Helium System Inc., Samsara Networks Inc., Beep Inc., Estimote Inc., Aaeon Technology Inc., Nexcom International Co. Ltd., STMicroelectronics NV, Eurotech SPA, Adlink Technology Inc., Volansys Technologies, Embitel Technologies, Mitsubishi Electric Corporation, Lantronix Inc., Cradlepoint Inc., and so on.

PLATFORMS

The final area in which there will be a lot of innovation is platforms. A platform is a business model that creates value by facilitating exchanges between two or more interdependent groups, usually consumers and product or service providers. Platforms harness and create large, scalable networks of users and the resources they seek to make these exchanges occur, which the provider can access on demand. Platforms create communities and markets with network effects, allowing users to interact and transact with vendors and other current or potential customers.

Platforms don't directly create and control inventory via a supply chain as linear businesses do. Platform businesses don't own the means of production; instead, they make the means of connecting the relationship between producer and consumer. This is shown in figure 8.5.

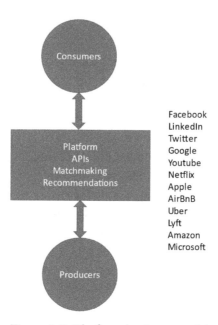

Facebook
LinkedIn
Twitter
Google
Youtube
Netflix
Apple
AirBnB
Uber
Lyft
Amazon
Microsoft

Figure 8.5. Platform business model
connecting producers to consumers

For example, Airbnb and Vrbo have created platforms for people who own homes and apartments so they may list their inventory of properties on their platform for customers who want to rent their homes or apartments for a day, week, or month. Hotels used to own the market for term rentals, which had a high maintenance cost. Airbnb does not own properties. They act only as middlemen, connecting the property owners and potential renters and advertising through Internet-based shopping sites.

Airbnb and Vrbo platforms have disrupted the hotel industry. Similarly, Uber and Lyft created a platform for people who drive cars to provide taxi-like service to customers who need to be gone somewhere. The taxi industry used to own the taxis and pay enormous fees for the licensing medallions at a high cost of maintenance and a salary to drivers. Instead, Uber and Lyft only create the platform that connect drivers and passengers, disrupting the taxi industry.

Facebook, WhatsApp, Instagram, and Twitter have created platforms for content creation, where writers upload content (blogs, pictures, and videos), users read the content, and like or share or comment, thereby creating engagement between content producers and consumers. In the past, of course, magazines and newspapers hired writers and photographers, owned printing presses, and bought paper and ink to create the content at a high cost. Now Facebook, WhatsApp, Instagram, and Twitter do this practically for free for all on their platform, disrupting the news publishing industry and the advertising business.

This platform shift has created many challenges concerning the types of content being created and uploaded on these platforms and the need to monitor this content's accuracy. Platform companies like Facebook have been criticized for permitting controversial content to generate more views, eyeballs, and revenue. This results in more daily active users on their platforms and bringing more advertisers to show their ads to these users.

YouTube, Netflix, and even Amazon Studios have created platforms for creative people to produce and distribute video content and for consumers to view it. Again, these Internet-based new platforms have been disrupted in the entertainment industry. And again, the challenges of monitoring the video content on these platforms have become an important issue. Amazon, eBay, Etsy, Alibaba, Whole Foods, Walmart, and hundreds, if not thousands, of other formerly brick-and-mortar retailers have disrupted business with their innovative and convenient shopping platforms as well.

The critical point on all these platforms is that they have created a way for both producers and consumers to be connected at scale. In each of these platforms, the business model is to charge either a flat fee or a percentage of the price of the sold item. For example, Uber takes 25 percent of the value of the ride as its fee. Amazon, similarly, collects a fee for every book, coffee maker, and movie rental to provide the platform's convenience. Creating a scalable platform to connect millions of producers and consumers is not easy, nor is it necessarily cheap. Yet this is where today's business innovation thrives. Perhaps most twenty-first-century innovations are founded on platforms, whether by building third-party apps or buying a book. And this platform-based intermediary has grown by leaps and bounds because of the pandemic.

Successful platforms facilitate exchanges by reducing transaction costs and by enabling externalized innovation. With the advent of connected technology, these ecosystems enable platforms to scale in ways that traditional businesses cannot. It is important to remember that a platform is a business model, not necessarily a piece of technology. Many people mistake conflating a platform with a mobile app or a website. Still, a platform is a holistic business model, obviously employing a variety of hardware, software, and networking technologies, creating value by bringing parties interested in some collaboration or transaction together.

Traditional, nonplatform companies operate linear businesses. Their operations are well-described by the linear supply chain. They build specific products or services, not opportunity networks. As such, they don't have the cost structure or the underlying economics or perhaps even the need to make a platform business model successful. In general, linear companies create value in goods or services and then sell them to someone downstream in their supply chain. Publishers publish books and sell them to bookstores, which sell them to consumers. That is linear. The platform design isn't about creating the underlying technology. It's about understanding and starting the whole business and creating value for and building a network.

The supply chain is no longer the central aggregator of business value in the twenty-first century. What a company owns matters less than the resources and connections between interested parties. In the old model, the scale resulted from investing in and growing a business's internal resources as large as possible. But in a networked world, scale comes from cultivating an external network built on top of your business. Growth becomes an organic event, not an abstract number to hope for. This is the essence of how platform business models work.

In the twentieth century, we saw rudimentary platform business models in the shopping mall and auction houses. Like their predecessors, these businesses relied upon brick-and-mortar locations to facilitate exchanges. But thanks to connected technology, platforms facilitate the exchange of value produced by decentralized networks of individuals. The result is that today's platform businesses can facilitate exchanges at an unprecedented scale.

The five most successful platforms are Google, Apple, Facebook, Amazon, and Microsoft. In finance, GAFAM is an acronym that refers to the stocks of five prominent American technology companies: Alphabet (GOOG, formerly known as Google), Amazon (AMZN), Facebook (FB), Apple (AAPL), Microsoft (MSFT). The term was coined in 2013 by Jim Cramer, the television host of CNBC's *Mad Money*, who praised these companies for being "totally dominant in their markets." In addition to being widely known among consumers, the five GAFAM stocks are among the largest companies in the world with a combined market capitalization of nearly $10 trillion as of December 21, 2021. (GOOG, $1.9 trillion; AMZN, $1.7 trillion; FB, $0.93 trillion; AAPL, $2.8 trillion; and MSFT, $2.45 trillion). In addition to GAFAM companies in the USA, the BAT (Baidu, Alibaba, and Tencent) companies in China have also achieved a similar market dominance globally. These companies have created platforms that have enabled an ecosystem of producers, developers, and consumers to innovate.

To create a successful platform business model, a company needs clean APIs using languages such as Python to allow third-party developers to develop applications on top of the platform. These APIs need to be easy to use and highly scalable to handle requests from millions of unskilled users. If the interface is not user-friendly, the customers will turn away. The second point is the business model. For example, Apple and Google charge their app developers a 20–30 percent fee for apps sold on their platforms. That fee is the transactional cost of doing business for both the developer and the platform company. Both will earn back, and the consumer will be enticed to download because there is little, if any, price.

The third point concerns the governance mechanism. Suppose a third-party developer builds an iOS or Google Play platform. Some platforms will simply let you install the app on their platform and permit any user to download or use the app. But there is often a governance mechanism, controlled by the platform creator, to approve an app (and its developer organization) only after a rigorous screening review. The platform company must be able to stand behind every app in its app store.

The global development platform market is projected to grow from $13.2 billion in 2020 to $45.5 billion by 2025 at a CAGR of 28.1 percent during the forecast period. The major players in the platform market include Apple, Google, Amazon, Salesforce, Microsoft, Netflix, Oracle, and Facebook. Key start-ups in this space include Magic Software Enterprises, AgilePoint, OutSystems, Appian, Zoho, Quick Base, LANSA (US), Netcall, WaveMaker, and K2.

Apps, APIs, and Technology Stacks for Platforms

Developers in start-ups can use technology stacks created by the platform companies to build microservices for their applications using APIs in Java or Python while leveraging innovation from others. This is the ultimate form of open innovation. Figure 8.4 showed the concept of platform innovation these software developers can leverage off cloud-based service providers' technology stacks.

Full-stack application developers in a start-up company can learn about AWS services, create a back end, add it to the front-end application, and simultaneously build storage. The developers can add user management, routing for traffic, and security features for the most common Internet attacks. They can also learn about the many services AWS cloud offers to make developing apps more straightforward and quicker. This allows developers to focus more time on building differentiated application logic to ensure the app stands out from the competitors.

These technology stacks are designed to help these developers conceive and develop cloud solutions using AWS. They can use AWS's software development kit (SDK) to interact with tested services and build compatible solutions. Developers can learn how to use Amazon DynamoDB data stores and integrate applications and data (Lambda, SWF). Developers can build secure, scalable, and fault-tolerant cloud applications.

PLATFORMS ARE THE ULTIMATE FORM
OF OPEN INNOVATION

Apple and Google have created the iOS platform and Google Play platform for applications on mobile phones or tablets. Some of these apps are free while others are paid apps. Apple and Google make 30 percent revenue for each app sold on their platforms. Why do app developers agree to pay 30 percent of their income to Apple/ Google? Because they have solved the problem of reaching their customer through their platform. All the app developer has to do is list the apps on the iOS or Google Play platform, and automatically, these apps are available to billions of phone and tablet users. Encouraging third-party developers to create applications on the iOS and Google Play platform is the ultimate model of open innovation as presented in this book. We will discuss this in more detail in chapter 9.

Consider this simple observation: When an app developer creates an app, it is typically rendered for a particular use case or vertical. For example, it can be a specific genre of video gaming or configured for finding only Italian restaurants. Say the total market for either of these apps is $1 million. Large companies will likely not invest in this type of vertical app, yet there are probably millions of customers for them if only they were created. Say the total market for such vertical market apps is $1 million $\times$ $1 million = $1 trillion. If a platform owner could attract all these app developers to its platform and charge each a 30 percent fee, it would generate $300 billion. This is why all companies are looking to do business on platforms.

It is not possible for the company that has built the platform to create the apps; that does not scale. But by enabling third-party developers to develop innovative apps, which they can market to their clientele, they are leveraging the power of open innovation.

CONCLUSION

This chapter reviewed some of the key digital technologies driving twenty-first-century product and service innovation. But the key takeaway is this: The innovator must determine how to drive business outcomes and realize real customer value by the judicious use of these technologies. One needs to start with a business strategy to drive the execution; then the execution will drive the technical implementation. For example, the business strategy may involve a digital OEM strategy, an operator strategy, a platform strategy, or a commercialization strategy.

The choice of business strategy will drive business execution, including cocreation, sourcing, business model, go-to-market, and rollout. The business execution will guide the selection of the technical implementation by leveraging the digital technologies, such as AI/ML or cloud or IoT discussed in this chapter. We should not create a start-up or a business in AI/ML simply because it is superior. We determine how to innovate strictly on the choice of which technology will improve business outcomes for our customers and drive value.

CASE STUDY: PRITH'S PERSONAL JOURNEY AS CTO OF ANSYS

This chapter has highlighted more than ten digital technologies to drive product innovation. Many companies are using many of these technologies to drive innovation. As CTO of Ansys, I have personally led the application of many of these digital technologies to innovate new products. The primary digital technology related to Ansys is CAD/CAE simulation-driven product innovation. There are numerous innovations that are being pursued at Ansys around different types of numerical methods, such as finite element and finite volume and finite-difference time-domain methods and isogeometric analysis.

There is a lot of interesting work being done on meshing to set up the solvers and post-processing to visualize the output of the solvers. Finally, there are a lot of innovations around multiphysics interactions among various solvers. The holy grail of simulation is accuracy, speed, robustness, and ease of use of the simulation. It turns out that one can get faster results if you run the simulation solvers at lower mesh sizes, but then you lose in accuracy. There is a lot of innovation that is being developed to design solvers that are accurate, fast, easy to use, and extremely robust.

The chapter mentioned semiconductor and nanotechnology as the next digital technology. Ansys is exploring the use of semiconductor simulation to simulate the power integrity, signal integrity, and thermal integrity of chips with tens of billions of transistors using 3D ICs and chiplet technology using the Redhawk-SC platforms. This is assisting customers in using semiconductor and nanotechnology to design new products.

The chapter also mentioned the use of photonic interconnects and opto-electronics as a digital technology. Ansys has acquired technologies such as Optics, Lumerical, and Zemax to perform simulations of optics and photonics and opto-electonic components in electronic chips. This is assisting customers using photonic technology to design new products.

Another digital technology that was described in this chapter was AI / machine learning. AI/ML involves training large neural networks with lots of training data where it learns the models and then applies the learning to different domains, such as natural language understanding or image recognition. Ansys is exploring the use of neural networks to train them for three-dimensional simulation for various inputs and boundary conditions using data-driven neural networks and physics-informed neural networks and machine-learning-based partial differential equation solvers. Some early work has shown one hundred times speedups using AI/ML methods on fluids simulations.

Another digital technology that Ansys is working on is high-performance computing. Across all the CAE solvers, such as Ansys Mechanical and Fluent and HFSS, there are four levels of parallelism that are being explored. First, there is independent parallelism, where one is running design optimization on multiple designs using CAE solvers in the inner loop. Second, there is domain decomposition, where a finite element domain is divided up into smaller domains and CAE solvers are solved on each domain with interactions among the domains using messaging passing. Third, within each domain, one can use multithreaded or loop-level parallelism to accelerate the tasks. Finally, researchers are exploiting fine-grained parallelism using GPUs that were mentioned in this chapter.

The next digital technology that Ansys is leveraging is the cloud. Many customers run CAE simulation solvers on high-performance workstations or HPD clusters on premise. But increasingly, the customers are running their CAE simulations on the cloud, on Microsoft Azure, Amazon Web Services, or Google Cloud Platform. Ansy solvers, such as Mechical, Fluent, and HFSS, now run seamless across all types of public clouds, private clouds, and hybrid clouds.

The chapter mentioned Internet of Things as a major digital technology. Customers are connecting their products using IoT to collect data from their products to the cloud. Using this IoT technology, customers are building digital twins of their physical assets, such as aircraft engines or chillers in air-conditioning systems for buildings. While the state of the art in digital twins is based on data analytics on the IoT data from the assets, Ansys is exploring the development of simulation-based digital twins and hybrid digital twins that combine data analytics with simulation.

Another digital technology that was mentioned in this chapter was augmented reality / virtual reality. Ansys is exploring the use of visualization of the physics simulations of the assets using AR/VR sets to visualize a digital twin using virtual reality. The final technology that the chapter discussed was platforms and APIs. Ansys is building a pervasive insights simulation platform, which is going to expose the APIs to all its core solvers, like Ansys Mechanical, Fluent, HFSS, and Redhawk, using Python-based APIs that will allow developers to run CAE simulation on the cloud using the simulation platform. Ansys is working with application developers, such as OptimEyes, to assist surgeons with eye surgery by connecting to Ansys solvers using APIs on the cloud.

CHAPTER 9

Building the Twenty-First-Century Innovation Factory

Interview: Henry Chesbrough, UC Berkeley Haas School of Business

Henry Chesbrough, who coined the term "open innovation," is the educational director of the Garwood Center for Corporate Innovation at Berkeley Haas. His research focuses on technology management and innovation strategy. He also teaches at Esade Business School in Spain's University Ramon Llull. He has been an adjunct professor at Harvard Business School and previously served as a product manager and vice president of marketing at Quantum Corporation, a manufacturer of data storage devices and systems. He earned a BA in economics from Yale University, an MBA from Stanford University, and a PhD in business administration from Berkeley Haas.

INTERVIEWER. Henry, thank you very much for agreeing to interview for my book The Innovation Factory. Tell me about your background. How did you arrive at your current role as director of the Garwood Center for Corporate Innovation at the Haas School at Berkeley?

INTERVIEWEE. I came out to California in 1981 and took a job at a hard disk drive manufacturer (Quantum) in 1983. In 1992, I left the HDD industry, got a PhD from Berkeley, and then took a job as an assistant professor at Harvard Business School. In 2003, my book *Open Innovation* came out, and I left Harvard for Berkeley. I've been at Berkeley ever since.

INTERVIEWER. You have pioneered the term "open innovation." Can you define it for us, and what is its benefit to larger companies? How do you differentiate it from closed innovation?

INTERVIEWEE. Traditionally, most business innovation processes have been closed. Companies often restrict their innovation inputs to their internal research labs and refuse to work with external knowledge sources that they do not own and control. Equally, companies start many more projects than they finish. There are numerous stranded projects with no place to go and no path forward. Not surprisingly, this impairs productivity.

The way to improve these processes is to open them up. Outside-in methods are required to bring more excellent external knowledge into the organization. Outside techniques encompass many mechanisms—from technology scouting, to crowdsourcing, to university collaboration, to in-licensing, and to engaging with start-up companies, among the more prevalent practices.

And there's another kind of opening up that's needed for more pathways for stranded internal technologies: the inside-out processes. These include outlicensing, joint development agreements, spinouts, internal start-up ventures, and lean start-up methods for discovering new business models inside large companies. These are only some of the more prevalent practices.

INTERVIEWER. I mention in my book that large companies do horizon 1 and horizon 2 innovation well but struggle with horizon 3 disruptive innovation. Is that where open innovation works?

INTERVIEWEE. In my view, horizon 1 and horizon 2 are focused on sustaining the firm's current business model in the short- and medium-term. Outside-in open innovation works well here, as shown in my previous answer. When we get to horizon 3, the business model is sometimes up for grabs. While there can be a substantial technical risk in horizon 3, the more significant risk is often whether the idea can be executed within the company's current business model or whether a new model must be created/discovered. Open innovation can help in horizon 3 by expanding the range of possible collaborators by developing POCs and other tangible demonstrations of technology and market potential. Lean start-up methods also have a role to play.

INTERVIEWER. Can you give some examples of companies that have practiced open innovation successfully and of companies where this open innovation did not work?

INTERVIEWEE. There is growing evidence that open innovation improves business performance. Some of this evidence comes from individual firms' experiences with open innovation. A consumer products firm, General Mills, analyzed sixty new product introductions in twelve months. They found that those with a substantial open innovation component outsold those that did not by more than 100 percent. Procter & Gamble has claimed that its use of open innovation has increased its revenues by billions of dollars. In the industrial sector, a recent study of 489 projects inside a sizable European manufacturer found that projects involving significant open innovation collaboration achieved a better financial return for the company than projects that did not. Open innovation also improved the time to market it took for many projects in this company.

One company that practiced open innovation twenty years ago was HP itself. They practiced using the outputs of each year's strategic planning process to initiate a call for proposals from academic researchers working in those areas of strategic interest. Successful responses would receive about $75,000 typically, enough to fund a professor and a grad student for summer. What was clever about the program was that before HP spent any money, they would receive responses from dozens of experts working in the specific fields of interest to HP. This environmental scanning came for free, and often, a successful summer project could be followed up with a consulting arrangement with the professor or hiring the graduate student working on the project.

The question of failures is fascinating, and there are some good ones. Quirky is one such situation. The company was founded in 2009 by serial entrepreneur Ben Kaufman and raised over $150 million in funding. The cool thing about Quirky was how it found its ideas. It invited individual inventors to submit their ideas for products to the company via its website. If the company selected the inventor's product for commercial development, the inventor would receive a portion of the revenues and develop the product to participate in a smaller amount of royalty payments. In turn, Quirky would handle the further development, merchandising, distribution, and advertising to promote the product.

In effect, Quirky outsourced the initial concept development for all its new products while building a solid marketing and distribution capability to sell all those products. This model celebrated the individual inventor and rewarded their ingenuity by paying these royalties. The company attracted a lot of attention and publicity with this model. Ideas came from many different people from different walks of life, and a wide array of possible products were proposed to Quirky.

The company also had some big hits with products like its Power Pivot, a flexible, multi-outlet plug extension cord, generating millions of dollars in revenues. In addition to attracting a lot of venture capital financing, the company signed a partnership with GE to manufacture and market its products (GE also invested in the company). So Quirky was well-backed and well-connected, and it was practicing an exceptionally expansive model of open innovation by relying on its external community for all its product ideas. Yet it all came to tears. By 2015, the company filed for bankruptcy, and founder Kaufman was forced out. In this case, open innovation didn't work, and it wasn't for lack of money or top management support.

INTERVIEWER. If you are a start-up company, how do you form an open innovation partnership with a larger company? What are the dos and don'ts? What should you avoid?

INTERVIEWEE. Just as there is a valley of death between the innovation units of companies and their downstream business units, there is also a big gap between external start-ups and corporates. This gap between the corporate and start-up ways of working poses real challenges to getting both sides together. Corporations are hard to approach for start-ups, cultural differences often lead to misunderstandings, and different organizational clock speeds for making decisions take their toll. In the beginning, start-ups fear that corporates would steal their idea. If they persist and engage, that fear soon gives way to another: that companies take way too long to make small decisions.

The critical flaw here is that a large company's processes to make a big, expensive decision, like building a new factory, are also used to make tiny decisions with start-ups, like which target market to start with. So large companies should avoid imposing their traditional work processes on these start-ups but instead craft an expedited path for small decisions so that the start-up and the corporate can work together at the pace of the start-up. For start-ups, corporate partners understand how to scale. And this, more than money, is where the start-up can benefit from working with a corporate partner.

INTERVIEWER. If you are a large company, how do you form an open innovation partnership with a start-up company? What works, and what does not?

INTERVIEWEE. The processes that a large company follows to make a big, expensive decision are also used to make very small decisions with start-ups, so large companies should avoid imposing their traditional work processes on these start-ups but instead craft an expedited path for small decisions so that the start-up and the corporate can work together at the pace of the start-up.

INTERVIEWER. What about open innovation with academia? How can large companies better partner with academia?

INTERVIEWEE. One lesson from the HP example in the fourth question is to focus your energies on relevant academic areas. There is too much going on in academia for companies to benefit from them unless there is consistent engagement over time and focus. In the beginning, a promising collaboration can begin with personal relationships. But if that collaboration is to sustain over time, the association must evolve between two institutions.

In the late 1990s, Intel did this well with Berkeley in its heyday. They were spending tens of millions of dollars annually on supporting academic research, and they devoted significant time in their senior R&D leadership to nurturing the relationship. A lesson for companies today is that many universities have success attracting donors for new buildings but have difficulty attracting funding for research programs. Companies should care less about getting their name on the building and benefit from influencing research programs with stellar faculty and outstanding graduate students. So they can be entirely complementary to private donors, who want their name on the building, but care less about what goes on inside.

INTRODUCTION

This final chapter focuses on applying some of the key take-aways from the previous chapters, particularly chapters 2 and 8, to create the innovation factory of the twenty-first century. The fundamental millennial change is in the way of thinking about innovation. In the twentieth century, innovation may or may not have happened at some time during business processes. In the twenty-first-century innovation factory, it is an essential aspect of business strategy. It is integrated into the value chain, therefore dealing with product and service development.

The innovation factory is the practice and the implementation of H2 and H3 open innovation, in which companies, whether large or small, partner outside their internal operations with universities, start-ups, and other business partners to develop innovative ideas and subsequently deliver them in the form of products and services to their customers. This was mentioned during the interview with Professor Henry Chesbrough in the beginning of the chapter and is shown in figure 9.1.

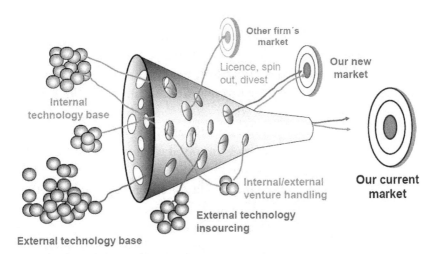

Figure 9.1. Open innovation funnel for large companies, a way to tap into horizon 2 and horizon 3 external ideas from start-ups, universities, and other companies (courtesy of Henry Chesbrough, *Open Innovation*)

ROADMAP FOR BUILDING AN INNOVATION FACTORY

The following is a roadmap to allow large companies to support long-term disruptive innovation in the twenty-first century:

- Continuously learn new ways to accelerate innovation.
- Actively seek and hire the best talent you can find, and retain them with a strong, supportive culture and business climate.
- Create a culture in which innovation is the highest goal for everyone.
- Increase your risk tolerance to the highest amplitude; it is okay to be uncomfortable and uncertain about outcomes to enhance clarity and confidence.
- If failure appears to be an alternative, fail quickly and move on.
- Explore the use of continuous innovation for both software and hardware product innovations.
- Try and leverage platforms and the cloud for your innovative software products.
- If you are a large company, you need to create a central research lab or core R&D group whose job is to explore long term R&D (H3 innovation).
- This group should be empowered to explore organic innovation and open innovation to identify potential partners in academia or start-ups to introduce innovative ideas from outside the organization.
- This central team should have an R&D role and a sales and marketing team of its own to sell what is being developed.
- This new business should be incubated in the central team and insulated from its main businesses even if it is disruptive. Everyone from the C-suite down must champion innovation and help the company accept and adapt to change, even in the possible threat to the cash cows of the leading business.
- Once the new business scales to a certain size, it needs to enter into the folds of the rest of the company as another of its business units under the aegis of the CEO.

- Use mergers and acquisitions of start-up companies as a very effective way to bring disruptive innovation to a large company. Leverage the central research team and its open innovation approach to feed into the M&A pipeline.

This new organizational structure for the innovation factory for the twenty-first century is shown in figure 9.2.

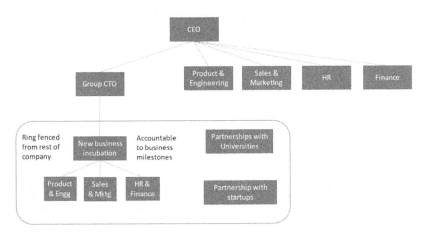

Figure 9.2. Organizational structure of the innovation factory. The central incubation team consisting of a central R&D team and sales team incubates the horizon 3 innovative products and solutions while building partnerships with universities and start-ups.

CASE STUDIES OF CISCO AND ALPHABET

As mentioned in chapter 6, the above organizational structure has been shown to work in many companies. For example, Cisco used the spin-in model to create several disruptive innovations over a decade. A group of entrepreneurs within Cisco would come up with an innovative idea, and the CEO would create a ring-fenced organization where they could develop this innovative product and sell the product to some key customers. The CEO would give these entrepreneurs different stages of funding similar to a start-up and hold them accountable for outcomes. This has been discussed in detail in chapter 6.

Another company that has adapted this principle successfully is Google. While Google's main business was around search, they explored new innovations around self-driving cars and quantum computing as Moonshot projects. However, it was difficult to fund such long-term innovations while responding to Wall Street's short-term expectations of profit and loss every quarter. Hence, Google created a larger entity called Alphabet in which the primary business of Google was housed. And all other new business incubations, such as Waymo and the Moonshot Sandbox, were directly part of Alphabet as a holding company. Google recently spun out the Moonshot Sandbox as a spin-out start-up.

Another recent example is a start-up company called Chipletz, which was recently spun out of AMD to explore a new way of connecting chips using interposers on a die. The technology was originally developed by researchers and executives at AMD, but AMD was not interested in proceeding with this technology, so they spun out the company and allowed the start-up to license their technology in exchange for equity ownership. The new company raised Series A funding from AMD and VC investors to pursue this innovation.

This is clearly the right organizational structure for large companies wishing to pursue long-term disruptive innovation.

ROLE OF MERGERS AND ACQUISITIONS TO DRIVE DISRUPTIVE INNOVATION

In addition to this incubation model, a very important approach for larger companies to perform disruptive innovation is through mergers and acquisitions. Most companies have a strong corporate development organization, whose role is to identify other companies to acquire and bring under the fold of the larger company. The central R&D team can play a very important role in identifying which start-up companies to partner with and which start-up companies to acquire. The most innovative companies, like Google and Amazon, have been able to enter some new disruptive markets using acquisition. For example, Google acquired YouTube to expand from search-based advertising to video-based advertising, and Amazon acquired Kiva to accelerate their logistics in distribution centers.

CHALLENGES TO AND CHARACTERISTICS OF INNOVATION FACTORY

As pointed out repeatedly in these pages, American business has long struggled to be more innovative. Management continually strives to lower costs, manage workflow, raise productivity, and myriad other concerns. Innovation too often takes a back seat to these more pressing problems, which have only grown more significant and insurmountable because of the coronavirus pandemic, which shows no sign of relenting. Companies, large and small, all face a set of common challenges to innovation initiatives: war for talent, culture challenges, such as resistance to risk-taking, and innovation in a globally diverse business environment.

Any company seeking to grow, whether a large company or a start-up, struggles with similar challenges. Shareholders expect continually rising returns, which means the companies must constantly innovate however they can, which results from hiring and nurturing innovative talent. The three critical assets for continuous growth in innovation are people, culture, and the environment. Hiring the most talented individuals and giving them all the environmental resources (workspace, software, hardware, and time) they need to develop new ideas within a culture that encourages, grows, and rewards their work make up the garden in which innovation will grow and flourish.

War for talent. The most crucial factor for innovative company culture is creative talent. A well-known saying among venture capitalists is that it is better to fund a start-up with an A-plus team and a B-minus business plan than a B-minus team with an A-plus business plan. Human capital will always find a way to pivot and change directions when encountering roadblocks or uncertainties. Wise leaders surround themselves with innovative employees.

The United States used to attract the best and brightest talent in the world. Students lacking sufficient opportunities in their home countries came here to pursue advanced degrees. I arrived in 1981 after completing my BTech degree at the Indian Institute of Technology Kharagpur, one of the top engineering colleges in India, to pursue an MS and PhD degree in electrical engineering at the University of Illinois Urbana-Champaign. More than 50 percent of the graduate students in my classes at UIUC were from China, India, and elsewhere.

These days, graduates from overseas engineering colleges, like the IITs in India, are recruited on their college campuses by multinational companies, like Microsoft and Google, to work in India. Significantly few ever come to the US to pursue graduate studies, so US grad schools suffer from a lack of fresh, top-quality talent. Exacerbating the situation, the more restricted immigration policies of the US further result in foreign nationals staying in their home countries. Many of these graduate students are now going to Canada and Europe. This will have an ever-deepening impact on the US. Therefore, global companies need to recognize this change and develop talent recruitment strategies for the worldwide market for innovative employees to work remotely from wherever they wish and still be part of their home team.

Culture. A culture that develops and sustains innovation is essential for growing healthy, productive innovators. This starts at the top with C-suite leadership encouraging more idea generation, risk-taking, and innovation. Yet creating an innovation factory demands it. When dealing with H2 and H3 innovation, the more disruptive and long-term the ideas, the riskier it gets and the higher the chance of failure is. Leadership needs to be tolerant of such risks and celebrate risk-taking, whether it is a success or failure. Only then will the innovators feel that the culture is safe enough to embark on more innovative projects.

Environment. Finally, the resources and funding to support long-term disruptive innovation must be in place to successfully support innovation in companies. The general rule of thumb when managing a large company portfolio of R&D projects is that about

70 percent of the investments are targeted to H1 or incremental or short-term innovation, about 20 percent of the investments are for H2 or medium-term innovation, and about 10 percent of the investments are for H3 or long-term disruptive innovation. Over the long term, more than 90 percent of these H3 investments will fail, but 10 percent of the remaining 10 percent will be successful, and it is these investments that will make the company successful in innovations.

Once a large company begins its innovation strategy in the manner just explained, they are effectively building their own private, proprietary innovation hub. As it is understood by most in business today, an innovation hub is a concept and a physical entity where innovators can interact, create, undertake, and work together. The idea has gained interest and has led to a network of innovation hubs around the globe.

WORLDWIDE INNOVATION HUBS

In the twenty-first century, innovation has become a necessity. Many businesses already consider it central to their strategy. According to *Forbes* magazine, innovation is vital for companies because it allows them to penetrate markets quicker, create original concepts, and grow more organically. But innovation is not only crucial in the business world. Today, its influence has become fundamental for the success of cities, counties, and states. The combination of innovation and talent in large cities has produced higher productivity and more significant, long-term economic growth. Like businesses, cities that combine these two characteristics are more resilient in the face of economic/financial crises. Looking to share their success and encourage others to share in it, some cities have created incentives to attract large companies and start-ups, hoping to attract talented citizens and enhance economic growth.

What does it take to be recognized as a hub for innovation globally?

- Access to talent
- Access to top universities

- Access to investors/capital
- Access to customers
- Support from C-suite

The *Innovation Geographies* report published in 2019 analyzed the most innovative cities and those with the highest innovation talent worldwide. The leading indicators used to assess innovation in a city where there is foreign direct investment (FDI) in high-tech industries, amount of venture capital spent, expenditures on R&D, and the number of international patent applications. Other leading indicators taken into account to measure the concentration of talent present in a given city were quality of higher education, standard of education among the population, percentage of the population between the ages of twenty and forty, and percentage of jobs in high-tech industries.

According to these criteria, JLL, a UK-based commercial real estate services company, has researched the ten most innovative cities in the world. They are the following:

1. *San Francisco and Silicon Valley (US)*. The Bay Area is home to the most significant number of start-ups globally. Furthermore, some of the most prestigious international universities (Stanford and UC Berkeley) are in the San Francisco Bay Area. Headquarters of tech firms such as Apple, Google, Oracle, Tesla, Facebook, Cisco, Xilinx, Intel, Juniper, and Altera are also based in the Bay Area. In addition, most of the top-tier venture capital firms are located in Silicon Valley. Finally, Silicon Valley is the hotbed of start-ups, and there is a lot of entrepreneurship talent in this area. The combination of the most prestigious universities, access to entrepreneurial talent, and investment capital makes Silicon Valley the world's innovation capital.

2. *Tokyo, Japan*. Japan's most populous city produces the highest number of patents globally. Similarly, it leads the field in diverse technologies—from electrical machinery to nanotechnology. It is home to two of the most prestigious

universities in Asia, the University of Tokyo and the Tokyo Institute of Technology. And it is the headquarters of many well-known multinational corporations, such as Sony, Panasonic, Honda, Mitsubishi, SoftBank, and Toyota.

3. *Singapore, Republic of Singapore.* This beautiful city-state is growing in terms of the number of start-ups and is an important hub for R&D. It is the home of two top-tier universities—the National University of Singapore and Nanyang Technological University. It is also the world's top destination for foreign direct investment (FDI) in high-tech industries.

4. *Beijing, People's Republic of China.* Beijing has a well-established innovation ecosystem, which has spawned many of the unicorn companies outside Silicon Valley. It is the world's third-highest destination for venture capital finance. It is the home of Tsinghua University and Peking University, the best universities in China. It hosts several exciting start-ups and large cloud companies, like Baidu, Tencent, and Alibaba. It ranks as the seventh city in the world for patent applications.

5. *London, United Kingdom.* Almost 15 percent of London's labor force is employed in high-tech. London also occupies the world's top position in the concentration of talent thanks to its first-class universities and highly educated workforce. It is close to the University of Oxford and Cambridge University and home to King's College London and Imperial College, all recognized as prestigious universities. London is called the financial capital of the world. Hence, there are lots of fintech start-ups.

6. *Berlin, Germany.* Berlin has long attracted innovators, scientists, and technologists to its thriving scene. It is home to top universities, such as Technical University of Berlin, Humboldt University of Berlin, and Berlin Institute of Technology. Some of the world's biggest companies, such as Tesla, have a presence in the region. VC funding backs Berlin as a center of growth and innovation.

7. *Paris, France.* European leader in patent applications, Paris is also a leader in technological innovations. It is the home of Université PSL, Institut Polytechnique de Paris, the Sorbonne University, and Université de Paris. It hosts headquarters for Airbus, Safran, and Schneider Electric.

8. *New York, US.* One of the most innovative places for innovation and talent, New York has long been a headquarters destination for notable companies, such as IBM, Verizon, and Pfizer, the first to bring a COVID-19 vaccine to market. It is home to many prestigious universities, such as Columbia, Princeton, NYU, Cornell, and Yale. New York is called the financial capital of the US with its proximity to Wall Street and the New York Stock Exchange and the headquarters of many banks, such as Citibank and JPMorgan Chase, and several financial technology start-ups.

9. *Boston, US.* Boston boasts over forty-five colleges and universities, including MIT and Harvard. Once considered second only to Silicon Valley in high-tech companies, such as Digital Equipment Corporation, Wang, and Data General, the 128 loop is home to over a thousand prominent biotech start-ups and pharma companies, like Biogen and Merck. It has also become a hotbed for start-ups and venture capital. In 2014, Google launched its 30 Weeks incubator for designers into entrepreneurs in Boston.

10. *Seoul, South Korea.* South Korea is third in the world of patent applications. One of the four Asian tigers (with Hong Kong, Singapore, and Taiwan, South Korea became an economic and innovation powerhouse by creating a nationwide collaboration between government, industry, and the academic community, an innovation factory), Seoul is the home of Seoul National University and KAIST, two of the most prestigious universities in South Korea. It is the headquarters of technology giants Samsung and LG and the renowned automaker of Hyundai, Kia, and Genesys. Seoul is also a hotbed for start-ups.

WHAT IS DIFFERENT ABOUT INNOVATING IN THE DIGITAL WORLD?

In the past, innovations were mostly for hardware products—cars, phones, and chips—and required a lot of investment. A start-up that was attempting to build a new ASIC chip might have needed $200 million to design, fabricate, test, and market the device. Software products developed in the past required less investment: hiring a team of developers, office, and workstations. A typical enterprise software company might have needed $50 million in funding to launch a new application. Since the software talent was concentrated in high-cost areas, like Silicon Valley, New York, or London, often where the hardware was also being developed, the investment required even for a start-up was relatively high.

USE OF CONTINUOUS PRODUCT IMPROVEMENT

The traditional waterfall development model for new product innovation, especially hardware products, breaks project development into distinct stages or phases, separated by decision points (gates). Continuing with the project is typically decided by a manager, steering committee, or governance board at each gate. The decision is made based on forecasts and information available at the time, including the business case, risk analysis, and availability of necessary resources (e.g., money, people with correct competencies, etc.).

The staged approach appeals to the team members because they can assess progress incrementally. It appeals to management because the make-or-break stages control funding more tightly. The traditional stage-gate process has five phases with four gates. The phases are scoping, building a business case, development, testing and validation, and launching. Ahead of this process, there is often a preliminary phase called ideation or discovery. After the fifth phase, the process typically ends with the postlaunch review. Significant new products go through the complete five-phase process.

Most products in the twentieth century were designed and built using these waterfall or stage-gate processes. In the twenty-first century, a software product is more often made using a fluid continuous innovation process where a new iteration or version is released to a small set of customers with some initial ideas. If it is well-regarded, it is then scaled to a more extensive collection of customers, usually incorporating more features and, in some instances, as a full beta release. The software may not be ready to be sold just yet, but every iteration helps make it a mature product prepared for the market.

In the past, software products had to be manufactured on transportable media—CDs or magnetic tape—and released on a dependable schedule—for example, once a year or every six months. Today, customers are partners in continuous innovation, suggesting bug fixes and improvements all the time. And with most software products available for download from the cloud, transport media has gone the way of the buggy whip. Author Eric Ries, an entrepreneur and start-up expert, proposed a methodology to use continuous innovation to create radically successful businesses.

A related approach in software engineering is the technology of continuous integration and continuous delivery (CI/CD), the combined practices of continuous integration (CI), and either continuous delivery or continuous deployment (CD). CI/CD bridges the gaps between developmental and operational activities and teams by deploying automation in the building, testing, and deploying applications. The process contrasts with traditional methods, where all updates were integrated into one large batch before rolling out the newer version. This became cumbersome and impractical for the reasons mentioned above and superseded by modern-day developmental operations, or DevOps. This practice shortens the software development life cycle (SDLC) and incorporates continuous development, continuous testing, continuous integration, continuous deployment, and continuous monitoring of the application build. The CI/CD practice, or CI/CD pipeline, forms the backbone of modern-day DevOps operations.

Continuous innovation inevitably leads to and complements all the other continuous methods described above. Continuous is a new way of thinking about both, making iterative product development seem quite antiquated. It is easy to commit to continuous releases of new software product features when they are served from the cloud. Likewise, it can be continuously tested by subsets of customers. In today's world of IoT-connected intelligent devices and over-the-air (OTA) software updates, such as iOS updates of iPhones or as-needed upgrades from HP, Microsoft, or Adobe, the same practice of continuous innovation used with software works equally well with technology-based hardware products, even an automobile.

For example, it is well-known that the Tesla electric car has more than one hundred million lines of software code that controls all aspects of the car, electrification, autonomous driving, navigation system, and entertainment system. It has more software than a Boeing 747 aircraft. Tesla has embraced continuous integration / continuous development in its software engineering. As soon as new software features are available, they are pushed out via wireless connectivity to the cars. In 2015, Tesla had some problems with fires in their vehicles since the battery packs were too low to the ground. Instead of doing an expensive recall, they solved the problem with a software update that raised the suspension by three inches and, thus, avoided the battery explosions. This is the kind of continuous innovation for hardware products enabled by digital technologies in the twenty-first century.

Innovators Can Work from Anywhere in the World

In another contrast, most workers in the twentieth century were required to work on the company's premises. Today's software applications are being developed on the cloud by software engineers who work remotely from their homes anywhere in the world provided they have a secure internet connection. Many software developers have found that they can collaborate remotely just as effectively using tools such as Teams, Webex, Zoom, Slack, Atlassian, or Jira. Employers can hire the best talent in the world wherever they are without all the costs and encumbrances of engaging in a specific location. Employees can end the endless commutes and be much more productive working in a home office environment. Both save time, money, and stress. During the Covid-19 pandemic in 2020, the world taught us all to work remotely. This is a permanent business transformation about how innovators will work from anywhere in the world.

DIGITAL TECHNOLOGIES DRIVING PRODUCT INNOVATION IN THE TWENTY-FIRST CENTURY

Chapter 8 discussed the role of key digital technologies that drive both the innovation process and product development in the twenty-first century. These technologies include the following:

- CAD/CAE simulation-driven product innovation
- semiconductors and nanotechnology
- photonics and optical interconnects
- quantum computing
- wireless communications
- additive manufacturing
- virtual reality / augmented reality
- blockchains
- cybersecurity
- high-performance computing
- cloud computing
- AI/machine learning
- Internet of Things (IoT)
- platforms

Twenty-first-century innovators need to think about how these digital technologies can be leveraged to drive new business results, contribute to top-line revenue growth, bottom-line cost savings, or improve customer relationship experiences for the company.

Chapter 8 explained how high-technology companies offering a development platform, such as Apple's iOS, Google's Android, Microsoft's Azure, the Salesforce Force, or Amazon with its AWS platform, encourage third-party developers to build applications for them. It is an evolutionary step forward from the freelance development methods of the twentieth century and even an advancement from making an app store. Developers can work remotely from the cloud. This is the ultimate expression of open innovation for the twenty-first century.

In addition, all these cloud service providers offer programs for start-ups to give free computing credits. For example, Amazon's AWS Activate provides start-ups with many benefits, including AWS credits of up to $100,000, AWS support plan credits, and architectural guidance to help grow their business. Similarly, Microsoft Azure has a program for start-ups to run lean, stay agile, and grow fast. Azure is truly open-source, supporting familiar, open-source software tools and technologies. Azure Marketplace supports various Linux distributions, including Debian and SUSE.

Google Cloud Platform offers a similar program for start-ups. Developers can get financial, business, and technology support, including product credits, access to growth opportunities and a global community, accelerators, mentoring, and more Google services. Select start-ups may qualify for tailored go-to-market opportunities.

Basic, Applied, and Use-Inspired Research

Traditionally, most academic research has been classified as either basic—that is, curiosity-driven and meant to create new knowledge within a field—or applied, performed in the service of some practical need or goal. In a recent article, Professor Randy Katz from UC Berkeley has defined a new term: "use-inspired research." It characterizes the work of scientists who search for fundamental knowledge yet select questions and methods based on their relevance to real-world issues (https://randyhkatz.medium.com).

THE ROLE OF GOVERNMENT, VCS, AND COMPANIES IN FUNDING INNOVATION

Throughout this book, I have stressed that to succeed with innovation in the twenty-first century, large companies need to engage in concerted, three-pointed innovation development. This premise has been widely acknowledged in the literature and practice worldwide.

Chapter 7 went into detail about the National Science Foundation, founded in 1950 based on a report by Vannebar Bush submitted to then president Eisenhower. The NSF is the model for practicing three-pointed innovation and has made a lot of progress over the past seventy-five years in supporting basic science and engineering research in the US.

As discussed in the interview in chapter 7, there have been a number of broad calls over the past couple of years for a new directorate at NSF. For example, the US Senate has passed the US Innovation and Competition Act, or USICA, which authorizes the establishment of a new Directorate for Science, Technology, and Innovation, focused on strengthening US leadership in critical technologies through basic research in key technology focus areas, such as artificial intelligence, high-performance computing, and advanced manufacturing, and the commercialization of those technologies to businesses in the US. Likewise, the US House of Representatives has passed the NSF for the Future Act, authorizing the establishment of a new directorate for Science and Engineering Solutions to advance research and development solutions to address societal and national challenges. In May 2021, the Biden-Harris administration issued its FY 2022 President's Budget Request, seeking a new Technology, Innovation, and Partnerships, or TIP, directorate.

The goal of TIP is to advance critical technologies, like advanced manufacturing, advanced materials, advanced wireless, artificial intelligence, biotechnology, quantum information science, and semiconductors and microelectronics, and to address pressing societal challenges, such as climate change, equity, and critical and resilient infrastructure. Indeed, we feel strongly about the bidirectional nature of critical technologies and societal challenges. Our climate change challenges prompt new artificial intelligence techniques, for example, just as advances in artificial intelligence offer new lenses for thinking about how to mitigate climate change.

Ultimately, the ambition of TIP is to engender a paradigm shift. Rather than an emphasis on pushing research results, including new technologies, out of the laboratory and out to the market and society, we would like to encourage the market to inspire research questions and specifically draw out research results. That is, this market-pull dynamic will enable the beneficiaries of research to motivate that work and, thus, become invested in seeing it translated and realized in society.

INNOVATIVE FUNDING MODELS FOR LARGE COMPANIES IN THE TWENTY-FIRST CENTURY

In the past, large companies commonly funded research in all three horizons. Many of them had a central research lab, as described in chapter 4. These CRLs would support work conducted in academia with solid research ties. Such companies were funded to facilitate a technology transfer to make commercial products and services. But more recently, because of increased pressure on corporate profit margins and the push for short-term benefits from innovation work, many companies have had to reduce funding for their CRLs.

That has resulted in the formation of research consortia that pool resources among multiple companies in a shared development area, which then fund one or more universities to pursue the research. Two examples of successful consortia-based research programs are the Semiconductor Research Corporation (SRC) and SEMATECH, as discussed in chapter 7.

FUTURE FUNDING MODELS

Many social and economic factors have contributed to shaking up how innovation R&D is funded in the US. In the past, the federal government funded research in universities and government labs, venture capitalists funded start-ups, and the company CEO and board financed the company's R&D. In the future; governments will support universities, large companies, and start-ups. In contrast, companies will fund universities, start-ups, and their own internal R&D. Figure 7.5 in chapter 7 showed the transition to the new funding model.

A Constantly Changing Business Landscape

The past one hundred years have seen a lot of innovation; but this has been taken place by innovators working in silos in universities, government labs, start-ups, and large companies. The following one hundred years will be the century during which innovation will break boundaries between organizations.

Silicon Valley was once the world's most important innovation center, but COVID has dispersed it across the country and the world. There are now Silicon Valleys in the Research Triangle Park of North Carolina; Austin, Texas; Boston; Berlin; London; Singapore; etc. We used to think of lines of businesses (LOBs) in companies and companies as independent and standalone, smokestacks, but this is no longer the norm.

Over the past thirty years, the US has attracted and hired the best and the brightest students, domestic and international. But now foreign national talent is graduating from our universities, then returning to their home countries. This creates immense new forms of technology transfer and levels the competitive playing field for innovation work. I believe it is vital that we think of innovation not as a trait of any particular nationality but as an outgrowth of the global enterprise we work with.

Today, we recognize the advantages of working in innovation teams, both internal and outside partners, whenever and however we can, because no single entity has the necessary knowledge or expertise. Partners may come from academia, start-ups, business partners, and product suppliers. We succeed most productively and reliably when we partner. That is what we call open innovation, and open innovation is a network spreading everywhere.

AUTHOR'S PERSONAL EXPERIENCE
IN DISRUPTIVE INNOVATION

From 2007 to 2012, I had the opportunity to be the director of HP Labs, the central research arm of Hewlett-Packard. During that period, I led a global team of about six hundred researchers in seven locations around the world—Palo Alto (US), Bristol (UK), Haifa (Israel), Bangalore (India), Beijing (China), St. Petersburg (Russia), and Singapore (Singapore). We were able to create global teams across the world to work on twenty big bet research projects on topics such as exascale computing, Moonshot server, optical interconnect for servers, memristor nonvolatile memory, commercial digital printing, cloud computing, scalable cloud storage, sustainable data center, Openet software-defined networking, Vayu personal digital device, color-reflective displays, CeNSE, and pervasive communications. These projects were worked on in collaboration with the businesses in the five divisions of HP (printing, personal computing, servers and storage, software, and services).

In addition, we had a very successful open innovation program with eighty universities around the world, where the professors at these universities worked closely with the research agenda of the twenty big bet projects. While the research projects were successful, the business success was limited to the projects that had the salespeople from the five divisions of HP aligned with them. The R&D projects that did not have sales support were not successful. I learned the importance of lacking an incubation organization at HP Labs. If we had our dedicated sales and marketing organization to take the innovations developed at HP Labs, these projects would have been more successful.

I have been CTO at Ansys since 2018. Ansys is a global leader in modeling and simulation. We have simulation tools based on numerical methods to solve structures, fluids, electromagnetics, semiconductors, optics, and systems. For the past three years (2018–2021), I have worked with the R&D developers on a long-term technology strategy that included twelve pillars: numerical methods, meshing, visualization, multiphysics platforms, AI and machine learning, high-performance computing, cloud computing, model-based software engineering, digital twins, integrated computational materials engineering, solutions around autonomy, electrification and IoT, and health care as a new vertical.

We have created centers of excellence in each area to bring researchers together to collaborate across the product areas and business units, along with these technical directions. We have organized a yearly TechCon to bring our two thousand developers and one thousand application engineers across Ansys to discuss the latest technology trends and innovations in each of these twelve areas. Finally, we have started a significant R&D team focused on AI / machine learning, high-performance computing, digital twins, and health care in the CTO office. These major R&D teams are working organically to advance state of the art in their fields and work with the R&D teams in the different product lines and business units.

Finally, we are practicing open innovation by working with universities, such as Stanford, Princeton, MIT, Carnegie Mellon, and Michigan, with start-up companies, such as Geminus, M-Star, and Neural Concept, and larger companies, such as Microsoft Azure, Google Cloud Platform, Rockwell Automation, Nvidia, and Intel. The Digital Twin group is in incubation mode, where they have their own sales overlay team to complement the regular sales team of Ansys, but they are focused 100 percent on selling digital twin solutions. This made a big difference in incubating this new business at Ansys.

Prith Banerjee is chief technology officer at Ansys, a leader in engineering simulation. In this role, he leads the evolution of Ansys's technology and champions the company's next phase of innovation and growth. Before that, he was executive vice president and chief technology officer of Schneider Electric. Formerly, he was managing director of the global technology R&D at Accenture. Earlier, he was chief  technology officer and executive vice president of ABB. Previously, he was senior vice president of research at HP and director of HP Labs. Formerly, he was dean of the College of Engineering at the University of Illinois Chicago, and he was the Walter P. Murphy professor and chairman of ECE at Northwestern University. Before that, he was a professor of ECE at the University of Illinois. In 2000, he founded AccelChip, which was then sold to Xilinx in 2006. From 2005 to 2011, he was founder, chairman, and chief scientist of Binachip.

His research interests are in electronic design automation and parallel computing. He has more than 350 research papers, 10 book chapters, and a graduate textbook on parallel algorithms for VLSI computer-aided design (Prentice Hall 1994). He has also supervised thirty-seven PhD students.

Banerjee currently serves on the board of directors of Turntide Technologies. He has served on the board of directors of Cray Inc., Cubic Corporation, AnitaB.org, and the Computer Science and Telecommunications Board for the National Academy of

Engineering. He has also served on the technical advisory boards of Ambit, Atrenta, Calypto, Cypress, Ingram Micro, and Virsec. He was listed in *Fast Company's* list of one hundred top business leaders in 2009. He is a fellow of the AAAS, ACM, and IEEE and a recipient of the 1996 ASEE Terman Award and the 1987 NSF Presidential Young Investigator Award. He received a BTech (President's Gold Medal) in electronics engineering from the Indian Institutes of Technology, Kharagpur, and an MS and PhD in electrical engineering from the University of Illinois Urbana.

The author brings his personal experiences with innovation in academia, start-ups, and the corporate world to write this exciting book called *The Innovation Factory*. The book is filled with practical examples of innovation that works.